CELL MEMBRANES

CELL
Biological and

edited by
GOETZ W. RICHTER, M.D.

Department of Pathology, The University of Rochester
Rochester, N.Y.

DANTE G. SCARPELLI, M.D., Ph.D.

Department of Pathology, University of Kansas
Kansas City, Kansas

series editor
NATHAN KAUFMAN, M.D.

Department of Pathology, Queen's University
Kingston, Ontario, Canada

MEMBRANES
Pathological Aspects

AMERICAN ASSOCIATION
OF PATHOLOGISTS AND BACTERIOLOGISTS
ST. LOUIS   1970

THE WILLIAMS & WILKINS COMPANY *Baltimore 1971*

Library of Congress Catalog Card Number 76-152763
SBN 683-07234-X

Composed and printed at the
Waverly Press, Inc.
Mt. Royal and Guilford Aves.
Baltimore, Md. 21202, U.S.A.

FOREWORD

For many years symposia on selected topics of immediate interest have been an important component of the annual meeting of the American Association of Pathologists and Bacteriologists. Carefully chosen individuals at the forefront of their fields have presented and integrated current, new and developing concepts in a particular area relative to pathology.

Unfortunately, the individual papers presented at each symposium were never published in book form. Their publication was scattered in many journals and over a long period of time. In answer to repeated requests that this material be made available under one cover and as quickly as possible, the American Association of Pathologists and Bacteriologists has arranged for the publication of the Annual Symposium in book form. *Cell Membranes* represents the first volume of our series.

The support of the Council of the American Association of Pathologists and Bacteriologists, the contributors, the symposium editors, and the publishers is gratefully acknowledged.

Nathan Kaufman, M.D.
Series Editor

PREFACE

Recent discoveries, as well as refinements of existing knowledge, have greatly raised the hopes of medical investigators that most diseases will be clarified at the subcellular level. Subcellular organization and function are, to a great extent, determined by the structure and disposition of cell membranes* which delimit cell organelles and domains. The evident compartmentalization of cells by membranes has given rise to discussions about what constitutes the outside and the inside of cells, and about the outside of the inside, and the inside of the outside. Topology has become a very significant part of subcellular biology not only because cells are intricate geometric structures, but also because the geometry defined by membranes is in turn a result of molecular geometry within the membranes, and this organization is closely associated with enzyme activities.

The creation of the famous Danielli-Davson model of biological membranes was a great advance and has been helpful in explaining various phenomena. After the introduction of electron microscopy into cell biology, it seemed for a time that the Danielli-Davson model was being confirmed, at least in its essential features; but today there is again much uncertainty and we seem to be far away from a satisfactory integration of physiological, biochemical, and morphological data on biological membranes. Ideas about the nature of various cell membranes are more deeply rooted in the methods used than many of us would like to admit. Because of the diversity of opinions rather than despite it, it is appropriate for pathologists to study membranes.

In the belief that the relation of biological membranes to the pathogenesis of diseases will become a major concern of pathologists, the American Association of Pathologists and Bacteriologists sponsored a symposium on biological and pathological aspects of cell membranes. The nine contributions published in this monograph leave no doubt about the great diversity of

---

* It has been suggested that the term "cell membrane" should not be applied to structures other than the plasma membrane. In the context of modern cell biology this distinction is no longer useful. Cell membranes are membranes of or in cells. Moreover, the plasma membrane is often continuous with intracellular membranes, and pinocytic vesicles as well as phagosomes have membranes derived from the plasma membrane. Perhaps the term "biological membranes" might be preferable if everybody would agree that "biological" includes "pathological."

relevant problems. Though the contributors have worked in various fields, all of the articles represent interdisciplinary approaches.

The editors take this opportunity to thank all those who have helped them: the authors, the Council of the American Association of Pathologists and Bacteriologists, Dr. Nathan Kaufman, and the publishers, whose care and efforts have been exemplary.

G. W. Richter

D. G. Scarpelli

CONTENTS

1

MOLECULAR STRUCTURE AND FUNCTION OF CELLULAR MEMBRANES

Fritiof S. Sjöstrand

When analyzing living systems at a molecular level we are in a position that allows us to look for some basic principles that are of decisive importance to explain life processes.

The genetic code is one such fundamental principle which gives a basis for the repetitive character of living systems, for the continuity of Life. But what is Life that is maintained this way? This is an ambitious question that we can try to answer at a fairly sophisticated level today.

Functionally, when looked upon from the outside, living systems are characterized by a complexity of chemical reactions maintained by a continuous input of energy; this process in itself depends on complex chemistry.

The characteristic features of these chemical reactions are the high rate at which they proceed, the efficient coordination of sequences of reactions, and the astonishing precision of the control of the numerous related and non-related reactions. The high reaction rate is only partially accounted for by the presence of catalysts. The small number of enzyme molecules in a cell is utilized with strikingly high efficiency.

Both the high rate and the precision in coordination of chemical reactions are incompatible with a system in which enzyme molecules and substrate molecules are randomly distributed within the cell. Light microscopy has revealed that the cell is subdivided into regions that can be distinguished because they show differences in their chemical composition. Light microscopy paved the way for revealing that the respiratory chain and the citric acid cycle enzymes were confined to particular regions in the cytoplasm of cells, the mitochondria. Already light and ultraviolet microscopy made it justifiable to relate protein synthesis to certain basophilic regions in the cytoplasm.

With electron microscopy contributing to our knowledge of cell structure, it became obvious that these cytoplasmic regions contained structural components of supramolecular dimensions. In the most common types of such structures the molecules were associated in the form of membranes. A large number of complex multistep chemical reactions were found to be associated with such membranes, like those associated with energy transduction in retinal receptor cells (1, 2), in chloroplasts (3), and in mitochondria (4–7).

Membranes had earlier been considered only in connection with barrier functions like that of the plasma membrane, and great energy has been invested into explaining these barrier functions on the

Department of Zoology, University of California, Los Angeles, California 90024.

This work was supported by Research Grants GB-7859 from the National Science Foundation and NB-02889 from the U.S. Public Health Service.

1

basis of purely physical phenomena. The preferred permeation of lipid-soluble molecules over non-lipid soluble molecules was thus explained by the presence of a lipid layer in the plasma membrane. Preferred permeation of certain non-lipid soluble molecules was assumed to reflect relationships between size of pores in the membrane and the diameter of the molecules, and so on.

The demonstration of membranes as basic structural components associated with complex chemical events led electron microscopists to propose that these membranes were important for the coordination of these reactions and that they were the actual sites of enzymes. Biochemical studies have confirmed these interpretations and cytoplasmic membranes today are generally looked upon as metabolic structures where the major part of the metabolism is not associated with maintaining certain permeability properties of the membrane. In this respect there might be some quantitative differences between cytoplasmic membrane systems and the plasma membrane.

It is obvious that a membrane structure would allow a very ordered arrangement of molecules like enzyme molecules, and would guarantee a localized high concentration of the enzymes in spite of a limited number of such molecules per cell. Such a structure would therefore eliminate randomness. While a membrane structure would leave large surfaces open for substrate molecules to bind to the enzymes and products to be released, it would secure a spatial arrangement of the enzyme molecules that would favor their interaction. We then ask ourselves whether these speculations can be confirmed. What kind of arrangement is favorable from this point of view and how can such an arrangement be maintained?

To move from speculation and guesswork with respect to how the molecular structure can determine membrane function it appears justifiable to collect information regarding the precise molecular structure of membranes. We then must choose a proper technique. Biochemical studies of the composition of various types of membranes are of basic importance to relate what functions are associated with what membranes and to clarify the complexity of the chemistry involved. But since we believe that it is the particular spatial arrangement of the enzyme molecules that is important we must study the membranes with this arrangement intact and still available for observation.

X-ray diffraction studies are not likely to be of great help since the amount of information obtained by X-ray crystallography decreases drastically when the object loses its similarity to a perfect crystal. With a large number of enzyme molecules of different types with varied molecular weights and shapes, it appears obvious that the membrane structure must be far from crystalline.

Optical methods can reveal information regarding the over-all relative content of helical and random coiled regions in the membrane proteins and of other types of asymmetric centers in the molecule. Although this information gives some important clues to the conformation of proteins associated with membranes it does not allow any conclusion regarding the arrangement of the molecules in the membranes.

The only technique that would allow collecting such information is electron microscopy. The application of electron microscopy to such problems imposes however, enormous technical problems that are not fully appreciated even among electron microscopists.

It is obvious that an analysis of the structural organization of membranes as a basis for their metabolic function must concentrate on an analysis of the arrangement of the enzymes, that is, of the proteins that are associated with the membrane. But such an analysis requires that the protein molecules are observed in their native conformation or with the conformation modified to only a limited extent. Furthermore, their topographical arrangement must be retained. Denaturation of the proteins not only changes the conformation of the molecules but also is likely to result in secondary aggregation of the molecules which is drastically different from the native type of aggregation. Furthermore, the denatured protein molecules have lost the properties with respect to shape and dimensions that would allow observing them with the electron microscope. The changes in the conformation associated with extensive denaturation of protein molecules would eliminate the possibilities to observe individual protein molecules in the electron microscope.

In order to appreciate this problem and also as a basis for the discussion of our concept of membrane structure, it is appropriate to review some of our present knowledge regarding protein conformation.

A particular conformation of a protein molecule is maintained mainly by secondary bonds like hydrogen bonds, hydrophobic interaction, and possibly electrostatic interaction. The conformation that a protein molecule assumes in a medium is primarily imposed on the molecule by that medium. In an aqueous medium hydrophobic interaction contributes in an important way. In spite of the fact that water molecules could compete efficiently as proton donors with the NH groups of the peptide links, helical regions are present together with randomly coiled regions in the native conformation of proteins.

X-ray crystallographic studies of protein structure have shown that the interior of protein molecules is occupied mainly by non-polar side chains. Such side chains are shown in Figure 1.1. They usually make up 35 to 50% of the amino acid residues of a protein molecule. To that we can add the non-polar parts of side chains carrying a polar group.

Perutz et al. (8) pointed to the fact that non-polar side chains are found at the side of an α-helix which faces the interior of the molecule, while polar side chains are positioned at the side which is located at the surface of the molecule. This dividing

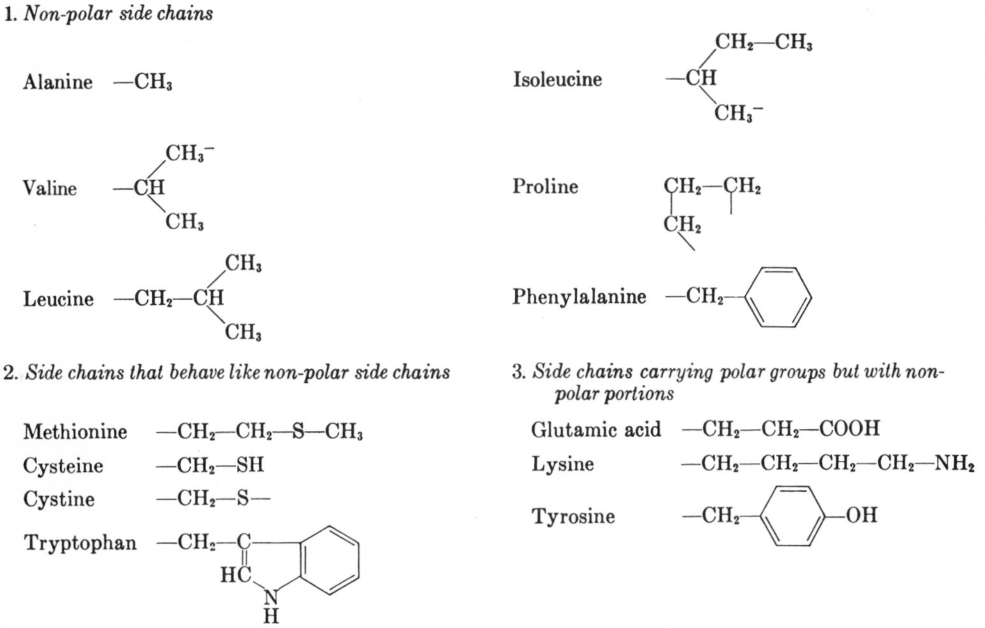

1. *Non-polar side chains*

Alanine   —CH$_3$

Valine   —CH(CH$_3^-$)(CH$_3$)

Leucine   —CH$_2$—CH(CH$_3$)(CH$_3$)

Isoleucine   —CH(CH$_2$—CH$_3$)(CH$_3^-$)

Proline   CH$_2$—CH$_2$, CH$_2$

Phenylalanine   —CH$_2$—⟨⟩

2. *Side chains that behave like non-polar side chains*

Methionine   —CH$_2$—CH$_2$—S—CH$_3$

Cysteine   —CH$_2$—SH

Cystine   —CH$_2$—S—

Tryptophan   —CH$_2$—C, HC, N, H

3. *Side chains carrying polar groups but with non-polar portions*

Glutamic acid   —CH$_2$—CH$_2$—COOH

Lysine   —CH$_2$—CH$_2$—CH$_2$—CH$_2$—NH$_2$

Tyrosine   —CH$_2$—⟨⟩—OH

Figure 1.1. Amino acid side chains that can interact through hydrophobic bonding.

the α-helix surface into half polar and half non-polar sides is due to the hydrophobic residues appearing with a certain periodicity along the helix. In the randomly coiled region of the molecules the polar and the charged side chains are also found positioned predominantly at the surface of the molecule.

Estimates of the volume of protein molecules in an aqueous medium have shown that the peptide chain is closely packed and that there are no indications of any voids in the molecules. This is confirmed by the X-ray crystallographic studies. In the myoglobin molecule only six water molecules are found inside the molecule and they are completely trapped.

Both theoretical deductions based on thermodynamics and actual observations of protein conformation agree with respect to the molecules exhibiting a predominantly non-polar interior allowing hydrophobic interaction between non-polar side chains and a predominantly polar surface in which the charged groups are located. Both hydrodynamic measurements of the volume of protein molecules and X-ray crystallographic data agree with respect to a compact arrangement of the peptide chains which makes the interior of the molecules inaccessible to water molecules and to ions or stains.

In the case of the cytochrome c molecule Dickerson *et al.* (9) showed by means of X-ray crystallographic analysis that a non-polar region extends all across the whole molecule and thus occupies certain areas at the surface of the molecule.

Such non-polar regions at the surface would allow hydrophobic interaction between protein molecules. The extent of any such interaction would depend upon the relative size of the non-polar areas and on whether the shapes of the surfaces allow any close packing of the molecules, since non-polar interaction is possible only over short distances.

When changing the medium in which the protein molecules are dispersed it is likely that more or less drastic conformational changes will occur. When changing from water to a non-polar medium the new medium can compete with the intramolecular hydrophobic bonding and this would lead to an opening up of non-polar regions in the molecule. A medium that is less polar than water and at the same time is a strong proton donor can in addition compete with the hydrogen bonding in the α-helices and favor a random coil conformation. The standard media used for dehydration of tissues for electron microscopy, ethanol and acetone, are considerably less polar than water and are known as strong denaturing agents.

There is no method that allows the complete analysis of changes in protein conformation that occur when subjecting proteins to various treatments. Optical rotatory dispersion allows, however, an estimation of the effect on, for instance, the over-all α-helix content of the molecules when the medium is changed. Hydrodynamic analysis gives important information with respect to changes in the volume over which the molecules are spread out and therefore can reveal any unfolding of the molecules. Enzymatic activity is assumed to be a sensitive test for native conformation but unfortunately such activites are difficult to measure in non-aqueous media. The reversibility of any conformational change has been proposed as an indication of a limited conformational change. Extensive conformational changes are considered likely to be irreversible.

When applying electron microscopy to the problem of the molecular structure of cellular membranes it is necessary to use thin sectioning techniques since only the analysis of extremely thin sections can be pursued at sufficiently high resolution to reveal enough details. On thin sections a resolution of 5 to 10 Å has been achieved while negative staining has a limit at about 20 Å and freeze-etching at 30 to 40 Å.

It is striking that practically no traces of globular proteins can be found in electron micrographs of sections through tissues that have been prepared with conventional techniques. Figure 1.2 shows mitochondrial membranes at a high resolution. The specimen was treated with conventional fixation and embedding techniques used in electron microscopy. The inner membranes consist of a pair of membranes or membrane elements which appear as triple-layered structures with three continuous layers, two opaque layers at the membrane surfaces and one lightly stained middle layer. The total thickness of each membrane element is only 50 Å. There is no indication of any globular structures in the range of 30 to 100 Å that could correspond to globular proteins of these dimensions, in spite of the fact that such molecules would constitute the major part of the membrane.

According to Fleischer *et al.* (10) the mitochondrial membranes appear identically triple-layered whether the mitochondrial lipids had been almost completely extracted before fixation and embedding for electron microscopy or whether the mitochondrion had been fixed fresh. Since the presence of membrane lipids therefore is of no importance in determining the triple-layered appearance of the membranes it appears justifiable to conclude that the triple-layered appearance does not reflect the arrangement of lipids in these membranes. So, this picture of the membranes does not show us the arrangement of either the membrane proteins or the membrane lipids. What then does it show?

Before answering this question, let us try to deduce how globular proteins would appear if present in the section.

The contrast in the electron microscopic picture that makes it possible to see any structural details is due to staining of the structures with electron stains, that is, stains containing heavy metal atoms. In order to achieve good enough contrast to obtain a resolution of 5 to 10 Å, it is necessary that the stain ions aggregate in clusters. These clusters must consist of pure, anhydrous stain. The size of these clusters or grains must not exceed the resolution at which the observations are intended to be made.

Let us now assume that we succeed in staining a globular protein molecule in this way and that the size of the stain grain allows a resolution of 10 Å. How would it look? First, it is obvious that the stain would be bound primarily to a small number of charged groups. There would be no binding to non-polar groups and the interior of the molecule would therefore remain unstained, both because of its non-polar milieu and because of the dense packing of the side chains that prevents any penetration of the stain into the molecule. On the other hand, the periphery of the molecule would be stained and stain ions would be located at certain sites at which they are bound. In order to obtain grains of stain that would show up in the electron micrograph it would be necessary either to have a number of such sites located very close together or to allow a precipitation or crystallization of the stain at the sites where one stain ion has already been bound. That site would then have to act as a kind of nucleation center for the stains.

It is obvious that the globular molecule would appear as a hollow rounded body delimited by a number of stain grains at the surface of the molecule. When looking at a projection of such a body onto a plane, which corresponds to looking at an electron microscopic picture of it, the body would appear as a ring of stain grains arranged around an almost unstained area. The center would be less intensely stained because only a few stained sites would be imaged by electrons passing through those parts of the stained surface of the molecule which are oriented perpendicularly to the electron beam, that is, the surface located over the center region of the molecule. The part of the surface of the molecule, on the other hand, which is oriented tangentially to the electron beam would appear more intensely stained because

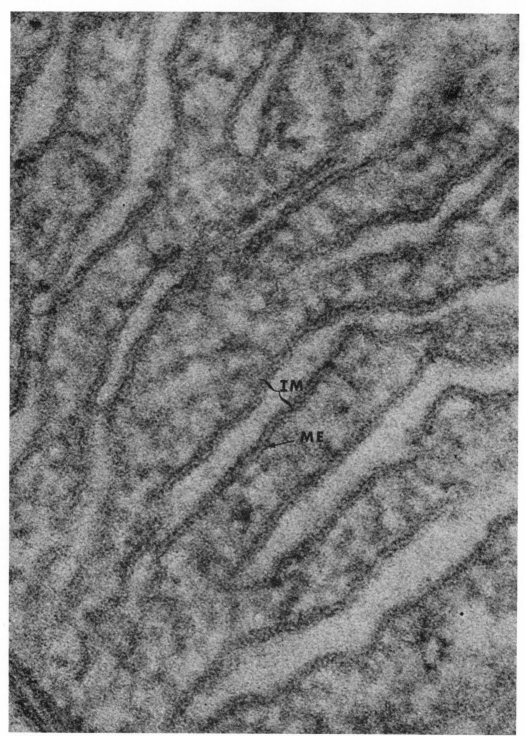

Figure 1.2. Inner mitochondrial membranes in kidney tissue fixed in osmium tetroxide, dehydrated in acetone, and embedded in Vestopal. The two individual membranes or membrane elements (ME) of the inner double membranes (IM) appear as triple-layered structures with a total thickness of 50 Å. The two membranes of the inner double membranes are separated by large spaces due to swelling of the double membranes. ×490,000.

here the images of stain sites become superimposed when the electrons strike in a tangential direction through the surface of the molecule.

If molecules are packed together due to hydrophobic interaction between non-polar surfaces the outlines of the individual molecules would be shown in an incomplete way and such associations would appear as structural units.

In experiments in which the tissue had been exposed to the fixative and the dehydrating agents for a minimum of time Figure 1.3, structures of this kind could be observed in mitochondrial membranes and cytomembranes (11, 12). On the basis of these observations Sjöstrand proposed that the core structure of these membranes consisted of globular proteins and not of a continuous lipid bilayer (13–15). This new concept of membrane structure stimulated new experiments aimed at revealing the membrane structure under conditions which would not alter the native conformation of globular proteins to the same extent that conventional preparatory procedures in electron microscopy were certain to do, whether short or long fixation and dehyration times were used.

It appeared that the transfer of the tissue from an aqueous medium to a nonaqueous medium, which is necessary for embedding, was the most critical part of the treatment of the tissue. This transfer is necessary to allow the cutting of sufficiently thin sections for high resolution electron microscopy, which requires embedding of the tissue in a proper plastic.

When choosing the method to embed the tissue in plastic in the experiments that were conducted in collaboration with L. Barajas (16) we tried to make best use of what is known about the effects on protein conformation of protein solvents that could be used as dehydrating agents. It then became obvious that ethylene glycol is a rather unique medium because optical rotatory dispersion measurements have shown that certain proteins can be dissolved in up to 100% ethylene glycol with little or no change in the α-helix content.

It has been used by Pease (17) for dehydration of tissues without prior fixation in order to eliminate fixation artifacts.

However, when trying to use ethylene glycol as a dehydrating agent this way we found that at a high resolution the membranes looked structurally very irregular, indicating damage to the membrane structure. This was to be expected, since ethylene glycol at 100% concentration has an effect on the α-helix content of many proteins that, however, can tolerate being exposed to 60 to 90% ethylene glycol. According to Sage and Singer (18) ethylene glycol has no observable effect on the helix content of ribonuclease even at a concentration of 100%, but it appears to affect the intramolecular hydrophobic bonding. They observed, namely, in spectrophotometric titrations, that all six tyrosine residues in ribonuclease titrated normally in ethylene glycol, while three of them titrate abnormally in an aqueous medium. The abnormal titration has been interpreted as due to these three tyrosine residues being buried in a non-polar region in the molecule and therefore being inaccessible for titration when the molecule is surrounded by an aqueous medium. Their accessibility in ethylene glycol would indicate an opening up of the molecule through a weakening of the intramolecular hydrophobic interaction.

We then looked for ways to stabilize the proteins in their native conformation and were advised by Alexander Glazer that glutaraldehyde had been used for cross-linking protein crystals, for instance, by Quiocho and Richards (19, 20) in their X-ray crystallographic analysis of carboxypeptidase A without introducing any significant changes in the X-ray diffraction pattern that would indicate conformational changes. The enzymatic activity of the crystals was also retained to an appreciable extent after cross-linking. On the other hand, the carboxypeptidase A crystals became both mechanically and enzymatically very stable after this treatment.

Glutaraldehyde was originally intro-

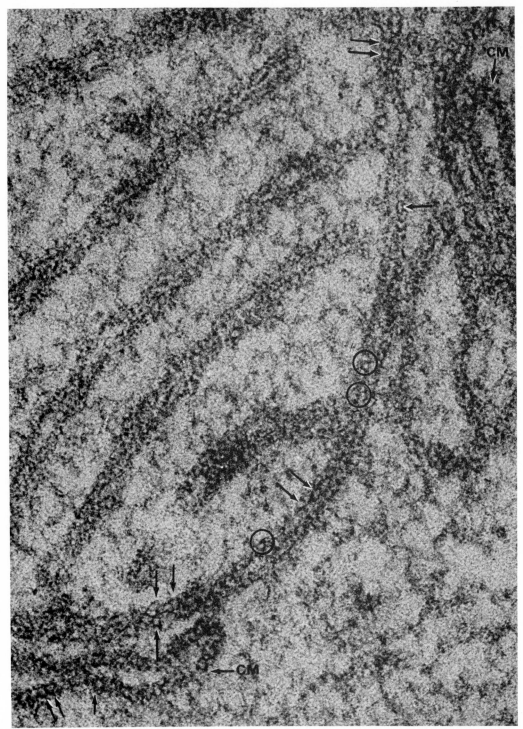

Figure 1.3. Part of mitochondrion in kidney tissue fixed short time through dripping of a potassium permanganate solution onto the surface of the kidney and short-time dehydrated in acetone. Vestopal embedding. The mitochondrial membranes show indications of a subdivision into globular subunits, (indicated by *arrows* and some encircled) with lightly stained centers and more intensely stained periphery. The thickness of the individual membranes is about 50 Å. The globular substructure is also seen in smooth-surfaced cytomembranes (CM). ×480,000. (From Sjöstrand, F. S., *J. Ultrastruct. Res. 9:* 340, 1963.)

duced in electron microscopy in connection with cytochemical studies. Its choice in this connection depended on the fact that many cellular enzymes are still active after glutaraldehyde fixation. This is another indication that some proteins are not greatly modified with respect to their native conformation by glutaraldehyde cross-linking.

The use of glutaraldehyde cross-linking and ethylene glycol dehydration appeared to allow preserving the mitochondrial membranes rather well as determined by their uniform dimensions and the fact that the membranes did not appear fragmented.

In order to limit the effects on the conformation of the proteins to a minimum, the tissues were exposed to glutaraldehyde and ethylene glycol for the shortest possible times, only 3 to 15 minutes cross-linking and 3 minutes dehydration.

In these preparations the mitochondrial membranes appear lightly stained against a more intensely stained matrix (Figs. 1.4–1.9). We expected that the membranes would be faintly stained if they would consist of closely packed globular proteins which would contribute a largely non-polar character to the membrane and where only certain areas at the surfaces of the proteins would be available for binding the stain. The more intense staining of the matrix was welcome because it enhanced the contrast by making the membranes appear in negative contrast in addition to the weak positive contrast due to staining of the membrane structure itself.

One striking observation that was made involved the dimensions of the mitochondrial membranes. The two components of the mitochondrial double membranes, which I call the mitochondrial membrane elements, measured 150 Å each in thickness as compared to only 50 Å after conventional fixation and embedding.

Within the lightly stained mitochondrial membranes stain grains line up to divide the membrane profile into subunits of varying dimensions and shapes. In a profile view there are considerable superposition effects because these subunits are smaller than the thickness of the sections.

When the membranes are oriented obliquely to the electron beam (Figs. 1.5, 1.8, and 1.9) such superposition effects are minimized particularly at the peripheral areas of the membrane projection. Looking at mitochondrial membranes that are oriented obliquely, we can see a particulate structure in the membranes considerably more clearly. The opacity of the matrix assists in delimiting the individual particles by making them appear in negative contrast.

In very obliquely oriented membranes the diameter of the particles was measured, and Figure 1.10 shows the distribution of the values. They ranged from below 40 Å to about 100 Å. The average diameter was 70 Å after 3 minutes cross-linking.

With increased time of cross-linking the thickness of the membrane elements increased slightly from 130 Å after 3 minutes to 150 Å after 15 minutes. No further increase was observed after 60 minutes cross-linking. The average diameter of the globules also increased from 70 Å after 3 minutes to 90 Å after 15 minutes and 110 Å after 60 minutes cross-linking. With increased cross-linking more and more sites presumably became inaccessible to the stain and therefore the particles presumably corresponded to larger complexes of molecules.

With our knowledge of the conformation of protein molecules as discussed above, it was expected that protein molecules in a state close to their native conformation would stain faintly in our preparations. The weak staining of the membranes, therefore, can be explained by an accumulation of densely packed globular protein molecules in these membranes.

From Table 1.1 it is obvious that the dominating components in various types of membranes are the proteins. This is particularly the case in mitochondrial membranes where the proteins make up

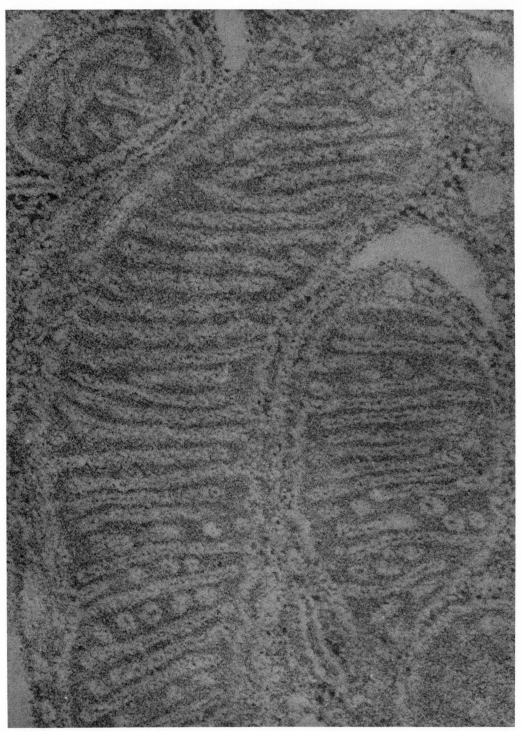

Figure 1.4. Mitochondria in kidney tissue which was cross-linked for 3 minutes by perfusion of 1% glutaraldehyde solution; about 50-μ thick tissue slices were then dehydrated for 3 minutes in 100% ethylene glycol and embedded in Vestopal. The mitochondrial membranes appear lightly stained against the more intensely stained matrix. They are considerably thicker than the membranes in Figures 1.2 and 1.3. When oriented parallel to the electron beam which allows a profile view they appear double with the two constituent membranes closely apposed. The light staining of the membranes reveals a particulate substructure. $\times$130,000. (From Sjöstrand, F. S. and Barajas, L., *J. Ultrastruct. Res. 25:* 121, 1968.)

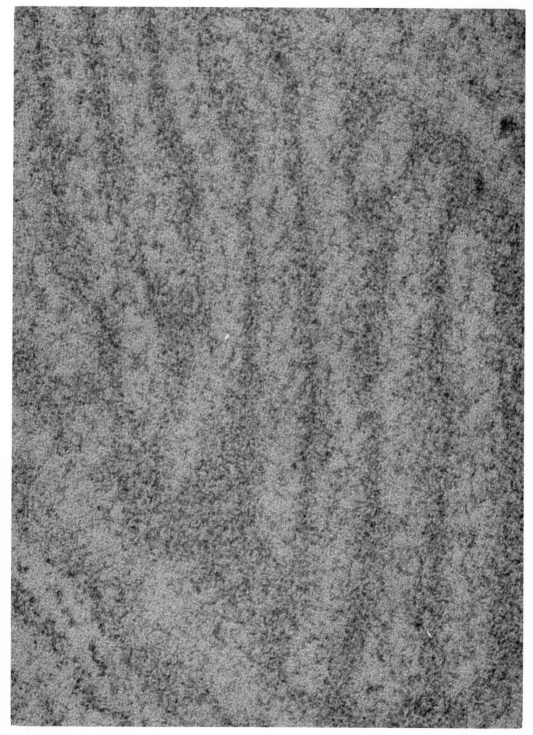

Figure 1.5. Higher magnification of area in Figure 1.4. The slightly obliquely oriented membranes appear broken up in lightly stained areas by irregularly arranged stained septa. ×400,000.

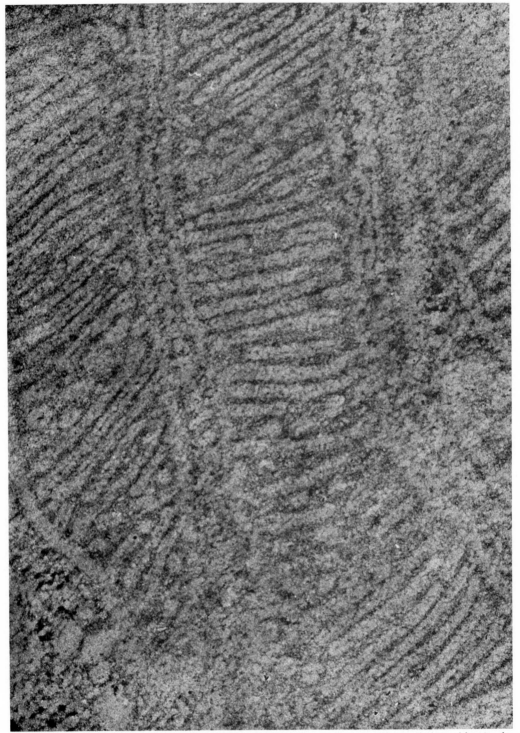

Figure 1.6. Mitochondria in rat kidney tissue cross-linked for 15 minutes by perfusion with 1% glutaraldehyde in phosphate buffer. Dehydration of 50-μ thick kidney slices in 100% ethylene glycol for 3 minutes and embedding in Vestopal. Notice the thickness of the mitochondrial membranes and their particulate substructure. The matrix spaces are furthermore very narrow. In contrast to material treated with conventional preparatory methods, this material shows very low contrast due to faint staining of the sections. ×120,000. (Sjöstrand and Barajas.)

12

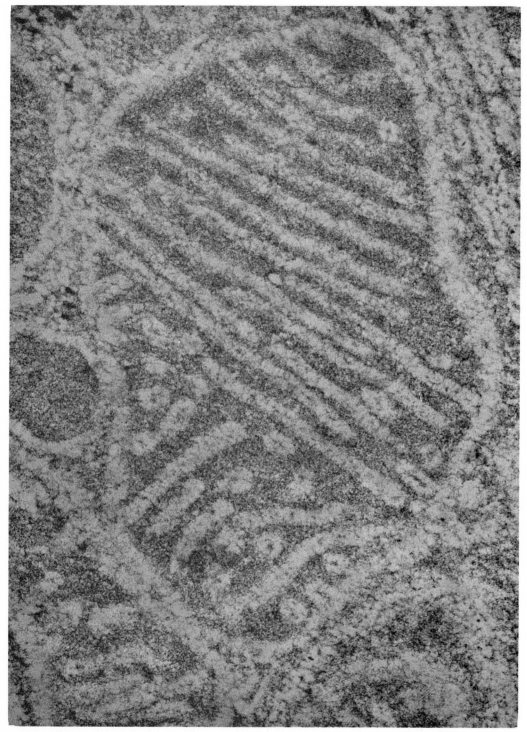

Figure 1.7. Kidney mitochondrion. Same treatment as described in figure legend for Figure 1.6. In this higher contrast picture the particulate substructure of the membranes is shown more clearly. ×140,000. (Sjöstrand and Barajas.)

13

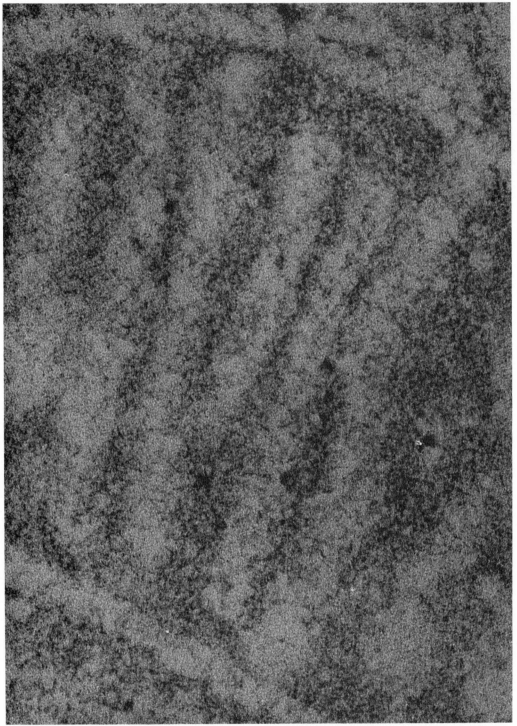

Figure 1.8. Kidney mitochondrion. Same treatment as described in figure legend for Figure 1.6. The mitochondrial membranes are oriented obliquely to the plane of the section. This allows observing the particulate substructure of the membranes with less interference of superposition effects. ×400,000. (Sjöstrand and Barajas.)

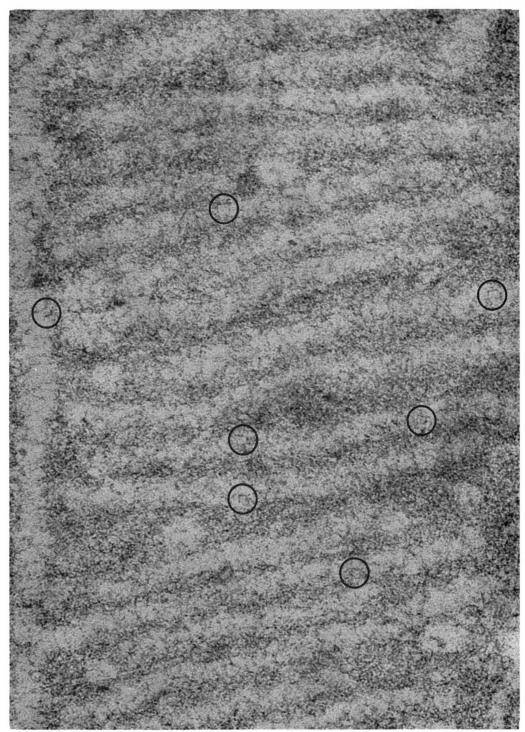

Figure 1.9. Mitochondrial membranes in specimen treated as described in figure legend for Figure 1.6. The obliquely oriented membranes show a particulate substructure. In several places the lightly stained particles show a rectangular or square shape (encircled). ×240,000. (From Sjöstrand, F. S. and Barajas, L., *J. Ultrastruct. Res. 25:* 121, 1968.)

15

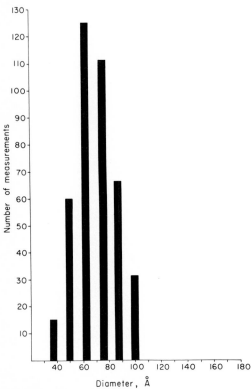

Figure 1.10. Distribution of particle diameters as measured in obliquely oriented mitochondrial membranes. Glutaraldehyde cross-linking for 3 minutes.

consists of a population of protein molecules of different types. Table 1.2 shows that these proteins differ widely with respect to molecular weights and dimensions, which range from 25 by 25 by 37 Å for cytochrome *c* to more than 100 Å for certain dehydrogenases. The delimited regions in the membranes and the particles we see in oblique sections therefore correspond to the dimensions of protein molecules that we know are present in the membranes.

It is then justifiable to conclude that these particles are protein molecules. No other material in the membranes is likely to form a structure of this kind.

If these particles are protein molecules and groups of protein molecules then they would disappear after denaturation of the proteins. Experiments were therefore conducted involving heat and low pH denaturation of the tissue. Heating for 400 minutes at 65° C and acetone dehydration led to a picture of the membranes which is completely different from that just described. The membrane elements now consisted of a continuous light layer about 50-Å thick (Fig. 1.12). Their appearance can be compared with that in cross-linked ethylene glycol-dehydrated material shown in Figure 1.13, taken at identical magnification as Figure 1.12. The light layers of the two membrane elements in Figure 1.12 are separated by a thin opaque layer.

After denaturation, the particulate

70 to 75% of the membranes, *versus* 25 to 30% accounted for by lipids.

It is obvious from the scheme in Figure 1.11 that already the respiratory chain

TABLE 1.1

Percent Lipid and Protein in Cellular Membranes

Membranes	Lipid	Protein	Source
	%	%	
Myelin	80	20	O'Brien and Sampson, 1965 (26)
Chloroplast	50	50	Park and Pon, 1961 (27)
Erythrocyte	40	60	Maddy and Malcolm, 1965 (28)
Mitochondria	26	74	Fleischer and McConnell, 1966 (29)
Retinal receptor cell			
outer segments	60	40	Fleischer and McConnell, 1966 (29)
	39	61	Sjöstrand, 1959 (30)
	32	68	Collins *et al.*, 1951 (31)
Microsomes	32	68	Spiro and McKibbin, 1956 (32)

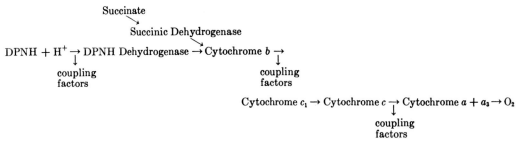

Figure 1.11. Respiratory chain components.

TABLE 1.2

Molecular Weights of Proteins Located in Mitochondrial Membranes and Their Estimated Dimensions

Compound	Molecular Weight	Diameter* $\overset{\circ}{A}$	Source
Cytochrome c	12,400	$25 \times 25 \times 37$†	Dickerson *et al.*, 1967 (9)
Structural protein	22,000	~ 45	Criddle *et al.*, 1962 (33)
Cytochrome b	30,000	~ 50	Goldberger *et al.*, 1961 (34)
Succinate dehydrogenase	200,000 (4 subunits)	4×55	Singer *et al.*, 1956 (35)
	49,000	~ 55	
Coupling factor F_1	280,000	~ 90	Racker, 1965 (36)
Cytochrome a	360,000 (pentamer)	$5 \times \sim 60$	Ambe and Venkataraman, 1959 (37)
	72,000 (monomer)	60	Criddle and Bock, 1959 (38)
Cytochrome c_1	51,000	~ 55	Criddle *et al.*, 1962 (33)
Choline dehydrogenase	850,000	100	Kimura and Singer, 1962 (39)
NADH dehydrogenase	1,000,000	100	Singer *et al.*, 1957 (40)
α-Glycerophosphate dehydrogenase	2,000,000	100	Ringler, 1961 (41)

* With the exception of cytochrome c, the dimensions of the molecules have been assumed on the basis of molecular weights and a spherical shape. For cytochrome c the dimensions were determined from X-ray crystallographic data by Dickerson *et al.* (9).

† These dimensions do not include side chains extending from peptide backbone structure at the surface of the molecule.

structure observed after glutaraldehyde cross-linking and ethylene glycol dehydration has disappeared. The structure of the mitochondrial membranes is identical to that observed after conventional glutaraldehyde fixation and acetone or ethanol dehydration.

As a conventional fixative, glutaraldehyde is mostly used at a concentration of 2 to 3% and the fixation time is several hours. For comparison, a 1% solution was used in our experiments and the tissue was exposed to the glutaraldehyde solution for only 3 to 15 minutes. For conventional fixation of tissues, the glutaraldehyde treatment is also frequently followed by a postfixation in osmium tetroxide. The picture of the mitochondrial membranes then appears somewhat different as compared to that after glutaraldehyde fixation and acetone or ethanol dehydration without postfixation. Postfixation with osmium tetroxide makes the membrane elements appear triple-layered and the matrix shows a low opacity, which makes the opaque layer of the membrane elements facing the matrix stand out with good contrast. Fixation in still higher concentrations of glutaraldehyde, for instance 6%, without postfixation in osmium tetroxide also

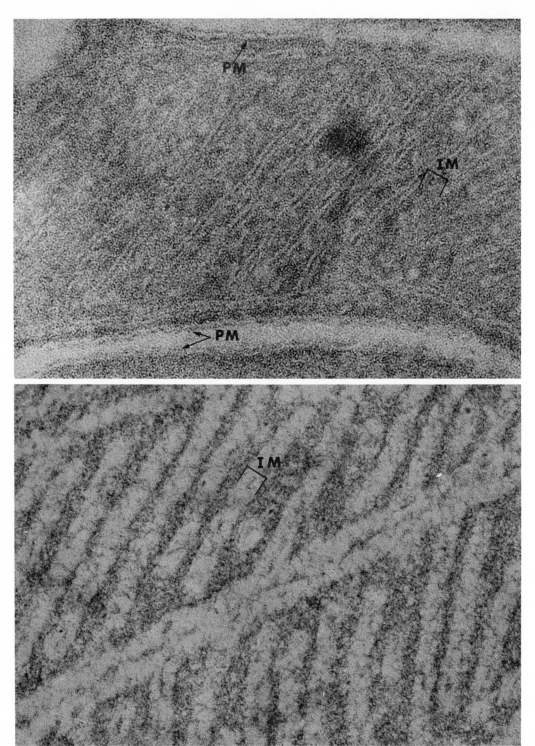

Figure 1.12. Kidney mitochondrion in heat-denatured tissue. Sections (50-μ thick) of glutaraldehyde cross-linked rat kidney tissue were kept at 65° C for 400 minutes and then embedded in Vestopal after acetone dehydration. Both mitochondrial membranes (IM) and the plasma membrane (PM) show an appearance similar to that after conventional fixation and embedding of tissues. The mitochondrial membrane elements measure only about 50 Å in thickness. The membrane dimensions can be compared with those shown in Figure 1.13. ×210,000. (From Sjöstrand, F. S. and Barajas, L., *J. Ultrastruct. Res. 25:* 121, 1968.)

makes the mitochondrial membrane elements appear triple-layered.

It is likely that the opaque layer in the middle of the mitochondrial membranes, which is seen in the denatured material as well as after conventional glutaraldehyde fixation, consists of the opaque layer of the membrane elements located at the surfaces which are facing each other, and that the close apposition of these membrane elements has made these layers fuse to a single opaque layer.

It is also likely that a second opaque layer is present at the surface of the membrane elements, that is, facing the matrix space. Such a layer would not show up as a distinct layer because the opacity of the matrix matches that of the opaque layers of the membranes. It is therefore likely that the membrane elements in fact are triple-layered after denaturation. Already the dimensions of the denatured membranes coincide so well with those observed after conventional treatment of tissues for electron microscopy to allow the conclusion that denaturation of the membranes has an effect on the membrane structure similar to conventional fixation and embedding.

These experiments clearly point to the conventional picture of the cellular membranes as reflecting drastic denaturation of membrane proteins. Such denaturation would unfold the protein molecules, expose non-polar side chains, and favor extensive intermolecular hydrophobic interaction. The non-polar side chains are likely to collect in the interior of the modified membrane removed from contact with water, while polar and charged side chains will assume positions at the surfaces of the membrane. It is these side chains that are likely to be stained while the non-polar interior of the membrane will form a continuous unstained layer. This explains the triple-layered structure of membranes after conventional treatment of the tissues for electron microscopy. The extensive denaturation of the membrane proteins also explains why no globular protein molecules can be seen in such preparations.

We then tried a different technique to check our observations. This technique would decrease the chances for an unfolding of the protein molecules during the preparatory procedure and would furthermore reduce the mobility of lipid molecules not associated firmly with the proteins.

Since all proteins investigated so far can tolerate ethylene glycol in water in concentrations up to 60 to 70% ethylene glycol without showing signs of conformational changes, it appeared reasonable to make use of ethylene glycol for a partial dehydration of the tissue. After dehydration in 25 to 50% ethylene glycol the tissue can be frozen rapidly in propane chilled to $-170°$ C without the formation of ice crystals. The frozen tissue was dried in a vacuum at $-80°$ C for several weeks. The temperature was then slowly raised to $-20°$ C and the tissue infiltrated in a vacuum with hydroxypropyl methacrylate chilled to $-20°$ After infiltration the plastic was polymerized at $-20°$ to $-30°$ C in a cold room using ultraviolet irradiation to initiate polymerization.

With this technique the basic features of the mitochondrial membranes as observed after ethylene glycol dehydration were confirmed. These preparations were, however, very difficult to stain and the specimens show extremely low contrast. It is typical that the staining becomes increasingly difficult the better the conditions are to prevent protein denaturation.

It should be pointed out that the obser-

Figure 1.13. Mitochondria in rat kidney tissue cross-linked with glutaraldehyde for 15 minutes and ethylene glycol-dehydrated for 3 minutes. The magnification is ×210,000, which is the same as Figure 1.12, to allow direct comparison of membrane dimensions. (From Sjöstrand, F. S. Molecular structure and function of cellular membranes. In *Regulatory Functions of Biological Membranes*, edited by Järnefelt, J., pp. 1–20, BBA Library 11. Amsterdam, Elsevier Publishing Company, 1968.)

vations made on the structure of the mitochondrial membranes after the new preparatory procedures described here are not dependent on any extreme high resolution electron microscopy. To determine the thickness of the mitochondrial membranes to 300 Å and of the membrane elements to 150 Å does not involve high resolution. Even the particulate structure with an average diameter of the particles of 70 Å can be observed at a rather limited resolution. The precision of the measurements will, however, improve with the resolution up to the limit set by the size of the stain grains.

There are today many assumptions made with respect to what resolution really can be made use of in electron microscopy when dealing with biological material. Certain pessimism is expressed with respect to the value of extreme high resolution work, that is, studies below 10 Å. To this I would like to comment that electron microscopy as applied to biological material of today has developed in spite of all predictions in the past that it would be impossible to see much of cell structure in the electron microscope. The situations have always been too complicated to allow any precise predictions, and methods have always been worked out to solve the technical problems. Instead of making predictions, it seems more profitable to try in practice to find the ultimate limit for the structural information that can be achieved. This limit has definitely not yet been reached even in the conventional use of the electron microscope, mainly because the procedures used in specimen preparation have not been suitable for extreme high resolution.

The observations made so far have allowed us to propose an entirely new type of membrane model (21, 21a, 22). This model fulfills the purpose of showing in a concrete way how our observations on mitochondrial membranes at various projections, profile views, and oblique face-on views can be interpreted in terms of molecular structure. It also fulfills the important purpose of leading us in our future research to design proper experiments to test the model and to add further information regarding membrane structure.

When building this model we have appreciated the important contributions of biochemists to our knowledge of the chemical composition of mitochondrial membranes. We have tried to put together all the present knowledge of mitochondrial membranes as well as of other types of membranes where permeability properties are better known.

The model was based on the following assumptions.

1. The particles observed in the electron micrographs are globular protein molecules and/or lipid-protein complexes.

2. Since the average thickness of the membrane elements is about twice the average diameter of the particles, it was assumed that the protein molecules were arranged in a three-dimensional packing and not distributed in a monolayer.

3. Since no continuous layer of the dimensions of lipid bilayers was found, it was assumed that no continuous lipid bilayer existed as a backbone structure of the membranes.

4. Since biochemical studies have shown that a large number of mitochondrial enzymes can be recovered in submitochondrial fractions consisting of membrane fragments, it was assumed that these enzymes were located *in* the membranes.

5. Since structural integrity of multimolecular complexes in mitochondria has been found important to the function of these complexes, it was assumed that the function depended on a particular favorable arrangement of the components of the complex facilitating alternate interactions between the active sites of the individual enzyme and carrier molecules.

The active sites would therefore be separated by minimum distances to allow alternate interaction of one component with adjacent components through thermal motions of the molecules.

6. It was assumed that several multi-

component complexes were present in and mixed in the mitochondrial membrane elements.

Most of the molecules in the model were assumed to have a spherical shape and a population of molecules representing varied molecular weights were made from Plastilina. Larger molecules were assumed to consist of a number of spherically shaped subunits.

One complex (complex I) was intended to reflect certain features of the respiratory chain (Fig. 1.14A). Since, however, the knowledge of the molecular composition of the respiratory chain and of the molecular weights of its components is incomplete, complex I represents a simplified version that has been built with no other intention than to represent one multimolecular complex in which mutual interaction between chain members and between these members and coupling factors is highly facilitated through a close packing of the molecules.

Complex II (Fig. 1.14B) has some features in common with pyruvate dehydrogenase, while complex III (Fig. 1.14C) is based on free imagination.

Figure 1.15 shows a photograph of the membrane model. A number of these three complexes were positioned in a closely packed arrangement on a surface. It then became obvious that the complexes could not be packed without leav-

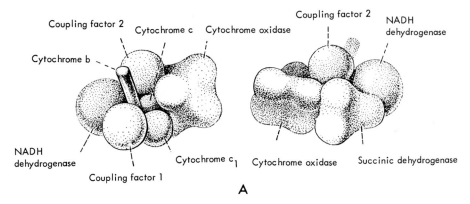

Coupling factor 2
Cytochrome c   Cytochrome oxidase
Coupling factor 2
NADH dehydrogenase
Cytochrome b
NADH dehydrogenase
Cytochrome c_1 Cytochrome oxidase   Succinic dehydrogenase
Coupling factor 1

A

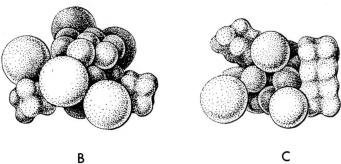

B   **C**

Figure 1.14. Three multimolecular complexes of globular protein molecules or lipoprotein complexes used to build a membrane model. *A*, complex I: a simplified respiratory chain viewed from two directions at 180° angle; *B*, complex II: a complex showing a certain degree of symmetry; *C*, complex III: an irregular appearing complex. (From Sjöstrand, F. S. and Barajas, L., *J. Ultrastruct. Res. 32:* 293, 1970.)

ing holes between the complexes. These holes were assumed to be filled partially through lipid molecules in bilayer arrangement (Figs. 1.15 and 1.16). This way a pool of lipids would be present in the membrane where lipid-lipid interaction would dominate. Another pool of lipids was assumed to be associated with the protein molecules in specific lipid-protein complexes.

The first aim of building the model was to see whether a model of this kind would look like the electron micrographs of mitochondrial membrane elements. It now became quite obvious that the lack of any simple repetitive pattern in these micrographs and the irregularity of the patterns were consistent with a model of this kind (Figs. 1.16 and 1.17). Rather large areas of the membranes observed in perfect projections without superposition effects, as in Figure 1.16, would be needed in order to observe a repetitive pattern. Such projections cannot be obtained in random sections through mitochondria.

The forces that are responsible for the stability of the membrane structure are assumed primarily to be hydrophobic interaction between non-polar surfaces of the protein molecules. This way the inte-

rior of the membranes would have a predominantly non-polar character which would favor the penetration of non-polar molecules and restrict the permeation of inorganic ions and of polar water-soluble molecules.

Polar and charged side chains would be found predominantly at the surfaces of the membrane. Separation of the charged groups at the surfaces by a predominantly non-polar interior milieu would account for the fairly high specific resistance and specific capacitance of cellular membranes. The specific capacitance of mitochondrial membranes has been estimated to 0.5 to 0.6 $\mu F/cm^2$ and to about 1 $\mu F/cm^2$ for the plasma membrane.

This model therefore accounts for some of the basic properties that have been known since the end of the last century and the beginning of this century to be associated with the plasma membrane. It is obvious that these properties can be accounted for without assuming the presence of a continuous lipid bilayer as a backbone structure of the membrane. The properties referred to only point to the presence of a highly non-polar zone in the membrane. Such a non-polar zone can be built by using lipid or protein molecules and

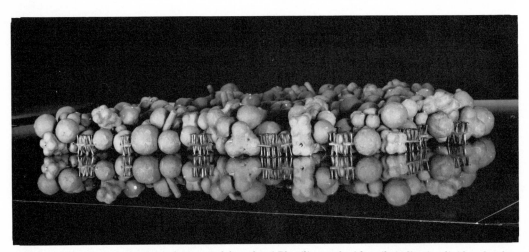

Figure 1.15. Photograph of membrane model made of Plastilina and with nails indicating lipid molecules. (From Sjöstrand, F. S. and Barajas, L., *J. Ultrastruct. Res. 32:* 293, 1970.)

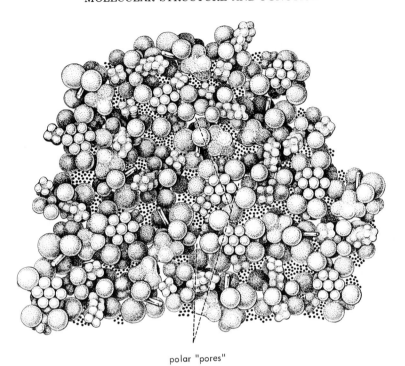

polar "pores"

Figure 1.16. The membrane model observed in face-on view, showing the arrangement of the complexes and the holes between the complexes filled with lipid molecules (circular dots). Some of the holes between the complexes are left open to illustrate the presence of polar pores. (From Sjöstrand, F. S. and Barajas, L., *J. Ultrastruct. Res. 32:* 293, 1970.)

Figure 1.17. The membrane model in profile view. Notice the irregular profile which becomes more evident if only the molecules in the foreground are considered. In a thin section the less shaded molecules would be confined in a cross-section of the membrane. (From Sjöstrand, F. S. and Barajas, L., *J. Ultrastruct. Res. 32:* 293, 1970.)

these properties therefore do not discriminate between the two building materials.

Measurements of the specific resistance of artificial lipid bilayers show values that are 1,000 to 10,000 times higher than those found for the plasma membrane. This makes it highly unlikely that even the plasma membrane consists of a continuous lipid bilayer as postulated by the Danielli-Davson model.

The most important feature of our model is its explanation of the efficiency of enzymes in multienzyme systems. Through the confining of the enzyme molecules to a membrane a locally high concentration of certain enzymes can be maintained permanently. There is experimental evidence that the space bounded by a membrane contains substrate at a high concentration. A high enzyme concentration would then be matched by a high substrate concentration within a limited region of the cell body.

The close packing in three dimensions of the components of a multienzyme complex allows alternate and successive interactions of members of the complex through small changes in the orientation of the molecules which would make the active sites acquire proper contact relations for interaction. Due to the relative position of the members, the correct sequence of interaction would be programmed.

The interaction between the members of the complex would then be associated with collisions of their active sites, which is in agreement with the observations by Chance and Spencer (23) that the spectra of cytochromes of yeast cells and cell particles were stabilized in a steady-state condition with partially reduced cytochromes when the particles were chilled to liquid nitrogen temperature. This observation shows a uniform inhibition of the electron transfer along the respiratory chain due to the low temperature. The most plausible explanation is that this inhibition was due to a decrease in the collision frequency of the molecules at the low temperature.

This model thus offers an explanation for the high efficiency and excellent coordination of enzymic activities in multistep reactions. These were some of the basic properties that we had identified as characteristic for living matter.

If we now turn to more specific permeability properties of a membrane of this type we recognize that even at a close arrangement of the complexes, holes appear between the complexes. If we assume that some of these holes are located between protein molecules with predominantly polar surfaces we would obtain a polar pore extending through the membrane. If there is a dominance of carboxyl groups at the surface of the proteins we would have a hole with an excess negative charge. Should amino groups dominate, a predominantly positive-charged pore would be the consequence. Pores favoring the trapping of either anions or cations would thus be a consequence.

The permeation of a molecule through the membrane involves a first stage at which the molecule is adsorbed or bound to the surface of the membrane and a second stage when it is displaced from the surface toward the inside of the cell or the compartment. With protein molecules forming the backbone structure of the membrane it is easy to conceive of a variety of sites at which specific types of molecules could be bound temporarily. The thermal motions of the molecules involving rotations of the molecules could account for the displacement of the molecule bound to the protein.

Such rotations of the molecules would mean that the polar areas at the surface of the molecules could dip into the non-polar milieu in the interior of the membrane and vice versa. This could lead to limited conformational changes that could change the conditions for binding the molecule that was picked up from the external milieu. This change could lead to its release in a position in the membrane favoring its expulsion into the inside medium.

The thermal motions of the molecules would thus change the relationships between polar and non-polar surfaces and could be considered to introduce oscillatory minor changes in the conformation of the molecules.

In studies of the permeability of the plasma membrane for inorganic ions the concept of the equivalent pore has been developed. This concept states that the permeability of the membrane for a certain ion can be theoretically accounted for if we assume a certain number of permanent pores of a diameter corresponding to the diameter of the hydrated ion and assuming free diffusion through such pores. This concept does not stipulate the existence of permanent pores in the membrane. However, paths must exist through which ions can pass through the membrane and the equivalent pore concept gives some quantitative estimate of how many such paths are needed at each instant to account for the permeability properties of the membrane under certain specified conditions.

Such estimates have led to the conclusion that only $1/1000$ of the total surface area of the red cell membrane is permeable to ions. This corresponds to about one pore per 10,000 Å^2. The pores would thus be about 100 Å apart. For the squid axon Villegas and Barnola (24) arrived at an estimate of 1.3×10^{10} pores/cm^2. In the resting axon the pores would then be 1,000 Å apart. In activation of the axon the specific resistance decreases from about 1,000 ohms/cm^2 to 25 ohms/cm^2. This would correspond to an opening of a large number of new pores in the membrane and the separation of the pores would be reduced to about 100 Å.

Electrophysiological observations of the effects of certain pharmacological agents on the permeability of the axonal membrane indicate that there are different paths or channels through the membrane for Na$^+$ influx and K$^+$ outflux, for Na$^+$ influx during rest and activation. Moore *et al.* (25) estimated the tetrodotoxin-sensitive sites or "pores" of the nerve membrane to 1.3×10^9/cm^2.

Reasonable estimates of the density of pores in the membrane led to one pore per 1,000 to 10,000 Å^2. The 1,000 Å^2 corresponds to the cross-sectional area of a molecule with a diameter of about 35 Å, which corresponds to a molecular weight of about 18,000. An area of 10,000 Å^2 is smaller than that covered by a face-on projection of a β-galactosidase molecule. The maximum porosity of the membrane would then be about one pore per protein molecule located at the membrane surface. The few pores per unit surface area would be an obvious consequence of the fact that no ions can pass through the protein molecules but must pass between these molecules.

The equivalent pore concept does not require permanent pores. It would be valid also as an expression for the average number of pores that are open at each instance. The model discussed here assumes that the molecules are in constant thermal motion, which is only restricted due to the association of the molecules in a membrane structure. Such thermal motions of the molecules would favor opening and closing of paths for ions through the membrane, a dynamic situation that could easily be affected in directions of increase or of decrease in ion leakage through the membrane. A particularly favorable arrangement of the protein molecules for leakage could then be conceived of as a consequence of nerve stimulation. Still, a predominantly non-polar milieu could be maintained in the interior of the membrane, accounting for the maintaining of a high capacitance in spite of a low specific resistance of the membrane.

The effects of transmitters and of different drugs on the neuronal plasma membrane and of hormones on plasma membranes point to the presence of receptor sites for these molecules at the membrane surface. A protein membrane would allow the high specificity of these interactions by the incorporation of receptor proteins in the membrane.

Active transport associated with ATPase activity is another example where proteins in the membrane would account for the energetic coupling of ion transport and dephosphorylation of ATP.

It is characteristic that oxidative phosphorylation as demonstrated in submitochondrial particles seems to require that these particles form vesicles. This could mean that oxidative phosphorylation requires that the medium on the two sides of the membrane would differ. This would be the case if the membrane permeability is selective.

One important consequence of such a situation could well be that the mitochondrial membrane element is charged and that the charge across the membrane affects the orientation and the conformation of the enzyme molecules. The existence of a selective permeability that is responsible for the charge would require the presence in the membrane of molecules that control the permeability. Such molecules can be considered as accessory factors.

It appears rather possible that the respiratory chain depends on such accessory factors to be functional. The isolation of a functional respiratory chain *per se* would therefore be impossible under such conditions.

If we now consider that functionally important accessory factors are present in the membrane which determine the permeability properties of the membrane and furthermore that an enzyme molecule can lose all enzymic activity when removed from its association with an enzyme complex, it then appears rather likely that a breaking up of the membrane structure would result in a rather large fraction of protein molecules that after isolation show no biological activity. These proteins would therefore be labeled structural proteins.

Since hydrophobic interaction is likely to be mainly responsible for the stability of the membrane, it immediately becomes evident that the association of protein molecules through such forces must represent a wide range of stability from very weak interaction represented by small areas of contact to very strong interaction

represented by large areas of contact and by a close fit of the contact surfaces (Fig. 1.18).

The electron microscopic observations made so far on the material treated with the new preparatory techniques make it justifiable to locate the citric acid cycle enzymes in the mitochondrial membranes because no large protein molecules or complexes of protein molecules could be observed in the matrix. The fact that the citric acid cycle enzymes are easily brought in solution would then reflect their weak bonding to the membrane structure.

The hydrophobic interaction will depend on the presence of predominantly non-polar surfaces on the interacting protein molecules. However, the hydrophobic interaction requires that the surfaces are brought in close contact since we are dealing with short-range forces. Therefore, the shapes of the surfaces must show a certain fit to establish good enough contact (Fig. 1.18). This could impose a certain specificity on the interaction of the molecules. It has been pointed out that hydrophobic interaction plays a role in many antigen-antibody reactions, indicating that such interaction can be rather specific.

Such specificity could account for the

Figure 1.18. Schematic illustration of globular protein molecules aggregated through hydrophobic interaction. The non-polar surfaces are indicated by shading. The drawing illustrates variations in the surface areas available for hydrophobic interaction and the requirement for a close fit of interacting surfaces. It also shows space restrictions that would allow only molecules of a small size to fit in certain places in the aggregate.

The presence of large polar surfaces prevents the aggregation from growing indefinitely in three dimensions and favors the extension of the aggregate in the form of a membrane by leaving polar surfaces free for interaction with the aqueous medium.

particular type of association of the components in a multienzyme complex and rule out a random aggregation.

The hydrophobic interaction would lead to only a relative stability of the membrane structure. Any factors interfering with the hydrophobic interaction could easily bring about drastic changes in the structure of the membrane. It is easy on this basis to understand that the mitochondrial membranes undergo spontaneous modifications when deprived of their normal substrates. Such changes are very obvious after shutting off the blood supply to a piece of tissue and thereby interfering with the normal metabolism of the tissue. These changes are furthermore speeded up and enhanced when mitochondria are exposed to osmotic shock by immersion in distilled water.

The observations made with these new techniques and the membrane model derived on the basis of these observations make it possible to explain certain basic aspects of membrane function. This model might have certain features that are universal in all cellular membranes, but it is likely also that, for instance, the plasma membrane differs in certain aspects from the model discussed here. Larger areas might be occupied by lipid bilayers in the plasma membrane than in the mitochondrial membranes.

The model fulfills a purpose in allowing one to draw certain conclusions that are of importance in defining conditions for future experiments that can add further information to the structure of membranes while either confirming or not confirming the model. Even if details in the model are wrong it appears rather certain that its basic features, the backbone structure formed by proteins, is correct.

This model is our answer today to the question, "How can the metabolism in living systems proceed with such efficiency, both with respect to rate of the reactions and their coordination?" The answer is the organization of multicomponent enzyme systems in aggregates of a particular organization. This is to our mind one of the basic principles that characterize living systems. It represents a special state of aggregation, *organized multi-molecular aggregates*.

SUMMARY

The molecular structure of mitochondrial membranes has been analyzed with the aim of revealing the arrangement of the membrane proteins. Electron microscopic examination of thin sections is the only method that can be applied for a systematic analysis of this kind as far as resolution is concerned. In order to apply this technique, methods were worked out which would allow embedding of tissue in plastic without introducing extensive changes of the native conformation of the membrane proteins. These methods revealed an entirely different picture of membrane structure as compared to conventional fixation and embedding techniques used in electron microscopy. The latter techniques lead to an extensive denaturation of membrane proteins, as was shown by the similarity of the membrane patterns observed in tissues conventionally fixed and embedded to those observed after exposing the tissue to extensive denaturation by heat or low pH.

A new type of membrane model was deduced from the observations made with the new techniques. Biochemical information regarding the mitochondrial membranes was incorporated into this model. The arrangement of enzyme molecules in multimolecular aggregates in membranes is one of the features of the model. This feature is considered of basic importance to the development of efficient and coordinated metabolic functions in living systems.

REFERENCES

1. Sjöstrand, F. S. An electron microscope study of the retinal rods of the guinea pig eye. *J. Cell. Physiol. 33:* 383, 1949.

2. SJÖSTRAND, F. S. The ultrastructure of the outer segments of rods and cones of the eye as revealed by the electron microscope. *J. Cell. Physiol. 42:* 15, 1953.

3. STEINMANN, E. An electron microscope study of the lamellar structure of chloroplasts. *Exp. Cell Res. 3:* 367, 1952.

4. PALADE, G. E. The fine structure of mitochondria. *Anat. Rec. 114:* 427, 1952.

5. PALADE, G. E. An electron microscope study of the mitochondrial structure. *J. Histochem. Cytochem. 1:* 188, 1953.

6. SJÖSTRAND, F. S. Electron microscopy of mitochondria and cytoplasmic double membranes. Ultrastructure of rod-shaped mitochondria. *Nature (London) 171:* 30, 1953.

7. SJÖSTRAND, F. S. The ultrastructure of the inner segments of the retinal rods of the guinea pig eye as revealed by electron microscopy. *J. Cell. Physiol. 42:* 45, 1953.

8. PERUTZ, M. F., KENDREW, J. C., AND WATSON, H. C. Structure and function of haemoglobin. II. Some relations between polypeptide chain configuration and amino acid sequence. *J. Molec. Biol. 13:* 669, 1965.

9. DICKERSON, R. E., KOPKA, M. L., WEINZIERL, J., VARNUM, J., EISENBERG, D., AND MARGOLIASH, E. Location of the heme in horse heart ferricytochrome *c* by x-ray diffraction. *J. Biol. Chem. 242:* 3015, 1967.

10. FLEISCHER, S., FLEISCHER, B., AND STOECKENIUS, W. Fine structure of lipid-depleted mitochondria. *J. Cell Biol. 32:* 193, 1967.

11. SJÖSTRAND, F. S. A new repeat structural element of mitochondria and certain cytoplasmic membranes. *Nature (London) 199:* 1262, 1963.

12. SJÖSTRAND, F. S. A new ultrastructural element of the membranes in mitochondria and of some cytoplasmic membranes. *J. Ultrastruct. Res. 9:* 340, 1963.

13. SJÖSTRAND, F. S. The structures of the cellular membranes and cell membrane contacts in the nervous system. In *Biochemistry and Pharmacology of the Basal Ganglia: Proceedings of the Second Symposium of the Parkinson's Disease Information and Research Center, Columbia University, New York, 1965*, edited by Costa, E., Côte, L. J., and Yahr, M. D., pp. 17–41. New York, Raven Press, 1966.

14. SJÖSTRAND, F. S. The structure of cellular membranes. *Protoplasma 63:* 248, 1967.

15. SJÖSTRAND, F. S. Molecular structure and function of cellular membranes. *Protides Biol. Fluids 15:* 15, 1967.

16. SJÖSTRAND, F. S., AND BARAJAS, L. Effects of modifications in conformation of protein molecules on structure of mitochondrial membranes. *J. Ultrastruct. Res. 25:* 121, 1968.

17. PEASE, D. C. The preservation of unfixed cytological detail by dehydration with "inert" agents. *J. Ultrastruct. Res. 14:* 356, 1966.

18. SAGE, H. J., AND SINGER, S. J. A spectrophotometric titration of ribonuclease in ethylene glycol. *Biochin. Biophys. Acta 29:* 663, 1958.

19. QUIOCHO, F. A., AND RICHARDS, F. M. Intermolecular cross-linking of a protein in the crystalline state: Carboxypeptidase-A. *Proc. Nat. Acad. Sci. U.S.A. 52:* 833, 1964.

20. QUIOCHO, F. A., AND RICHARDS, F. M. The enzymic behavior of carboxypeptidase-A in the solid state. *Biochemistry (Wash.) 5:* 4062, 1966.

20a. SJÖSTRAND, F. S. A new ultrastructural element of the membranes in mitochondria and of some cytoplasmic membranes. *J. Ultrastruct. Res. 9:* 340, 1963.

21. SJÖSTRAND, F. S. Morphological aspects of lipoprotein structures. In *Structural and Functional Aspects of Lipoproteins in Living Systems*, edited by Tria, E., and Scanu, A. M., pp. 73–128. New York, Academic Press, Inc. 1969.

21a. SJÖSTRAND, F. S. Molecular structure and function of cellular membranes. In *Regulatory Functions of Biological Membranes*, edited by Järnefelt, J., pp. 1–20. Amsterdam, Elsevier Publishing Company, 1968.

22. SJÖSTRAND, F. S., AND BARAJAS, L. A new model for mitochondrial membranes based on structural and on biochemical information. *J. Ultrastruct. Res. 32:* 293, 1970.

23. CHANCE, B., AND SPENCER, E. L., JR. Stabilization of "steady states" of cytochromes at liquid nitrogen temperatures. *Discuss. Faraday Soc. 27:* 200, 1959.

24. VILLEGAS, R., AND BARNOLA, F. V. Characterization of the resting axolemma in the giant axon of the squid. *J. Gen. Physiol. 44:* 963, 1961.

25. MOORE, J. W., NARAHASHI, T., AND SHAW, T. I. An upper limit to the number of sodium channels in nerve membranes? *J. Physiol. (London) 188:* 99, 1967.

26. O'BRIEN, J. S., AND SAMPSON, E. L. Fatty acid and fatty aldehyde composition of the major brain lipids in normal gray matter, white matter, and myelin. *J. Lipid Res. 6:* 545, 1965.

27. PARK, R. B., AND PON, N. G. Correlation of structure with function in *Spinacea oleracea* chloroplasts. *J. Molec. Biol. 3:* 1, 1961.

28. MADDY, A. H., AND MALCOLM, B. R. Protein conformation in the plasma membrane. *Science 150:* 1616, 1965.

29. FLEISCHER, S., AND MCCONNELL, D. G. Prelimi-

nary observations on the lipids of bovine retinal outer segment disks. *Nature (London) 212:* 1366, 1966.

30. SJÖSTRAND, F. S. The ultrastructure of the retinal receptors of the vertebrate eye. *Ergebn. Biol. 21:* 128, 1959.

31. COLLINS, F. D., LOVE, R. M., AND MORTON, R. A. The preparation of rhodopsin and the chemical composition of rod outer segments. *Biochem. J. 48:* xxxv, 1951.

32. SPIRO, M. J., AND MCKIBBIN, J. M. The lipides of rat liver cell fractions. *J. Biol. Chem. 219:* 643, 1956.

33. CRIDDLE, R. S., BOCK, R. M., GREEN, D. E., AND TISDALE, H. Physical characteristics of proteins of the electron transfer system and interpretation of the structure of the mitochondrion. *Biochemistry (Wash.) 1:* 827, 1962.

34. GOLDBERGER, R., SMITH, A. L., TISDALE, H., AND BOMSTEIN, R. Studies of the electron transport system. XXXVII. Isolation and properties of mammalian cytochrome *b*. *J. Biol. Chem. 236:* 2788, 1961.

35. SINGER, T. P., KEARNEY, E. B., AND BERNATH, P. Studies on succinic dehydrogenase. II. Isolation

and properties of the dehydrogenase from beef heart. *J. Biol. Chem. 223:* 599, 1956.

36. RACKER, E. *Mechanisms in Bioenergetics*, New York, Academic Press, Inc., 1965.

37. AMBE, K. S., AND VENKATARAMAN, A. Depolymerization of cytochrome oxidase to a water-soluble monomeric protein. *Biochem. Biophys. Res. Commun. 1:* 133, 1959.

38. CRIDDLE, R. S., AND BOCK, R. M. On the physical-chemical properties of water-soluble cytochrome oxidase. *Biochem. Biophys. Res. Commun. 1:* 138, 1959.

39. KIMURA, T., AND SINGER, T. P. Choline dehydrogenase from rat liver. In *Methods in Enzymology*, edited by Colowick, S. P., and Kaplan, N. O., Vol. 5, p. 562. New York, Academic Press, Inc., 1962.

40. SINGER, T. P., MASSEY, V., AND KEARNEY, E. B. Newer knowledge of succinic dehydrogenase. *Advances Enzym. 18:* 65, 1957.

41. RINGLER, R. L. Studies on the mitochondrial α-glycerophosphate dehydrogenase. II. Extraction and partial purification of the dehydrogenase from pig brain. *J. Biol. Chem. 236:* 1192, 1961.

2

ELECTRON MICROSCOPY OF MEMBRANES IN THE NATURAL STATE

D. F. Parsons

This appears to be an appropriate time to review the achievements and problems of analysis of the structure of membranes using the electron microscope and to discuss future approaches. I will do this quite broadly, and mainly in relation to the questions of whether the images so far obtained are useful or mainly artifact.

The introduction of a practical thin-sectioning method for cells in 1948 revealed that all cells are compartmentalized by numerous membranes of nearly uniform thickness (60–100 Å). Robertson (1) then pointed out the striking triple-layered appearance of most cell membranes and suggested that many membranes have the same unit structure. This appeared to confirm the unitary bilayer structure model proposed much earlier by Davson and Danielli (2). At this time there was considerable optimism that the electron microscope images were sufficiently free from artifacts to be reliable and that all membranes might be built on quite a simple bilayer basis. Subsequently, as the working magnifications progressed upward into the hundreds of thousands, more and more questions began to be raised about the fidelity of the thin-section im-

age. Fortunately, the recent introduction of the much less objectional freeze-etching technique has confirmed the main features of the distribution, shape, and approximate thickness of cell membranes. The main uncertainties are in the reliability of images showing details of the surface structure and details of the interior of membranes.

ELECTRON IMAGES OF THE SURFACE STRUCTURE OF MEMBRANES

The topography of the mucopolysaccharide coats of cell membranes remains a virtually unexplored field. This is very unfortunate because of its relevance to such questions as the nature of cell adhesion, the separation of cell surfaces, antigenicity of cell surfaces, the structural basis of loss of contact inhibition, and metastasis. Because of the highly charged character of the polysaccharide coat it probably, also, influences ion transport. It may also be involved in phagocytosis.

The polysaccharide is visualized less well in the electron microscope than with special stains in the light microscope. Usually, with ascites cells that obviously have thick mucopolysaccharide layers in the light microscope, no sign of the layers is seen in the classical thin-section technique using osmic acid-fixed material. The polysaccharide layers of intestinal epithelial cells show more frequently with some variants of the glutaraldehyde-osmic acid fix-

Roswell Park Memorial Institute, Buffalo, New York 14203 and Department of Biophysics, State University of New York at Buffalo, Buffalo, New York 14214.

Supported by National Science Foundation Grants GB-8235 and GB-7130 and National Institutes of Health Grant GM 16454-01.

ing and embedding technique, but the rationale of chemical fixing or cross-linking of mucopolysaccharide has never been successfully worked out. Probably, the problem here is the chemical instability of the sugars in the polysaccharide toward strong oxidants such as osmium tetroxide. Even if chemical fixation is improved, the reliability of the thin-section images will depend on having confirmation by at least one other technique. Unfortunately, the thin-section appearances (long strands) reported for the mucopolysaccharide of intestinal villi surfaces (3) were not confirmed by negative staining studies (4) where the long strands were not seen. Perhaps the polysaccharide layer is too loose and hydrated and becomes embedded in the negative stain. Freeze-etching has provided little or no evidence of the structure of the polysaccharide external layer of membranes, possibly because of the large water content of this structure and because of the limited resolution of the metal shadowing used to reveal the structures on the cleared and etched ice surface. In the near future we look forward to the possibility of high voltage electron microscopy of the surfaces of cells in the natural state using a hydration chamber and dark field microscopy. Isolated, cultured normal and cancer cells and cells in contact with each other could be examined in this way.

Negative staining has shown several interesting features of surface projections of cell membranes. The surface of the inner membranes of mitochondria was found to be covered with 90-Å diameter knob-like projections (5, 6) now thought to be ATPase molecules. The identification of these as normal structures is made difficult by the necessity of fragmenting mitochondria in order to expose the structures to the negative stain, and by the fact that the structures are not seen consistently by the thin-section or the freeze-etch technique. In addition, negative stains vary in their effect on such structures since neutral phosphotungstate preserves the struc-

tures while neutral silicotungstates tend to break up the structures.

ELECTRON IMAGES OF THE INTERIOR STRUCTURE OF MEMBRANES

The contribution of the electron microscope to visualizing the interior structure of membranes has been as disappointing as attempts to show surface structures. Now that commercial microscopes are available with 4-Å point resolution, it is puzzling that the arrangement of protein and lipid molecules inside the membrane cannot be established by direct visualization. It may be just feasible to do this using positive staining techniques, although the large size of the stain deposits (10–15 Å) and their ill-defined location makes this doubtful. In any case, it will be necessary before accepting either the triple layer structure of Robertson (1) or the globular structure of Sjöstrand (7) to establish that the proteins and lipids were not lost or rearranged as a consequence of the thin-section embedding process. Recently, in our laboratory (8, 9), we have shown by comparing X-ray diffraction and electron microscopy of myelin that severe changes occur during electron microscope processing of myelin. Figure 2.1a shows the X-ray pattern of the fresh frog sciatic nerve and Figure 2.1b the same after glutaraldehyde fixation. All purification procedures tried resulted in a shift of intensity distribution indicating a significant molecular rearrangement even though the periodicity did not change. The intensity distribution of the osmium tetroxide-fixed nerve (Fig. 2.1c) is difficult to interpret since the scattering of the osmium predominates. However, the shrinking in periodicity indicates that molecular rearrangement has occurred because our recent X-ray analysis (10–12) of the structure of fresh frog sciatic nerve shows that there are no water layers thicker than 10 Å between membranes.

However, apart from these modifications

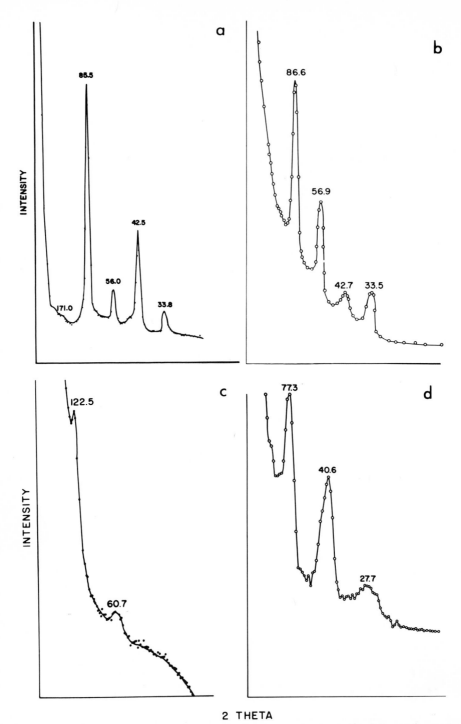

2 THETA

Figure 2.1. X-ray diffraction of the myelin membrane of frog sciatic nerve at different stages of the electron microscope thin-section fixing and embedding procedures. a, Fresh nerve; b, Nerve fixed in buffered, redistilled glutaraldehyde; c, Nerve fixed in Palade's osmium tetroxide; d, Osmium tetroxide-fixed nerve dehydrated with acetone. Data taken with a Kratky camera and proportional detector.

by the fixative, there is a more serious change discernible by X-ray diffraction following dehydration by acetone, ethanol, or methanol (Fig. 2.1d). These solvents extract a large fraction of the cholesterol and a variable fraction of the acid lipids, and may also have the effect of rearranging lipids as a result of substituting the polar water interface for a less polar solvent one. The X-ray patterns show a complete rearrangement of intensity and a shrinkage in periodicity. The loss of successive orders of reflections indicates that not only is the molecular arrangement inside the fixed and dehydrated myelin membrane completely different from that of the fresh nerve, but also it is less regular in its internal structure. X-ray diffraction of the subsequent (final) step of embedding in resin showed little further change.

This type of approach of cross-correlating the structures derived from X-ray diffraction and electron microscopy can only be applied to the two known examples of membranes which occur naturally in a regularly stacked arrangement, myelin and retinal rods. Numerous attempts in our laboratory to stack purified fragments of other types of membranes were only partially successful. Only if the membranes form a very regular stack is sufficient detail obtained in the X-ray pattern to give an adequate electron density map across the membrane. However, even if phasing is not available to calculate the electron density map, the X-ray check of the embedding and fixing procedure in terms of redistribution of intensity and change in periodicity is a valuable one.

Reluctantly, we have to conclude that no satisfactory electron microscope method is available for settling our seemingly interminable discussions about the arrangement of lipid and proteins inside membranes. The time has come to review the whole process of specimen preparation and the various possible imaging mechanisms in order to see if the electron microscope approach can be re-utilized and the pres-

ently available 4-Å point resolution made effective. The ultimate objective is to be able to recognize different kinds of molecules in the membrane and to obtain some indication of their conformation.

THE MAIN CAUSES OF ARTIFACTS IN ELECTRON MICROSCOPE IMAGES OF CELL MEMBRANES

From the above discussion we can list the following.

1. Rearrangement by chemical fixation.
2. Lipid extraction by dehydration solvents with possible reorientation due to change in dielectric constant.
3. Incapability of metal staining or contrasting techniques to show detail at the small molecule level because of the large size (10–15 Å) of the metal deposits formed and their arbitrary placement around the molecules.

Basically, what is required is the possibility of examining fresh, non-chemically treated and non-stained membranes in their natural state. This requires the solution of three technical problems.

1. Obtaining contrast electron optically (by phase contrast or dark field contrast).
2. Examining membranes in the hydrated state in order to eliminate the known lipid rearrangements that occur on vacuum drying.
3. Protecting the non-cross linked unstained membranes from their presumably increased susceptibility to electron beam damage.

NEW APPROACHES TO ELECTRON MICROSCOPY OF MEMBRANES IN THEIR NATURAL STATE

Because of the success of the Zernicke phase contrast microscope in light optics as a method of examining unstained material, we are naturally hopeful about the possibilities for an analogous in-focus phase contrast system. In its simplest form a thin carbon film of 240-Å thickness (for

$\pi/2$ phase shift at 100-kV acceleration voltage) with a central hole of 6-μ diameter is placed in the back focal plane of the objective lens. The primary beam passes through the hole while the scattered beam is phase retarded by the film to provide the phase contrast in the image. In practice, there are many difficulties connected with charging and contamination of the phase plate. Astigmatism is especially troublesome. H. M. Johnson of our laboratory is now working on phase-shifting systems dependent on a particular electrostatic potential distribution which appears more promising.

Recently, there has been a revival of interest in dark field microscopy of unstained biological objects. There are indications that the resolution is mainly controlled by chromatic aberration arising from the specimen and only influenced by spherical aberration to a lesser extent. A necessary condition for obtaining good resolution is to use thin ($<$50-Å thickness) carbon support film and to only attempt to visualize thin objects such as single molecules, tails of bacteriophage viruses, etc. At high voltage (1 million volts) thicker objects can be examined with good resolution because of the marked decrease in chromatic aberration with increasing voltage. Recently, Dupouy *et al.* (13) have shown high contrast for single surface-spread DNA molecules and Ottensmeyer (14) has shown dark field images of single molecules of transfer RNA. Recently, in our laboratory, we have quantitatively compared strioscopic (central beam stop) dark field and bright field contrast of very thin layers of carbon (15) and find that in bright field at 25-Å step on a 100-Å film is visible (5% contrast), while in strioscopic dark field a 5-Å step is visible on a 100-Å film. The strioscopic method gives even larger improvements in contrast for unsupported thin objects. The prospects for obtaining details of unstained membrane structure by dark field now appear good.

There are many advantages to examining membrane preparations at extra high voltage (1 million volts) (16). These include the improvement in dark field microscopy as a result of the reduction in chromatic aberration, the possibility of a point resolution approaching 1 Å, increased penetration allowing stereoscopy of thick sections (up to 1-μ thickness), and reduction of beam damage over the 100-kV level by a factor somewhere between 4 and 10 times as a result of the reduction in the ratio of inelastic scattering cross-section/ elastic cross-section. A further factor of beam damage reduction of about 10 times is possible by use of an image intensifier with TV camera and video-disc recording.

In recent work in our laboratory, by R. Moretz and V. Matricardi, we have constructed a differentially pumped specimen chamber for maintaining the specimen in a hydrated state for electron microscopy and electron diffraction. In this system water vapor at 34° C and 32 torr pressure is admitted to a microchamber at 34° C closed by two 70-μ apertures. The wet specimen grid is placed between these apertures. Water vapor escapes through the apertures and is pumped off by a cryogenic pump and a diffusion pump, leaving the rest of the microscope at normal vacuum pressure. To date, with this system, we have carried out electron microscopy (Fig. 2.2) and electron diffraction on water droplets. Single droplets remain in the beam for more than 40 seconds. Using an image intensifier to reduce beam heating the droplets would probably remain much longer. In current work electron diffraction of wet, unfixed catalase crystals is being attempted. If successful, we shall proceed to collect the electron diffraction patterns of hydrated preparations of many types of membranes. We expect the electron diffraction patterns from wet membranes to give important symmetry and subunit constraints on the possible models for any particular membrane.

At this time it appears that optimum biological electron microscopy will be obtained on 1-million volt instruments fitted

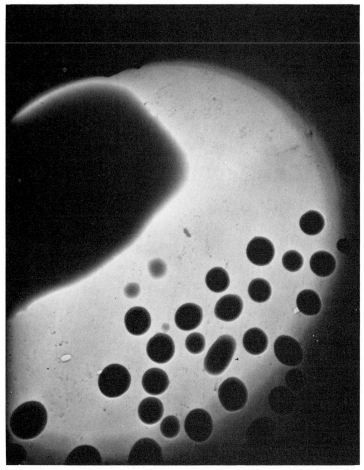

Figure 2.2. Various types of water droplets formed by condensation in a hydration chamber (beam current, 15 μA; 80 kV). The drops can be observed to grow and coalesce. If the water vapor supply is shut off, the water drops disappear (Negative no. 4442). $\times 4,700$.

with an image intensifier. Techniques are also available for on-line analog and digital (fast Fourier transform) image processing. With the increased penetration and decreased chromatic aberration there appear to be real possibilities for examining the surfaces of living cells using the type of hydration chamber described above.

CONCLUSIONS

1. Artifacts and limitations in current electron microscopy of membranes have prevented the reliable establishment of any features of the external surfaces or interior structure of cell membranes.

2. The new field of topography of the external polysaccharide layer of membranes remains virtually unexplored.

3. The only reliable evidence of internal organization of a membrane comes from recent improvements in the X-ray analysis of sciatic nerve myelin.

4. All metal-contrasting techniques are unsatisfactory and there is an urgent need for electron optical methods of obtaining contrast.

5. Both phase contrast and dark field

methods appear promising as high contrast imaging modes.

6. Differentially pumped hydration chambers have been successfully constructed and promise to allow electron microscopy and electron diffraction of wet membranes. At 1 million volts there now appears to be a real possibility of examining the surfaces of whole mounts of living cells.

SUMMARY

Further details of membrane structure are no longer readily forthcoming as a result of simple modifications of the specimen preparation technique and a new approach to electron microscopy is required. Positive and negative staining techniques require to be replaced by electron optical contrast methods (phase contrast and dark field). The recent introduction of differentially pumped specimen hydration chambers, especially when used at extra high acceleration voltage (1 MeV), opens up possibilities of electron microscopy and electron diffraction of cell membranes in a near natural state.

Small angle X-ray diffraction of myelin at different stages of the electron microscope thin-section processing technique, shows that severe artifacts occur and the significance and interpretation of the three-layered appearance of sectioned membranes must be reconsidered.

Acknowledgments. It is a pleasure to acknowledge collaboration and discussions with my students, C. K. Akers, H. M. Johnson, and R. C. Moretz; also with Drs. V. Matricardi and W. Claffey of this laboratory.

REFERENCES

1. ROBERTSON, J. D. The ultrastructure of cell membranes and their derivatives. *Biochem. Soc. Sympos. 16:* 1, 1959.
2. DAVSON, H., AND DANIELLI, J. F. *The Permeability of Natural Membranes*, New York, Cambridge University Press, 1943.
3. ITO, S. The enteric surface coat on cat intestinal microvilli. *J. Cell Biol. 27:* 475, 1965.
4. OVERTON, J., EICHHOLZ, A., AND CRANE, R. K. Studies on the brush border in intestinal epithelial cells. II. Fine structure of fractions of Tris-disrupted hamster brush borders. *J. Cell Biol. 26:* 693, 1965.
5. FERNANDEZ-MORAN, H. Cell membrane ultrastructure, low-temperature electron microscopy and x-ray diffraction studies of lipoprotein components in lamellar systems. *Circulation 26:* 1039, 1962.
6. PARSONS, D. F. Mitochondrial structure: Two types of subunits on negatively stained mitochondrial membranes. *Science 140:* 985, 1963.
7. SJÖSTRAND, F. S. A new ultrastructural element of the membranes in mitochondria and some cytoplasmic membranes. *J. Ultrastruct. Res. 9:* 340, 1963.
8. MORETZ, R. C., AKERS, C. K., AND PARSONS, D. F. Use of small angle x-ray diffraction to investigate disordering of membranes during preparation for electron microscopy. I. Osmium tetroxide and potassium permanganate. *Biochim. Biophys. Acta 193:* 1, 1969.
9. MORETZ, R. C., AKERS, C. K., AND PARSONS, D. F. Use of small angle x-ray diffraction to investigate disordering of membranes during preparation for electron microscopy. II. Aldehydes. *Biochim. Biophys. Acta 193:* 12, 1969.
10. AKERS, C. K., AND PARSONS, D. F. X-ray diffraction of myelin membrane. I. Optimal conditions for obtaining unmodified small angle diffraction data from frog sciatic nerve. *Biophys. J. 10:* 101, 1970.
11. AKERS, C. K., AND PARSONS, D. F. X-ray diffraction of myelin membrane. II. Determination of the phase angles of the frog sciatic nerve by heavy atom labeling and calculation of the electron density distribution of the membrane. *Biophys. J. 10:* 116, 1970.
12. PARSONS, D. F., AND AKERS, C. K. Neutron diffraction of cell membranes (myelin). *Science 165:* 1016, 1969.
13. DUPOUY, G., PERRIER, F., ENJALBERT, L., LAPCHINE, L., AND VERDIER, P. Accroissement du contraste des images d'objets amorphes en

microscopie electronique. *C. R. Acad. Sci. [D] (Paris) 262B:* 1341, 1969.

14. OTTENSMEYER, F. P. Macromolecular fine structure by dark field electron microscopy. *Biophys. J. 9:* 1144, 1969.

15. JOHNSON, H. M., AND PARSONS, D. F. Enhanced contrast in electron microscopy of unstained biological material. I. Strioscopy (dark field microscopy). *J. Micr. 90:* 199, 1969.

16. DUPOUY, G. Electron microscopy at very high voltages. *Advances Opt. Electron Micr. 2:* 167, 1968.

3

ENZYMATIC PROPERTIES OF MEMBRANE-AS-SOCIATED CELL FRACTIONS AS RELATED TO DRUG METABOLISM

Sten Orrenius and Lars Ernster

It is the purpose of this chapter to give a survey of current knowledge concerning the microsomal hydroxylating enzyme system of various mammalian tissues, with special reference to drug metabolism.

It is now 15 years since Brodie and associates (1) discovered the drug-metabolizing activity of liver microsomes. They showed (1–3) that in the presence of NADPH and molecular oxygen, liver microsomes catalyze the hydroxylation of a variety of drugs and that, depending on the chemical nature of the drug, the reaction may lead to the oxidation of an aromatic ring or a hydrocarbon side chain, an oxidative dealkylation or deamination, or the formation of a sulfoxide. The system was similar to that first described 7 years earlier by Mueller and Miller (4, 5) who had found that liver homogenates supplemented with NADH or NADPH in the presence of O_2 catalyzed the oxidative demethylation of the carcinogenic dye 4-dimethylaminoazobenzene to 4-amino-azobenzene and formaldehyde. Later it was found (*cf.* reference 6 for review) that microsomes from liver, adrenal cortex, testis, ovary, and placenta catalyze an NADPH- and O_2-dependent hydroxyla-

tion of various steroids and that a steroid-hydroxylating system is also present in adrenal cortex mitochondria. Furthermore, the same system was found to be involved in the hydroxylation of aliphatic hydrocarbons and the ω-oxidation of fatty acids (7–9).

COMPONENTS AND REACTIONS OF THE HYDROXYLATING ENZYME SYSTEM

The hydroxylating enzyme system has been termed as a "mixed function oxidase" (10) or "monooxygenase" (11), since in the course of the reaction, one of the oxygen atoms of O_2 is incorporated into the compound undergoing hydroxylation, and the other into H_2O. The process may be described by the general equation:

$$RH + NADPH + H^+ + O_2 \rightarrow ROH + NADP^+ + H_2O$$

where RH is the substrate and ROH the product of the hydroxylation reaction.

It is now fairly well established that the microsomal hydroxylating system consists of at least two catalytic components: a cytochrome called P-450 (12, 13); and the flavoprotein catalyzing the reduction of this cytochrome by NADPH, suitably termed NADPH-cytochrome P-450 reductase. Cytochrome P-450 is characterized by a sensitivity to carbon monoxide (14, 15), which binds to the reduced form of the cytochrome, giving rise to a

Department of Biochemistry, University of Stockholm, Stockholm, Sweden.

Work quoted from the authors' laboratory has been supported by grants from the Swedish Cancer Society.

characteristic absorption spectrum with a maximum at 450 nm. The cytochrome is easily denatured and converted into a hemochromogen with a shift of the absorption maximum of its CO-complex to 420 nm (12, 13). It is only recently that successful attempts have been reported toward an extraction of cytochrome P-450 from microsomes in its native form (16, 17) by a procedure that involves the use of glycerol and deoxycholate. The "solubilized" cytochrome P-450 has been used for a reconstruction of the hydroxylating system, with NADPH-cytochrome P-450 reductase and a phospholipid fraction as additional components. A cytochrome P-450 has been purified from *Pseudomonas putida*, where it is involved in the hydroxylation of camphor (18).

The flavoprotein NADPH-cytochrome P-450 reductase most probably is closely related to the enzyme known since 1950 as NADPH-cytochrome *c* reductase (19), which in recent years has been purified and studied in great detail by several groups of investigators (20–22). The purified enzyme has the interesting property of catalyzing a one-electron transfer from NADPH to cytochrome *c*, its prosthetic group FAD undergoing cyclic oxidoreductions between the half-reduced (free radical) and fully reduced states (23). Cytochrome *c* appears to serve merely as an artificial electron acceptor for the enzyme, as does vitamin K_3 (menaquinone) and various redox dyes.

Whether the flavoprotein interacts directly with cytochrome P-450 in the course of the hydroxylation process is not known, and there are indications that this may not be the case. For example, neotetrazolium chloride can serve as an electron acceptor for NADPH oxidation in liver microsomes through a reaction that is insensitive to CO, *i.e.*, that does not involve cytochrome P-450, but shares the sensitivity of the hydroxylating system to sulfhydryl reagents, in contrast to the NADPH-cytochrome *c* and -menaquinone reductase reactions (24). Neotetrazolium

chloride thus appears to interact with the system at a site intermediate between the flavoprotein and cytochrome P-450. The same holds true for the iron-pyrophosphate catalyzed peroxidation of microsomal lipids (25, 26). The possibility has been considered (27) that unsaturated microsomal lipids may serve as intermediate electron carriers between the NADPH-oxidating flavoprotein and cytochrome P-450.

There is also evidence (28, 29) for an interaction of the NADPH-linked hydroxylating system with the NADH-cytochrome *c* reductase present in liver microsomes (*cf.* reference 30), consisting of the flavoprotein NADH-cytochrome b_5 reductase and cytochrome b_5. Such an interaction is indicated by the fact that, in liver microsomes, NADH is capable of reducing cytochrome P-450 and, conversely, NADPH can serve as a reducing agent for cytochrome b_5, although the rates of these "cross-reactions" are lower than those of the NADPH-cytochrome P-450 reductase and NADH-cytochrome b_5 reductase, respectively. Recent evidence (31, 32) suggests that these cross-reactions are not due to lack of specificity of the flavoproteins with respect to the reduced nicotinamide nucleotides, but rather to an interaction between the two electron-transport chains in the flavin → cytochrome region, through intermediates that yet remain to be identified.

The hydroxylating system of adrenal cortex mitochondria also contains cytochrome P-450, but differs from the microsomal system with respect to the flavoprotein (33). The NADPH-oxidizing flavoprotein of adrenal cortex mitochondria does not react as such with cytochrome *c*, and its interaction with cytochrome P-450 is mediated by a non-heme iron protein (33–36), which also can serve as an electron-transport link of the flavoprotein to cytochrome *c*. The system utilizes intramitochondrial NADPH as the electron donor (37) and is localized in the inner membrane of the mitochondria (38).

Liver mitochondria also have been reported to contain a hydroxylating system which catalyzes an NADPH-dependent hydroxylation of kynurenine, and which is localized in the outer mitochondrial membrane (39, 40). The latter contains little if any NADPH-cytochrome c reductase and no cytochrome P-450 (41), and it has been suggested (40) that the kynurenine hydroxylase reaction, which is insensitive to CO, may involve the cytochrome b_5-like hemoprotein present in the outer membrane of liver mitochondria (41).

BINDING OF SUBSTRATE TO CYTOCHROME P-450

There is now ample evidence that the reaction catalyzed by the hydroxylating system involves a binding of the substrate to cytochrome P-450. Such a binding has been demonstrated by means of experiments involving incubation of microsomal suspensions with isotopically labeled drugs and subsequent determination of the drug in the reisolated microsomes (42) and, in a more specific manner, by spectral changes that occur when various substrates capable of undergoing hydroxylation are added to a suspension of microsomes (43–45). The spectral changes obtained with various substrates can be divided into two classes as illustrated in Figure 3.1: a type I spectral change, characterized by a peak at about 385 nm and a trough at about 420 nm; and a type II spectral change, characterized by a trough in the 400-nm region and a peak in the 430-nm region of the difference spectrum of the microsomes. That these spectral changes reflect binding of the substrate to cytochrome P-450 is shown by the fact that they are also observed with solubilized microsomal cytochrome P-450 (17) as well as with the cytochrome P-450 purified from *P. putida* (46). Of the two types of spectral changes, type I is generally believed to be due to a binding of the substrate to the apoprotein

of the cytochrome, whereas type II may at least partly be due to an interaction between the substrate and the heme prosthetic group. It is the type I spectral change that appears to be directly related to the hydroxylating activity. Strong evidence for this relationship comes from the finding that the binding constants (K_s) of various substrates, defined as the concentrations giving half-maximal type I spectral change, closely parallel their Michaelis constants (K_m) with respect to the hydroxylation system; data in Table 3.1 illustrate this correlation.

The reaction sequence catalyzed by the microsomal hydroxylating system may thus be visualized to consist of the following steps (*cf.* reference 47): (a) Reduction of the flavoprotein by NADPH; (b) Binding of substrate to the oxidized form of cytochrome P-450; (c) Reduction of the cytochrome P-450-substrate complex by the reduced flavoprotein; (d) Binding of O_2 to the reduced complex; (e) Dissociation of the oxidized cytochrome P-450 and the oxidized product.

SUBSTRATE SPECIFICITY

A problem of considerable interest concerns the substrate specificity of the hydroxylating system. The overwhelming evidence now available for a direct interaction between the substrate and cytochrome P-450 in the course of the hydroxylating process makes it very unlikely that any further enzymes would be involved in the activation of the various substrates. The question therefore arises as to whether one and the same cytochrome P-450 participates in the hydroxylation of the great variety of compounds that can serve as substrates of this enzyme system, or whether there exist different molecular species of cytochrome P-450, each specific for a given compound or group of compounds. If the latter is the case, a further question is whether the various species of cytochrome P-450 are reduced through a common NADPH-cy-

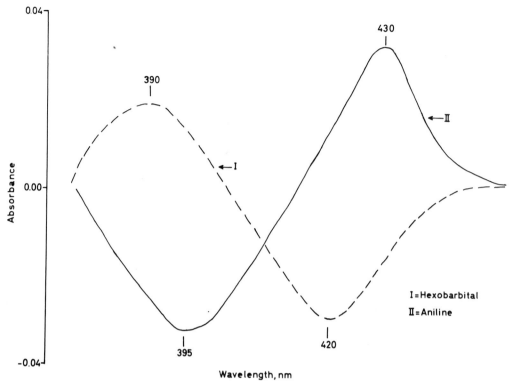

Figure 3.1. Spectral changes produced by the addition of hexobarbital (I) and aniline (II) to suspensions of rat liver microsomes. Each cuvette contained, in a volume of 2.9 ml, 3 mg of microsomal protein and 50 mM Tris-Cl buffer, pH 7.5. Hexobarbital or aniline was added to the sample cuvette in a final concentration of 3.3 mM.

TABLE 3.1

Concentrations of Substances Required for Half-Maximal Enzyme Activities (K_m) and Half-Maximal Spectral Changes (K_s)

Substrate	K_m	K_s	Reference
	μM	μM	
Hexobarbital	100	80	(45)
Testosterone	10	8	(85)
Laurate	6	4	(49, 85)

tochrome P-450 reductase or each one is reduced through a separate reductase.

It has been shown (48–50) that various substrates inhibit in a competitive manner the hydroxylation of each other when added in combination to liver microsomes in the presence of an excess of NADPH and oxygen. This effect which is illustrated in Figure 3.2, and which has also been demonstrated with the isolated, perfused liver (51), is of considerable pharmacological interest, since it explains the well-known clinical finding that drugs administered in combination may prolong each other's action and suggests, furthermore, that a similar interaction may occur between drugs and other substrates of the hydroxylating system, *e.g.*, steroid hormones. The competitive relationship among various substrates with respect to their metabolism appears to eliminate the involvement of separate NADPH-cytochrome P-450 reductases in the hydroxylating system. However, it does not exclude the existence of several species of cytochrome P-450. Clearly, if the NADPH-cytochrome P-450 reductase portion of the hydroxylating system is rate-limiting for the over-all process, and

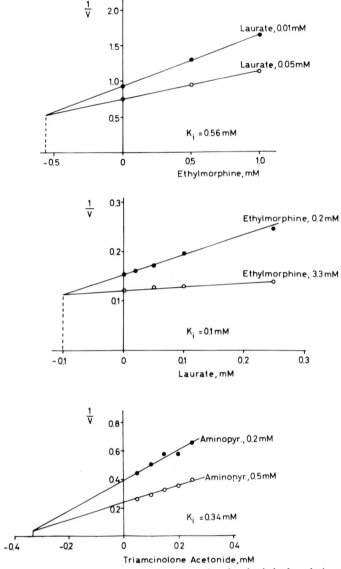

Figure 3.2. Competitive inhibition by various substances of each other's hydroxylation in rat liver microsomes. For experimental conditions see references (49) and (50).

there are reasons to believe that so indeed is the case (47, 52), then different substrates will compete with each other's hydroxylation regardless of whether they utilize the same or different species of cytochrome P-450.

A further approach to this problem may be based on investigation of the effect of various substrates of the hydroxylating system on their binding to cytochrome P-450. It is logical to assume that, if two substrates were bound to two different species of cytochrome P-450, they would give rise to an additive spectral change when both are added to microsomes. If, on the other hand, they interact with the same species of cytochrome P-450, then saturation of the microsomes with respect to one substrate would eliminate the occurrence of a further spectral change upon the addition of the second substrate. Experiments shown in Figure 3.3, performed with hexobarbital and testosterone as substrates, clearly demonstrate that the latter alternative is the case, indicating that these two substrates

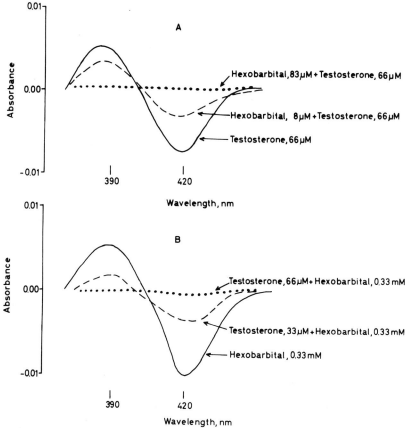

Figure 3.3. Interaction of hexobarbital and testosterone in their binding to cytochrome P-450 of rat liver microsomes.

A. Inhibition by hexobarbital of the magnitude of the type I spectral change produced by testosterone. Each cuvette contained, in a volume of 2.9 ml, 4 mg of microsomal protein in a 50 mM Tris-Cl–15 mM KCl medium, pH 7.5. ——, Testosterone (66 μM) was added in 20 μl of ethanol to the sample cuvette; – – –, Hexobarbital (8 μM) was added to both the sample and reference cuvettes. Testosterone (66 μM) was added in 20 μl of ethanol to the sample cuvette; · · · ·, Hexobarbital (83 μM) was added to both the sample and the reference cuvettes. Testosterone (66 μM) was added in 20 μl of ethanol to the sample cuvette. When testosterone was absent the same amount of ethanol was added.

B. Inhibition by testosterone of the magnitude of the type I spectral change produced by hexobarbital. Each cuvette contained, in a volume of 2.9 ml, 4 mg of microsomal protein in a 50 mM Tris-Cl–15 mM KCl medium, pH 7.5. ——, Hexobarbital (0.33 mM) was added to the sample cuvette; – – –, Testosterone (33 μM) was added in 20 μl of ethanol to both the sample and the reference cuvettes. Hexobarbital (0.33 mM) was added to the sample cuvette; · · · ·, Testosterone (66 μM) was added in 20 μl of ethanol to both the sample and the reference cuvettes. Hexobarbital (0.33 mM) was added to the sample cuvette. When testosterone was absent the same amount of ethanol was added.

interact with the same species of cytochrome P-450. Moreover, as shown in
Figure 3.4, combinations of varying concentrations of the two substrates, as well
as a number of other combinations of
substrates, mutually influence their binding constants in a competitive fashion.
Thus, all of these substrates appear to
bind to the same species of cytochrome
P-450 in liver microsomes.

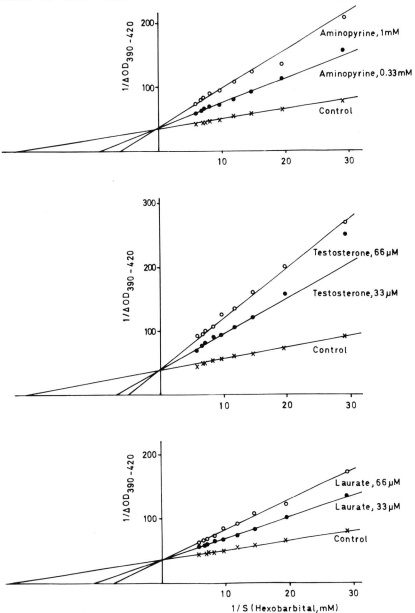

Figure 3.4. Competitive inhibition by aminopyrine, testosterone, and laurate of the magnitude of the type I spectral change produced by the addition of hexobarbital to suspensions of rat liver microsomes. For experimental conditions see reference (85).

Whereas liver microsomes readily catalyze the hydroxylation of various aromatic compounds (including many drugs), certain steroids, and the ω-oxidation of fatty acids, the hydroxylating systems of adrenal cortex microsomes and mitochondria seem to be "specialized" on steroids (*cf.* reference 6). The adrenal cortex microsomal system has a relatively weak capacity to handle drugs and virtually none to catalyze the ω-oxidation of fatty acids (53). Kidney microsomes, on the other hand, which contain only very small amounts of cytochrome P-450, are remarkably active in catalyzing the ω-oxidation of fatty acids (54) while exhibiting little or no activity toward drugs and steroids (55). There is also a pronounced specialization among the hydroxylating systems of various tissues and organelles in regard to their way and ability to handle compounds within a given group of substrates, *e.g.*, steroids (*cf.* reference 6). It is difficult at the present time to rationalize these variations in specificity in relation to the concept of a single molecular species of cytochrome P-450. A possible explanation is that there exist various subspecies (isoenzymes) of cytochrome P-450 with different patterns of substrate specificity and varying in relative abundance within the hydroxylating systems of various tissues and organelles. Alternatively, it is conveivable that the same cytochrome P-450 molecule may assume different patterns of substrate specificity under influence of regulatory devices, *e.g.*, allosteric effectors, present in the particular environments in the membrane structures which surround the cytochrome in the different tissues and organelles.

There is now some evidence (55) that compounds giving rise to a type II spectrum, and thus apparently binding to the cytochrome at a site different from its catalytic site, may promote the binding and metabolism of a substrate. Preliminary experiments show, for example, that testosterone and laurate, both of which are substrates of the hydroxylating system of liver microsomes, giving rise to type I spectral changes and competing with each other in terms of both binding and metabolism, reveal an entirely different relationship in kidney microsomes. Here, laurate is an active substrate, with a well marked type I spectral shift and a high rate of metabolism, whereas testosterone gives rise to a type II-like spectral shift and is not metabolized at an appreciable rate. On the other hand, testosterone in low concentrations enhances the rate of laurate oxidation in kidney microsomes with a simultaneous decrease in binding constant. It thus appears that, whereas in liver microsomes both laurate and testosterone bind to the catalytic site of cytochrome P-450, in kidney microsomes laurate binds to the catalytic site of the cytochrome while testosterone binds to another locus of the enzyme which may have the function of a regulatory site.

TOPOLOGY OF THE HYDROXY-LATING SYSTEM

A problem of considerable current interest concerns the topology of the hydroxylating enzyme system in the microsomal membrane. Studies based on the use of trypsin and other proteolytic enzymes to digest various protein components of liver microsomes have revealed that the flavoprotein component of the hydroxylating system, NADPH-cytochrome *c* reductase, is readily solubilized (21, 22, 56, 57), with a parallel loss of the over-all hydroxylating activity as well as other activities involving the NADPH-linked electron-transport system, such as cytochrome P-450 reductase, neotetrazolium reductase, and lipid peroxidation (31). Cytochrome P-450 as such showed a low trypsin sensitivity and was converted into the P-420 form only after extensive trypsin treatment, without solubilization of the hemochromogen. Interestingly, the converse picture was found (56–58) with the NADH-cytochrome c reductase system, in that the cytochrome moiety of the system, cytochrome b_5, was readily solubilized upon trypsin treatment (although not as readily as NADPH-cytochrome c reductase), whereas its flavoprotein component, NADH-cytochrome b_5 reductase, proved to be highly resistent to solubilization by trypsin. Again, the solubilization of cytochrome b_5 was accompanied by a loss of the over-all NADH-cytochrome c reductase activity (31), and there are indications that this may be due to a modification of cytochrome b_5 (57). From the available information it appears that the two microsomal electron-transport systems are localized in the microsomal membrane with an opposite transversal orientation, in a manner schematically illustrated in Figure 3.5, with the NADPH-linked system having its flavoprotein component, and the NADH-linked system its cytochrome component located near the outside surface of the membrane. Localization of cytochrome P-450 in the inner protein layer of the membrane may account for the well recognized need of lipid solubility for drugs in order to serve as substrates of the hydroxylating system (59).

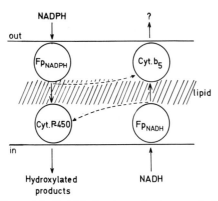

Figure 3.5. Possible topology of microsomal electron-transport systems.

Much work has recently been devoted to the question as to whether the enzymes associated with the microsomal membrane, including the two electron-transport systems, are distributed at random along the endoplasmic reticulum, or whether different enzymes are concentrated in different regions of the reticulum, with a consequent functional specialization of the different regions. As far as the ribosome-carrying and ribosome-free ("rough" and "smooth") segments of the reticulum are concerned, it now appears that these are closely similar in terms of relative enzyme composition (60). Yet an important exception is the case when an enzyme or an enzyme system is in the stage of active induction, in which case there may be a disproportion in the enzyme contents between the two segments. Thus it is found, for example, that during the drug-induced synthesis of the hydroxylating enzyme system, a topic that we shall deal with in greater detail later, the concentration of its enzyme components is higher in the rough than in the smooth microsomes in an early stage of the induction (61), whereas the converse relationship holds in a later stage (61, 62).

Attempts have been made to demonstrate an uneven distribution of various enzymes in subfractions of microsomes obtained by various procedures (63, 64). Such studies have revealed a certain heterogeneity among the various fractions with respect to the relative contents of *e.g.*, the NADPH- and NADH-linked electron-transport systems. This would indicate a functional heterogeneity of different parts of the endoplasmic reticulum. It has also been found (56) that different microsomal enzymes, such as NADPH-cytochrome c reductase and cytochrome b_5, have different turnover rates *in vivo*. It appears, therefore, that in the case of the endoplasmic reticulum, just as in those of other cellular membrane structures, enzyme components may have their individual locations and lifetimes, and thus that a membrane-bound enzyme system represents a strictly organized but still highly dynamic entity, with its components being renewed at different rates.

DRUG-INDUCED ENZYME SYNTHESIS

Administration of drugs in animals is known to induce an increased capacity of the hydroxylating system of liver microsomes (65, 66). It is now well established that the induction process leads to a selective increase in the levels of both the flavoprotein and cytochrome components of the hydroxylating system (67–69), and involves increased rates of both protein and RNA synthesis, as indicated by its sensitivity to puromycin and actinomycin D (68, 70). Simultaneously, there occurs a decrease in the rate of breakdown of at least the flavoprotein (71, 72) which may also contribute to the increased enzyme level. Whether the induction proceeds by way of a direct interaction of the inducing drug with the genetic system, or by way of some mediator of cellular origin, is not known. There are indications of a need for steroid hormones in the induction process (73) and it has been speculated that, since drugs probably alter steroid metabolism by way of the hydroxylating system, steroid hormones might in turn act as mediators in the drug-induced enzyme synthesis.

Various drugs have been shown to have an inducing effect on the metabolism of other drugs (74) as well as steroid hormones (75). This is to be expected, if all of these substances are metabolized through a common enzyme system, and, this phenomenon of mutual inducibility has, in fact, constituted an important argument in favor of the conclusion that the various substrates are metabolized through a common enzyme system. There is, however, an important exception to this rule, which was first recognized by

Conney and associates (*cf.* reference 76) and which concerns a group of carcinogenic compounds, the polycyclic hydrocarbons. When such a compound, *e.g.*, 3,4-benzpyrene or 3-methylcholanthrene, is administered to an animal, already after a single treatment it induces a greatly enhanced liver microsomal hydroxylating activity toward polycyclic hydrocarbons, whereas the activity toward other drugs increases only slightly or not at all. Because of the great interest of these compounds from the point of view of the mechanism of carcinogenesis, much interest has been devoted to this problem over the past years.

Recently several groups of investigators (77–79) made the important observation that the absorption maximum of the cytochrome P-450-CO complex of liver microsomes shifts from 450 to 448 (or 446) nm when a polycyclic hydrocarbon is administered to an animal *in vivo*. It was further found (80) that when a polycyclic hydrocarbon is administered together with a drug exhibiting a normal induction effect, *e.g.*, phenobarbital, the large elevation of the cytochrome content induced by the latter will all be accounted for by the P-448 type (Fig. 3.6). Under these conditions the hydroxylating activity of the microsomes will be increased with respect to both 3,4-benzpyrene and aminopyrine. Yet, both the activity and the affinity toward the latter drug is decreased as compared to the controls or to the animals treated with phenobarbital only, just as in the case of 3,4-benzpyrene treatment alone (Fig. 3.7). It would appear, therefore, that polycyclic hydrocarbons interfere with the induction or synthesis of the hydroxylating enzyme system in such a way as to modify the configuration of cytochrome P-450, giving rise to a form, cytochrome P-448, that exhibits an increased affinity for polycyclic hydrocarbons and a decreased affinity for other drugs and for steroid hormones (32). Alternatively, as suggested by Hildebrandt *et al.* (79),

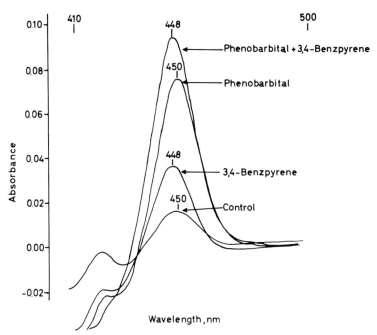

Figure 3.6. Effects of pretreatment of rats *in vivo* with 3,4-benzpyrene, phenobarbital, and 3,4-benzpyrene + phenobarbital on the absorption maximum of the reduced CO-bound cytochrome P-450 of liver microsomes. 3,4-Benzpyrene (20 mg/kg body weight), dissolved in corn oil, and/or sodium phenobarbital (80 mg/kg body weight) was injected intraperitoneally once daily for 3 days. The controls received the same amount of corn oil. Each cuvette contained 1 mg of microsomal protein and 50 mM potassium phosphate buffer, pH 7.5, in a final volume of 3 ml.

both types of cytochrome may exist in the normal liver. In that case, administration of polycyclic hydrocarbons would promote the synthesis of the P-448 form and simultaneously repress the synthesis of the P-450 form. Further work will be needed before a decision can be made regarding the two alternatives.

A striking phenomenon accompanying drug-induced enzyme synthesis is the proliferation of endoplasmic membranes (81). From the available evidence it appears that the induced enzyme synthesis begins in the rough-surfaced areas of the endoplasmic reticulum, and leads eventually to the accumulation of smooth-surfaced profiles, rich in hydroxylating enzyme content (61). The situation is similar to that found during the neonatal development of the liver endoplasmic reticulum which is characterized by a dramatic rise in membrane content and in certain enzyme activities, *e.g.*, glucose-6-phosphatase (82). In both cases, the synthesis of new membranes seems to be geared to the formation of new enzymes by a mechanism that may involve an outgrowth and budding off of smooth-surfaced membrane profiles from the rough-surfaced endoplasmic reticulum at the sites where the enzyme synthesis takes place. The drug-induced membrane proliferation is accompanied by an increased rate of phospholipid synthesis (68), although, here again, a simultaneous slowing-down of lipid catabolism may be a contributory factor (83, 84). The drug-induced synthesis of the microsomal hydroxylating system is a beautiful example of the now widely studied phenomenon of

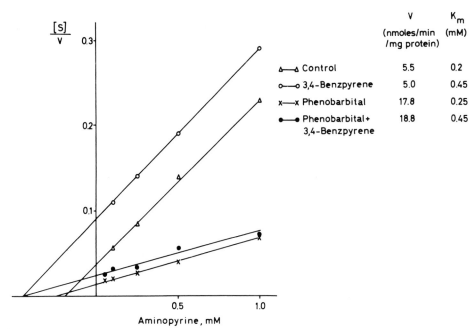

	V (nmoles/min /mg protein)	K_m (mM)
△—△ Control	5.5	0.2
○—○ 3,4-Benzpyrene	5.0	0.45
×—× Phenobarbital	17.8	0.25
●—● Phenobarbital+ 3,4-Benzpyrene	18.8	0.45

Figure 3.7. Effects of pretreatment of rats *in vivo* with 3,4-benzpyrene, phenobarbital and 3,4-benzpyrene, + phenobarbital on the oxidative demethylation of aminopyrine by liver microsomes. The rats were pretreated as described in Figure 3.6. Aminopyrine demethylation was assayed as described previously (32).

the induction of a membrane-bound multienzyme complex, and one of the few instances presently available where this phenomenon can be studied in a multicellular organism.

SUMMARY

Current information relating to the microsomal drug-hydroxylating enzyme system has been surveyed. Present knowledge concerning the catalytic components, reaction mechanism, and substrate specificity of the system were reviewed. Structural aspects of the hydroxylating system were considered in relation to the enzyme topology of the endoplasmic reticulum. The phenomenon of drug-induced enzyme synthesis was discussed with special reference to the effects of polycyclic hydrocarbons. Some aspects of the relationship between drug-induced enzyme synthesis and endoplasmic membrane biogenesis were considered.

REFERENCES

1. BRODIE, B. B., AXELROD, J., COOPER, J. R., GAUDETTE, L., LA DU, B. N., MITOMA C., AND UDENFRIEND, S. Detoxication of drugs and other foreign compounds by liver microsomes. *Science 121:* 603, 1955.

2. LA DU, B. N., GAUDETTE, L., TROUSOF, N., AND BRODIE, B. B. Enzymatic dealkylation of aminopyrine (Pyramidon) and other alkylamines. *J. Biol. Chem. 214:* 741, 1955.

3. BRODIE, B. B., GILLETTE, J. R., AND LA DU, B. N. Metabolism of drugs and other foreign compounds by enzymatic mechanisms. *Ann. Rev. Biochem. 27:* 427, 1958.

4. MUELLER, G. C., AND MILLER, J. A. The metabolism of 4-dimethylaminoazobenzene by rat liver homogenates. *J. Biol. Chem. 176:* 535, 1948.

5. MUELLER, G. C., AND MILLER, J. A. The metabolism of methylated aminoazo dyes. II. Oxidative demethylation by rat liver homogenates. *J. Biol. Chem. 202:* 579, 1953.

6. HAYANO, M. Oxygenases in lipid and steroid metabolism. In *Oxygenases*, edited by Hayaishi, O., p. 181. New York, Academic Press, Inc., 1962.

7. ROBBINS, K. C. Enzymatic omega oxidation of fatty acids. *Fed. Proc.* 20: 272, 1961.

8. WAKABAYASHI, K., AND SHIMAZONO, N. Studies *in vitro* on the mechanism of ω-oxidation of fatty acids. *Biochim. Biophys. Acta* 48: 615, 1961.

9. DAS, M. L., ORRENIUS, S., AND ERNSTER, L. On the fatty acid and hydrocarbon hydroxylation in rat liver microsomes. *Europ. J. Biochem.* 4: 519, 1968.

10. MASON, H. S. Mechanisms of oxygen metabolism. *Advances Enzym.* 19: 79, 1957.

11. HAYAISHI, O. (editor). History and scope. In *Oxygenases*, p. 1. New York, Academic Press, Inc., 1962.

12. OMURA, T., AND SATO, R. The carbon monoxide-binding pigment of liver microsomes. I. Evidence for its hemoprotein nature. *J. Biol. Chem.* 239: 2370, 1964.

13. OMURA, T., AND SATO, R. The carbon monoxide-binding pigment of liver microsomes. II. Solubilization, purification and properties. *J. Biol. Chem.* 239: 2379, 1964.

14. GARFINKEL, D. Studies on pig liver microsomes. I. Enzymic and pigment composition of different microsomal fractions. *Arch Biochem.* 77: 493, 1958.

15. KLINGENBERG, M. Pigments of rat liver microsomes. *Arch. Biochem.* 75: 376, 1958.

16. LU, A. Y. H., STROBEL, H. W., AND COON, M. J. Hydroxylation of benzphetamine and other drugs by a solubilized form of cytochrome P-450 from liver microsomes: Lipid requirement for drug demethylation. *Biochem. Biophys. Res. Commun.* 36: 545, 1969.

17. LU, A. Y. H., JUNK, K. W., AND COON, M. J. Resolution of the cytochrome P-450-containing ω-hydroxylation system of liver microsomes into three components. *J. Biol. Chem.* 244: 3714, 1969.

18. KATAGIRI, M., GANGULI, B. N., AND GUNSALUS, I. C. A soluble cytochrome P-450 functional in methylene hydroxylation. *J. Biol. Chem.* 243: 3543, 1968.

19. HORECKER, B. L. Triphosphopyridine nucleotide-cytochrome *c* reductase in liver. *J. Biol. Chem.* 183: 593, 1950.

20. LANG, C. A., AND NASON, A. A triphosphopyridine nucleotide-cytochrome *c* reductase from heart muscle. *J. Biol. Chem.* 234: 1874, 1959.

21. WILLIAMS, C. H., AND KAMIN, H. Microsomal triphosphopyridine nucleotide-cytochrome *c* reductase of liver. *J. Biol. Chem.* 237: 587, 1962.

22. PHILLIPS, A. H., AND LANGDON, R. G. Hepatic triphosphopyridine nucleotide-cytochrome *c* reductase: Isolation, characterization, and kinetic studies. *J. Biol. Chem.* 237: 2652, 1962.

23. KAMIN, H., MASTERS, B. S. S., GIBSON, Q. H., AND WILLIAMS, C. H. Microsomal TPNH-cytochrome *c* reductase. *Fed. Proc.* 24: 1164, 1965.

24. ERNSTER, L., AND ORRENIUS, S. Substrate-induced synthesis of the hydroxylating enzyme system of liver microsomes. *Fed. Proc.* 24: 1190, 1965.

25. HOCHSTEIN, P., AND ERNSTER, L. Microsomal peroxidation of lipids and its possible role in cellular injury. In *Cellular Injury*, edited by de Reuck, A. V. S., and Knight, J., p. 123. London, J. and A. Churchill, Ltd., 1964.

26. ERNSTER, L., AND NORDENBRAND, K. Microsomal lipid peroxidation. In *Methods in Enzymology*, edited by Estabrook, R. W., and Pullman, M. E., Vol. 10, p. 574. New York, Academic Press, Inc., 1967.

27. ERNSTER, L., NORDENBRAND, K., ORRENIUS, S., AND DAS, M. L. Microsomal lipid peroxidation. *Hoppe Seyler Z. Physiol. Chem.* 349: 1604, 1968.

28. COOPER, D. Y., NARASIMHULU, S., ROSENTHAL, O., AND ESTABROOK, R. W. Spectral and kinetic studies of microsomal pigments. In *Oxidases and Related Redox Systems*, (edited by King, T. E., Mason, H. S., and Morrison, M., p. 838. New York, John Wiley and Sons, Inc., 1965.

29. SATO, R., OMURA, T., AND NISHIBAYASHI, H. Carbon-monoxide-binding hemoprotein and NADPH-specific flavoprotein in liver microsomes and their roles in microsomal electron transfer. In *Oxidases and Related Redox Systems*, edited by King, T. E., Mason, H. S., and Morrison, M., p. 861. New York, John Wiley and Sons, Inc., 1965.

30. STRITTMATTER, P. Protein and coenzyme interactions in the NADH-cytochrome b_5 reductase system. *Fed. Proc.* 24: 1156, 1965.

31. ORRENIUS, S., BERG, A., AND ERNSTER, L. Effects of trypsin on the electron transport systems of liver microsomes. *Europ. J. Biochem.* 11: 193, 1969.

32. GNOSSPELIUS, Y., THOR, H., AND ORRENIUS, S. A comparative study on the effects of phenobarbital and 3,4-benzpyrene on the hydroxylating enzyme system of rat-liver microsomes. *Chem.-Biol. Interactions* 1: 125, 1969.

33. OMURA, T., SATO, R., COOPER, D. Y., ROSENTHAL,

O., AND ESTABROOK, R. W. Function of cyto-chrome P-450 of microsomes. *Fed. Proc. 24:* 1181, 1965.

34. SUZUKI, K., AND KIMURA, T. An iron protein as a component of steroid 11β-hydroxylase com-plex. *Biochem. Biophys. Res. Commun. 19:* 340, 1965.

35. KIMURA, T., AND SUZUKI, K. Enzymatic reduction of non-heme iron protein (Adrenodoxin) by reduced nicotinamide adenine dinucleotide phosphate. *Biochem. Biophys. Res. Commun. 20:* 373, 1965.

36. KIMURA, T., AND SUZUKI, K. Components of the electron transport system in adrenal steroid hydroxylase and purification of a non-heme iron protein (Adrenodoxin). *J. Biol. Chem. 242:* 485, 1967.

37. ESTABROOK, R. W., SCHENKMAN, J. B., CONNER, W., REMMER, H., COOPER, D. Y., NARASIMHULU, S., AND ROSENTHAL, O. Cytochrome P-450 and mixed function oxidations. In *Biological and Chemical Aspects of Oxygenases*, edited by Bloch, K., and Hayaishi, O., p. 153. Maruzen Co., Ltd., Tokyo, 1966.

38. SOTTOCASA, G. L., AND SANDRI, G. Intramito-chondrial distribution od cytochrome P-450 in ox adrenal cortex. *Biochem. J. 116:*16P, 1970.

39. OKAMOTO, H., YAMAMOTO, S., NOZAKIM., AND HAYAISHI, O. On the submitochondrial locali-zation of *l*-kynurenine-3-hydroxylase. *Bio-chem. Biophys. Res. Commun. 26:* 309, 1967.

40. MAYER, G., ULLRICH, V., SCHMELING, U., AND STAUDINGER, H. Possible involvement of cytochrome b_5 in *l*-kynurenine 3-hydroxylase. *Hoppe Seyler Z. Physiol. Chem. 349:* 1616, 1968.

41. SOTTOCASA, G. L., KUYLENSTIERNA, B., ERNSTER, L., AND BERGSTRAND, A. An electron-transport system associated with the outer membrane of liver mitochondria. A biochemical and morphological study. *J. Cell Biol. 32:* 415, 1967.

42. ORRENIUS, S., AND ERNSTER, L. Interactions be-tween liver microsomes and compounds capable of undergoing enzymic hydroxyla-tion. *Life Sci. 6:* 1473, 1967.

43. REMMER, H., SCHENKMAN, J. B., ESTABROOK, R. W., SASAME, H., GILLETTE, J. R., NARASIMHULU, S., COOPER, D. Y., AND ROSENTHAL, O. Drug interaction with hepatic microsomal cyto-chrome. *Molec. Pharmacol. 2:* 187, 1966.

44. IMAI, Y., AND SATO, R. Substrate interaction with hydroxylase system in liver microsomes. *Bio-chem. Biophys. Res. Commun. 22:* 620, 1966.

45. SCHENKMAN, J. B., REMMER, H., AND ESTABROOK, R. W. Spectral studies of drug interaction with hepatic microsomal cytochrome. *Molec. Pharmacol. 3:* 113, 1967.

46. GUNSALUS, I. C. A soluble methylene hydroxylase system: Structure and role of cytochrome P-450 and iron-sulfur protein components. *Hoppe Seyler Z. Physiol. Chem. 349:* 1610, 1968.

47. ESTABROOK, R. W., HILDEBRANDT, A., REMMER, H., SCHENKMAN, J. B., ROSENTHAL, O., AND COOPER, D. Y. The role of cytochrome P-450 in microsomal mixed function oxidation reac-tions. In *Biochemie des Sauerstoffs*, edited by Hess, B., and Staudinger, Hj., p. 142. New York, Springer-Verlag, 1968.

48. TEPHLY, T. R., AND MANNERING, G. J. Inhibition of drug metabolism. V. Inhibition of drug metabolism by steroids. *Molec. Pharmacol. 4:* 10, 1968.

49. ORRENIUS, S., AND THOR, H. Fatty acid interac-tion with the hydroxylating enzyme system of rat liver microsomes. *Europ. J. Biochem. 9:* 415, 1969.

50. KUPFER, D., AND ORRENIUS, S. Interaction of drugs, steroids and fatty acids with micro-somal cytochrome P-450. *Europ. J. Biochem. 14:* 317, 1970.

51. VON BAHR, C., SJÖQVIST, F., AND ORRENIUS, S. The inhibitory effect of hydrocortisone and tes-tosterone on the plasma disappearance of nortriptyline in the dog and the perfused rat liver. *Europ. J. Pharmacol. 9:* 106, 1970.

52. GIGON, P. L., GRAM, T. E., AND GILLETTE, J. R. Studies on the rate of reduction of hepatic microsomal cytochrome P-450 by re-duced nicotinamide dinucleotide phosphate: Effect of drug substrates. *Molec. Pharmacol. 5:* 109, 1969.

53. KUPFER, D., AND ORRENIUS, S. Characteristics of guinea pig liver and adrenal monooxygenase systems. *Molec Pharmacol. 6:* 221, 1970.

54. ICHIHARA, K., KUSUNOSE, E., AND KUSUNOSE, M. Some properties and distribution of the ω-hy-droxylation system of medium-chain fatty acids. *Biochim. Biophys. Acta 176:* 704, 1969.

55. JAKOBSSON, S., AND ORRENIUS, S. Unpublished observation.

56. KURIYAMA, Y., OMURA, T., SIEKEVITZ, P., AND PALADE, G. E. Effects of phenobarbital on the synthesis and degradation of the protein com-ponents of rat liver microsomal membranes. *J. Biol. Chem. 244:* 2017, 1969.

57. ITO, A., AND SATO, R. Proteolytic microdissection of smooth-surfaced vesicles of liver micro-somes. *J. Cell Biol. 40:* 179, 1969.

58. STRITTMATTER, P., AND VELICK, S. F. The isolation and properties of microsomal cytochrome. *J. Biol. Chem. 221:* 253, 1956.

59. GAUDETTE, L. E., AND BRODIE, B. B. Relationship between the lipid solubility of drugs and their oxidation by liver microsomes. *Biochem. Pharmacol. 2:* 89, 1959.

60. DALLNER, G. Studies on the structural and enzymic organization of the membranous elements of liver microsomes. *Acta Path. Microbiol. Scand.* (Suppl. 166) 1963.

61. ORRENIUS, S. Further studies on the induction of the drug-hydroxylating enzyme system of liver microsomes. *J. Cell Biol. 26:* 725, 1965.

62. REMMER, H., AND MERKER, H. J. Drug-induced changes in the liver endoplasmic reticulum: Association with drug-metabolizing enzymes *Science 142:* 1657, 1963.

63. DALLNER, G., BERGSTRAND, A., AND NILSSON, R. Heterogeneity of rough-surfaced liver microsomal membranes of adult, phenobarbital-treated, and newborn rats. *J. Cell Biol. 38:* 257, 1968.

64. DALLMAN, P. R., DALLNER, G., BERGSTRAND, A., AND ERNSTER, L. Heterogeneous distribution of enzymes in submicrosomal membrane fragments. *J. Cell Biol. 41:* 357, 1969.

65. REMMER, H. Der beschleunigte Abbau von Pharmaka in den Lebermikrosomen unter dem Einfluss von Luminal. *Naunyn Schmiedeberg Arch. Pharm. 235:* 279, 1959.

66. CONNEY, A. H., AND BURNS, J. J. Stimulatory effect of foreign compounds on ascorbic acid biosynthesis and on drug-metabolizing enzymes. *Nature (London) 184:* 363, 1959.

67. ORRENIUS, S., AND ERNSTER, L. Phenobarbital-induced synthesis of the oxidative demethylating enzymes of rat liver microsomes. *Biochem. Biophys. Res. Commun. 16:* 60, 1964.

68. ORRENIUS, S., ERICSSON, J. L. E., AND ERNSTER, L. Phenobarbital-induced synthesis of the microsomal drug-metabolizing enzyme system and its relationship to the proliferation of endoplasmic membranes. *J. Cell Biol. 25:* 627, 1965.

69. REMMER, H., AND MERKER, H. J. Effect of drugs on the formation of smooth endoplasmic reticulum and drug-metabolizing enzymes. *Ann. N. Y. Acad. Sci. 123:* 79, 1965.

70. CONNEY, A. H., AND GILMAN, A. G. Puromycin inhibition of enzyme induction by 3-methylcholanthrene and phenobarbital. *J. Biol. Chem. 238:* 3682, 1963.

71. SHUSTER, L., AND JICK, H. The turnover of microsomal protein in the livers of phenobarbital-treated mice. *J. Biol. Chem. 241:* 5361, 1966.

72. JICK, H., AND SHUSTER, L. The turnover of microsomal reduced nicotinamide dinucleotide phosphate-cytochrome *c* reductase in the livers of mice treated with phenobarbital. *J. Biol. Chem. 241:* 5366, 1966.

73. ORRENIUS, S., GNOSSPELIUS, Y., DAS, M. L., AND ERNSTER, L. The hydroxylating enzyme system of liver endoplasmic reticulum. In *Structure and Function of the Endoplasmic Reticulum in Animal Cells*, edited by Gran, F. C., p. 81. Oslo, Universitetsforlaget, 1968.

74. CONNEY, A. H. Pharmacological implications of microsomal enzyme induction. *Pharmacol. Rev. 19:* 317, 1967.

75. CONNEY, A. H., AND KLUTCH, A. Increased activity of androgen hydroxylases in liver microsomes of rats pretreated with phenobarbital and other drugs. *J. Biol. Chem. 238:* 1611, 1963.

76. CONNEY, A. H. Enzyme induction and drug toxicity. In *Drugs and Enzymes*, edited by Brodie, B. B., and Gillette, J. R., p. 277. New York, Pergamon Press, 1965.

77. SLADEK, N. E., AND MANNERING, G. J. Evidence for a new P-450 hemoprotein in hepatic microsomes from methylcholanthrene treated rats. *Biochem. Biophys. Res. Commun. 24:* 668, 1966.

78. ALVARES, A. P., SCHILLING, G., LEVIN, W., AND KUNTZMAN, R. Studies on the induction of CO-binding pigments in liver microsomes by phenobarbital and 3-methylcholanthrene. *Biochem. Biophys. Res. Commun. 29:* 521, 1967.

79. HILDEBRANDT, A., REMMER, H., AND ESTABROOK, R. W. Cytochrome P-450 of liver microsomes—one pigment or many? *Biochem. Biophys. Res. Commun. 30:* 607, 1968.

80. ORRENIUS, S., GRUNDIN, R., AND KUPFER, D. Unpublished observation.

81. REMMER, H., AND MERKER, H. J. Enzyminduktion und Vermehrung von Endoplasmatischem reticulum in der Leberzelle während der Behandlung mit Phenobarbital (Luminal). *Klin. Wschr. 41:* 276, 1963.

82. DALLNER, G., SIEKEVITZ, P., AND PALADE, G. E. Biogenesis of endoplasmic reticulum membranes. II. Synthesis of constitutive microsomal enzymes in developing rat hepatocyte. *J. Cell Biol. 30:* 97, 1966.

83. HOLTZMAN, J. L., AND GILLETTE, J. R. The effect

of phenobarbital on the turnover of microsomal phospholipid in male and female rats. *J. Biol. Chem. 243:* 3020, 1968.

84. ORRENIUS, S. Liver enzyme-membrane responses in drug induction. In *The Interaction of Drugs and Subcellular Components of Animal Cells,* edited by Campbell, P. N., p. 97. London, J and A. Churchill, Ltd., 1968.

85. ORRENIUS, S., KUPFER, D., AND ERNSTER, L. Substrate binding to cytochrome P-450 of liver and adrenal microsomes. *Fed. Europ. Biochem. Soc. Lett. 6:* 249, 1970.

4

THE PLASMA MEMBRANE AS A MODEL OF COMPLEX ORGANIZATION OF BIOLOGICAL STRUCTURES

E. L. Benedetti and Daniele Delbauffe

Knowledge concerning the chemical composition, enzymatic activity, and immunological properties of cellular membranes has progressed considerably in recent years. Improvements and refinements in the techniques for the isolation of various cellular membranous components have permitted the identification of specific functional markers for each membrane type. Differences in the relative proportion of the main constituents, proteins, lipids, and carbohydrates, and the specific enzymatic spectrum have made it possible to distinguish one type of membrane from the other. Yet, in spite of this progress, the molecular configuration of membranes and the spacial interrelation between their components remain uncertain.

The reason for this difficulty lies in the great complexity of membrane properties and features. Biological membranes are ordered structures characterized by a condensed and coherent hydrophobic phase separating two hydrophilic phases, and limiting two compartments of different composition. The membrane thus constitutes a closed boundary having multiple enzymatic properties and polarity; the latter character provides the basis for vectorial transmission of impulses and metabolites through transverse and tangential directions, and ensures the exposure of specific binding sites to regulatory ligands and the recognition of stereospecific signals (1–3).

Furthermore, membrane excitability and non-linear and cooperative responses to increased or threshold concentrations of ligands have been tentatively explained in terms of reversible conformational changes of the membrane structure comparable to allosteric interaction in regulatory enzymes (1).

Structural modulation and plasticity should also allow membrane relaxation and contraction. On the other hand the membrane must have the possibility of forming a rigid shell in order to impart shape and polarity to cells.

Membrane differentiation in organized areas of cell contact should provide the appropriate configuration ensuring cell-to-cell interaction and the transfer of information from one cell to another. Since cell membranes are involved in many functions and their principles of organization must fulfill the requirement of complex tasks, the assumption that membranes are built according to a common and unique design is highly questionable.

Institut de Biologie Moléculaire, Centre National de la Recherche Scientifique, Faculté des Sciences, Paris, France.

The research has been supported by Centre National de la Recherche Scientifique, Délégation Générale pour la Recherche Scientifique et Technique, and Fondation pour la Recherche Médicale Française.

Available biochemical and morphological evidence concerning the structure and composition of biological membranes is more consistent with most of the models proposed thus far, rather than confirming the validity of a particular one. A globular arrangement of lipoprotein within the plane of the membrane has been deduced from electron microscopic observations of both natural and artificial membranes (4–6).

On the other hand, the triple-layered structure observed in several biological or manufactured membranes may support the "unit membrane" model in which lipids are arranged in a bimolecular leaflet (7). However, observations showing that, at least for certain types of membranes, the triple-layered structure is retained after lipid extraction (8, 9) strongly suggest that the lipid bilayer is probably penetrated by peptide chains forming links across the membrane element. Evidence for the coexistence of different molecular models based on lipid configuration is also provided by a number of elegant experiments showing that lipids characteristic of biological membrane may artificially aggregate, alone or together with proteins, in a variety of structural arrangements and undergo polymorphic transition under circumstances, (temperature, water, and ion concentration) that often remain within a physiological range for cell systems (10–13). Studies using optical rotary dispersion, circular dichroism, infrared and fluorescent spectroscopy, and nuclear magnetic resonance have further developed the view that the protein as well as the lipids should be regarded as an important determinant of membrane configuration (cf. reference 14).

These observations, although still controversial, have indicated that the spacial interaction of proteins and lipids in membrane is mainly hydrophobic in nature rather than hydrophilic, as it has been considered in the traditional lipid bilayer model (15–18). Membrane circular dichroism spectra reported by several authors are not consistent with a β-configuration for membrane proteins. On the contrary, at least 50% of the membrane protein was found to have an α-helical configuration (15–17).

Lenard and Singer (18) have deduced from the protein spectra the existence of strong interactions between α-helical regions of adjoining proteins. According to Wallach (17) the correct folding of peptide chains, the spacing of protein subunits, and the complete conformation of the polypeptide chains are affected a great deal by direct molecular interactions with lipids, which impose a highly polarizable solvent environment. The aforementioned concepts, regarding protein-protein and lipid-protein interactions, affecting the versatility of both protein and lipid configuration, may provide the basis for better understanding of the mechanism of membrane transition caused by regulatory ligands operating on lipid- and protein-specific binding sites.

In the present contribution we would like to discuss some results of studies on isolated liver plasma membranes which are probably relevant to the demonstration of the structural complexity of the membrane element and of the variation of membrane architecture according to regional specialization within a single membrane type.

The study of membranes separated from other cell components has many advantages. Isolated membranes may be considered as a system that still displays many if not all the physiological and structural characteristics of the membranes in vivo. On the other hand, isolated membranes can easily be submitted to different analytical procedures and to experimental conditions conceivable only for an artificial membrane system.

The plasma membrane of liver cells has well defined regions characterized by specific functional properties, in particular regions devoted to secretion and/or absorption and others involved in cell contact and intercellular communication. Liver plasma membranes have been isolated as a rather pure fraction which appears to be representative of the plasma membrane *in situ* (19). The main components are proteins and lipids, with smaller quantities of carbohydrates. The protein content is about 65% of the dry weight. A substantial part of the protein (20–25%) is soluble in physiological saline and appears to be antigenically, electrophoretically, and ultracentrifugally heterogeneous (20). Three different classes of phosphoproteins have been characterized in rat liver plasma membranes by Blat and Harel (21).

At most 35% of the dry weight of rat liver plasma membranes consists of lipids (22, 23). Choline-containing phospholipids are particularly abundant. The content in cholesterol, saturated fatty acids, sphingomyelin, and gangliosides, per unit weight of protein, is higher than in other cell organelles (24, 25).

In the saline-insoluble membrane fraction, the hexoses, hexosamines, and sialic acids (predominantly N-acetylneuraminic acid) amount to 65, 61, and 33 mμmoles/ mg of membrane protein, respectively (20). In comparison with other cell membranes rat liver plasma membrane contains (per unit weight of membrane protein) more hexosamine and sialic acid. More than 20 enzyme activities have been identified in rat liver plasma membrane (26, 27).

Based on a larger number of physiological, biochemical, and histochemical studies, the following enzymes are considered to be representative of both the isolated plasma membrane and the plasma membrane *in situ*: Mg^{2+}-Ca^{2+}-dependent ATPase, Na^+-K^+-Mg^{2+}-ATPase, K^+-p-nitrophenylphosphatase, K^+-acetylphosphatase, 5'-mononucleotidase, NAD-pyrophosphatase, alkaline glycerol phosphatase and phosphodiesterase, and L-leucyl aminopeptidase (L-leucyl-β-naphtylamidase) (26, 28). In addition, phosphatidate phosphohydrolase activity has been found in isolated rat liver plasma membrane by Coleman (29). In bovine liver plasma membrane, glycosidases capable of hydrolyzing uridine diphosphogalactose and uridine diphosphoglucose as well as o-nitrophenyl-α- or -β-galactosides have been identified (30). Morphologically, the isolated liver plasma membranes consist of large sheets interconnected by junctional complexes identical to those existing *in situ*. Plasma membranes originating from the bile spaces are represented by large circular and oval profiles enclosing microvilli ghosts. Vesicles are also found either adhering or in close proximity to the cytoplasmic inner surfaces of the lateral plasma membrane.*

STRUCTURAL POLARITY OF THE MEMBRANE ELEMENT

In the isolated material, high magnification electron microscopy shows that the typical triple-layered structure of the membrane element is still retained (19).

---

*These vesicles are probably smooth endoplasmic reticulum elements. The triple-layered structure and the width of the membrane element forming these vesicles is identical with that of the adjoining plasma membrane. The cytochemical reaction for glucose-6-phosphatase shows within some of these vesicles the lead salt product of the enzymic reaction. Widnell (31) has reported a similar finding. In liver tissue, histochemical evidence has already been provided that glucose-6-phosphatase, which is a typical endoplasmic reticulum enzyme marker, is found within smooth-surfaced vesicles along the lateral plasma membrane or in close proximity of the sinusoids (32). The present observation that vesicles having some structural and enzymic markers for both plasma membrane and endoplasmic reticulum are still adhering to the main plasma membrane sheets after isolation indicates the existence of persistent structural and functional integration of these two cooperative membranous organelles in the liver cells. Under these circumstances the criteria of "purity" for a subcellular fraction are difficult to determine, since the presence of a "contaminant" may be the expression of the integration of two membranous cell compartments rather than an indication of the inadequacy of the separation techniques.

Furthermore, in spite of the isolation, it is possible to identify the extra- and the intracellular side of the isolated membrane since they are held together by means of intact junctional complexes, preserving thus, the relationship of the two opposite plasma membranes. It is, therefore, possible to study more readily than in the intact tissue, the structural polarity and the position of ionic, enzymatic, and antigenic components, which may be located at the outer or the inner membrane surface.

The aim of this approach is to search for the existence of a specific sequence and orientation of macromolecules through, or along, axes perpendicular to the plane of the membrane.

A number of experimental studies have already shown that biological membranes possess functional polarity based on stereospecific asymmetrical localization of membrane constituents (1, 2, 33). For instance, specific pharmacological agents (acetylcholine and tetrodotoxin) affect the action potential only if applied to the outer surface of the specific membrane system (34–36).

In studying the asymmetry and the specific orientation of a liver plasma membrane one has to determine the outward and inward borderlines of the membrane element. Two components of the cell periphery are to be taken into consideration: the cell coat and the ectoplasmic layer.

After isolation the latter component, which is involved in essential functions such as relaxation and contraction of the cell surface, remains partially attached to the inner membrane surface, particularly in association with the junctional complexes (19).

The question of whether the cell coat or "glycocalyx" should be considered as an integral part of the plasma membrane or as an extraneous layer has been repeatedly discussed (37–40). Many observations support the view that at least in certain types of cells, including hepatocytes, the cell coat and the plasma membrane should be regarded as a single integrated structure: "the greater membrane" (41). This concept has been further developed by Lehninger (34), who postulated that the molecular interface between cooperative cells consists of the plasma membrane, the cell coat, and the immediately surrounding intercellular space. The contact between cell surfaces would then be topologically restricted and would allow molecular interactions within a specific environmental space (34).

The postulate that cell coat and plasma membrane form a unitary structure has been reinforced by the observation that glycoproteins and glycolipids containing sialic acid, which are considered specific components of the cell coat, are found as an integral constituent in the insoluble fraction of isolated membranes (22, 42).

Further information on the localization of sialic acid has been obtained by the application of cytochemical methods and high resolution electron microscopy to the isolated liver plasma membrane (42, 43). The staining with "positively" charged colloidal iron hydroxide has revealed that the carboxyl group of N-acetylneuraminic acid is exposed at the outer surface of the membrane element (42) (Fig. 4.1). On the other hand, after incubation with "negatively" charged colloidal iron according to the methods of Gasic et al. (43), the outer surface of the membrane element remains unstained, whereas a coarse agglomeration of the iron particles appears irregularly attached to the inner cytoplasmic surface of the plasma membrane (Fig. 4.1). These results, however, do not exclude the existence of positively charged groups at the outer surface of the liver plasma membrane. Most likely the free carboxyl or other acidic charged groups, determining the net negative charge of the cell surface, prevent the staining of the basic groups by predominant electrostatic repulsion of the negatively charged iron. In mouse ascites adenocarcinoma cells, Gasic et al. (43)

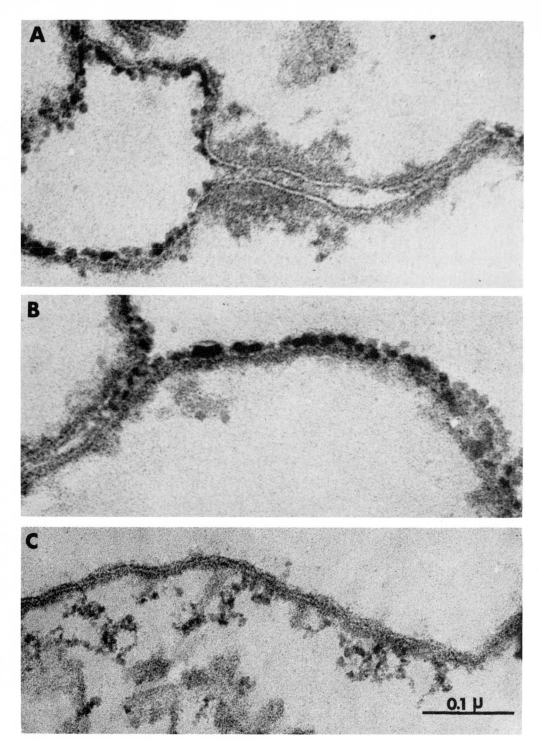

Figure 4.1. Isolated plasma membranes stained with colloidal iron. A and B, positively charged particles on the outer surface. C, negatively charged particles on the inner surface.

showed that the staining of the outer leaflet of the plasma membrane by negatively charged iron may occur if the staining reaction is preceded by neuramidase treatment. The staining is also enhanced by blocking the carboxyl groups by methylation. It seems therefore very likely that functional groups of different electrical charges are located at various levels within the hydrodynamic plane of the shear. The interplay of the exposed groups with the deeper ones exerts a great influence on the electrokinetic properties of the cell surface (44). Further experiments on the isolated rat liver plasma membrane are required, in order to have additional information on the relative position of the charged groups of glycoprotein and glycolipid, in particular of the sialic acid. Actually, there is not yet sufficient information with regard to the function of sialic acid in the plasma membrane of liver cells, nor to the contribution of N-acetylneuraminic acid to the negative charge of the liver cell surface as it has been established for other cell types by electrokinetic studies (44, 45). Furthermore, recent studies have led to the conclusion that sialic acid may be considered as a primary determinant of the plasma membrane configuration and the expression of antigenicity of the cell surface (46, 47).

The structural and functional polarity of membrane constituents is also demonstrated by the localization of some enzymatic end products as revealed by electron microscopic cytochemistry on isolated plasma membranes.

Using the Wachstein and Meisel method (48, 49) for nucleoside phosphatase activities, with ATP and AMP as substrates, the reaction products for both activities were found at the outer surface of the plasma membrane lining the bile spaces (Fig. 4.2).

In both cases electron dense lead deposits were also observed in other regions of the plasma membrane, namely where two membranes are adjoining and running together quite parallel. The reaction product was also located in close contact with the membrane outer leaflets (Fig. 4.3). On the other hand, the inner cytoplasmic surfaces of the close junctions were studded with lead dense granules, indicating the presence of both ATPase and AMPase activities (Fig. 4.3). According to critical evaluation (50, 51), the interpretation of the results of the Wachstein and Meisel method for the localization of nucleoside phosphatases is uncertain. Apparently, the K^+-Na^+ ATPase activity is strongly affected by the high lead concentration. On the other hand, if the lead concentration is brought down to a level compatible with a good preservation of the enzymatic activity, the reaction product for the demonstration of this activity is negligible (52, 53).

The Mg^{2+}-Ca^{2+} ATPase seems to be more resistant to the lead concentration suitable for the cytochemical reaction (50). It is, therefore, likely that nucleotidase shown on the plasma membrane should be referred to as Mg^{2+} and Ca^{2+} ATPase. In agreement with the previous study of Marchesi and Palade (53) we did not find any difference in the localization of the lead precipitates when the medium containing ATP was supplemented with Mg^{2+}, K^+-Na^+-Mg^{2+}, or Mg^{2+}-K^+-Na^+-ouabain, respectively. Furthermore, the presence of an ADPase activity in liver plasma membrane (54, 55) casts even more doubt on the possibility of differential and specific localization by means of cytochemical methods of the various nucleoside phosphatases associated with the liver plasma membrane.

The asymmetrical localization of the reaction end product at the outer surface of the isolated plasma membrane does not necessarily indicate the original location of the enzyme. It might, however, be related to the vectorial flow of matter within the asymmetric membrane element.

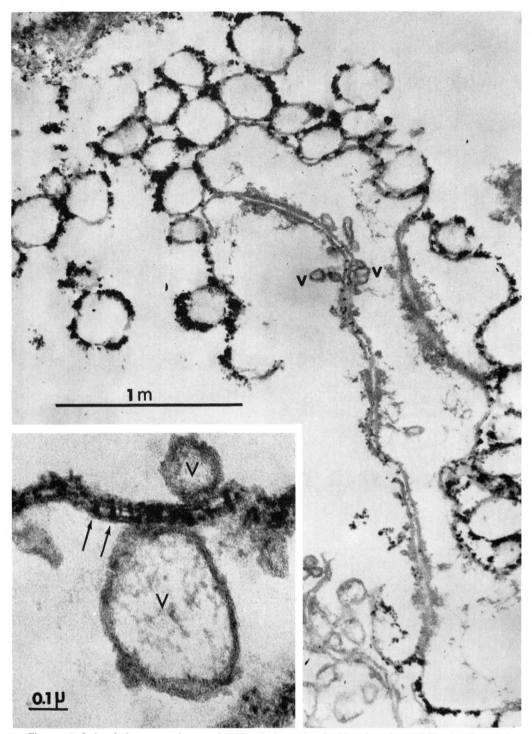

Figure 4.2. Isolated plasma membranes. Cytochemical reaction for 5′-nucleotidase (AMPase). The reaction product is localized at the outer surface of membranes lining the bile spaces. In the inset the arrows point to the lead precipitates on the outer surfaces of two adjoining plasma membranes. Vesicles (v) associated with the plasma membrane and the intermediate junctions are devoid of lead precipitates.

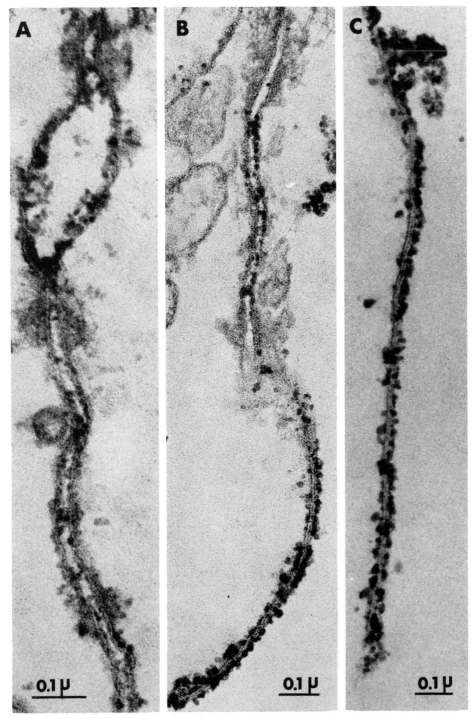

Figure 4.3. Isolated plasma membranes. Cytochemical reaction for ATPase. The reaction product is on the outer surface of the membrane and on the cytoplasmic sites of the close junction.

PLASMA MEMBRANE REGIONAL DIFFERENTIATION AS RE-VEALED BY NEGATIVE STAIN-ING AND FREEZE-ETCHING

The Membrane Subunit

The term of membrane subunit has been applied to a wide class of membrane entities, visualized by electron microscopy and has been invoked to explain the functional organization of membranes and the process of membrane reaggregation after solubilization. The arguments in support or against the "subunit membrane model" have been the subject of many reviews (56–58). In the present discussion the term membrane subunit will be restricted to those entities visualized by electron microscopy and which may be referred to as morphological subunits or "electron microscopic subunits." A crucial question is whether these types of subunits are forming the membrane element as a bidimensional lattice of repeating protomers, or whether they are associated with the surface of a continuous bimolecular layer. Electron microscopic observations on isolated liver plasma membrane negatively stained with potassium phosphotungstate have revealed the existence of remarkable differences in the appearance of the membrane surfaces. In some regions the membrane is found relatively smooth while in other areas both the edge and the surface are covered by small globular subunits with an average diameter of 60 Å (Fig. 4.4). The globular units viewed at the edge of the membrane appear as projections from a uniform leaflet, being attached to it either directly or *via* a short stem (59).

The notion of the presence of globular repeating units at the plasma membrane surface has been reinforced by the subsequent observations of Overton *et al.* (60) and Cunningham and Crane (61) on isolated brush border of intestinal epithelium and on fragments of membrane in liver homogenate. Moreover the relevance of these globular repeating units to membrane function has further been established by showing that membrane enzymatic activities were associated to the globular repeating units (62–64, 26). Multienzyme particles have been released from the plasma membrane by treatment with low concentration of papain and they were further purified by gel filtration (26, 63, 64). In the case of the isolated rat liver plasma membrane, globular repeating units similar to those found in negatively stained preparations of plasma membranes are also present in the gel filtration fraction in which the leucyl-β-naphtylamidase activity is most concentrated (26). The globular repeating units observed on the surface of negatively stained plasma membranes may be considered as a structural marker for this type of membrane, and are easily distinguished from the mitochondrial inner membrane elementary particles by their dimension and enzymatic properties (65), as well as from the small (30–40 Å) globular constituents described in negatively stained vesicles derived from endoplasmic reticulum (66).

The globular repeating units, often ascribed to artificial deterioration of the membrane during the negative staining, have been consistently observed in freeze-etched preparations of biological membranes (67–69). This technique provides useful information on the fine structure of membranes since freeze-etching avoids the utilization of chemical fixation or drastic dehydration and staining of the specimens. By this means it has been possible to show a remarkable degree of structural complexity of biological membranes in close correlation with their functional specialization (70–73). Gloubles of different dimension and array of subunits have been revealed by freeze-etching in surface view as well as in cross-section of a variety of membranes.

However the manner in which these subunits are arranged at the molecular level is not readily apparent. Alternative interpretations have been proposed; yet

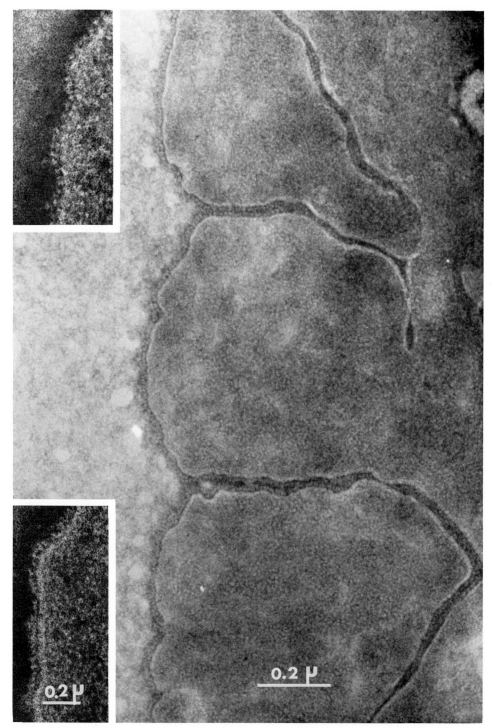

Figure 4.4. Isolated plasma membranes. Negatively stained with potassium phosphotungstate. The surface and the edge of the membranes are dotted with repeating units having globular shape (see insets).

63

it is not completely settled whether the freeze-etching exposes the two outer or inner membrane surfaces (68), or if it splits the membrane elements in half thus revealing its two hydrophobic faces (74). Another alternative is that the fracture plane shows true membrane surfaces as well as the split inner faces (70).

Freeze-etching of isolated plasma membranes shows several structural features of the membrane element. The preservation of the relationship between two opposite plasma membranes makes it possible to identify both outer and inner fracture surfaces of the membrane element (Fig. 4.5). In a high quality replica most of the exposed outer fracture surface is dotted by 60- to 90-Å particles of rather irregular shape (round, oval, or star-like) (Figs. 4.6 and 4.7).

The identity of these globular subunits is not easily understood. Their dimension and shape, as revealed by freeze-etching, support the view that they may correspond to the globular repeating subunits, observed in negative stained preparations of liver plasma membrane, which are found associated with leucyl-β-naphtylamidase. However, doubt on the identity of these two classes of particles visualized by the different techniques is cast by the observation that papain treatment, which releases from the membrane most of the particles visualized in negative staining (26), does not remove the units, which were found in freeze-etched plasma membrane (Fig. 4.8). However, the evaluation of the ratio of globular subunits released by papain and those resistant to the latter enzyme activity is not easy, since areas devoid of particles are also not uncommon in replica of untreated membrane. Previous observations on isolated plasma

membrane have demonstrated that, in contrast to leucyl-β-naphtylamidase, papain treatment does not release from the isolated liver plasma membrane 5'-nucleotidase, inosinediphosphatase, ATPase, K^+-Na^+ ATPase, alkaline phosphodiesterase, and alkaline glycerophosphatase (26). Thus, the possibility remains that the residual enzyme activities could be associated with globular repeating units resistant to the papain treatment. On the other hand, the association of an enzymatic activity with a repeating subunit does not imply that structural form of the enzyme protein and the repeating subunit are one and the same entity. Recent work still in progress in our laboratory indicates that in rat liver plasma membranes reassociated after solubilization with detergents, the globular subunits are not reformed (Fig. 4.9) but a fair amount of dipeptidase activity is present in the membrane fraction.

The inner fracture surface of the isolated plasma membrane is found studded by rodlike structures or short filaments arranged in a rather parallel array and interspaced by a few 90-Å particles (Fig. 4.5). The significance of the rod-like structure observed at the inner surface is questionable. Tentatively, similar rod-like structures and filaments observed in the inner cytoplasmic surface of frozen and cleaved red blood cell membrane (75) have been related to the protein "spectrin" isolated from the same material by Steers and Marchesi (76). Evidence for the presence of structural proteins, which have an assembly function in membrane, and some common properties with actin and the protein of microtubules has also been provided by Mazia and Ruby (77), who proposed the term of "tektins" to characterize this class of protein. An actomyosin-like

Figure 4.5. Isolated plasma membranes, treated with 5 mM EDTA at pH 6.0 for 30 minutes. Replica of freeze-etched preparation (30% glycerol). A, two adjoining plasma membranes. OS corresponds to the outer membrane surface which is dotted with globular subunits, and I C corresponds to the inner cytoplasmic surface which shows rod-like structures and filaments. B, higher magnification of the inner cytoplasmic surface showing rod-like structures interspersed with globular subunits.

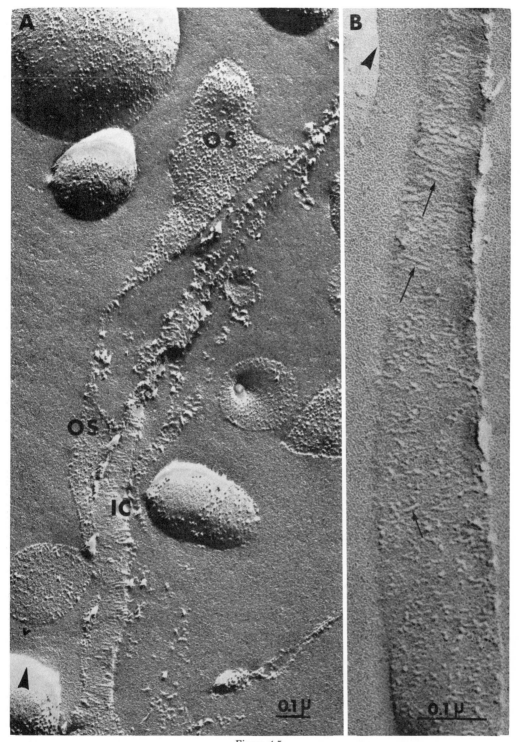

Figure 4.5

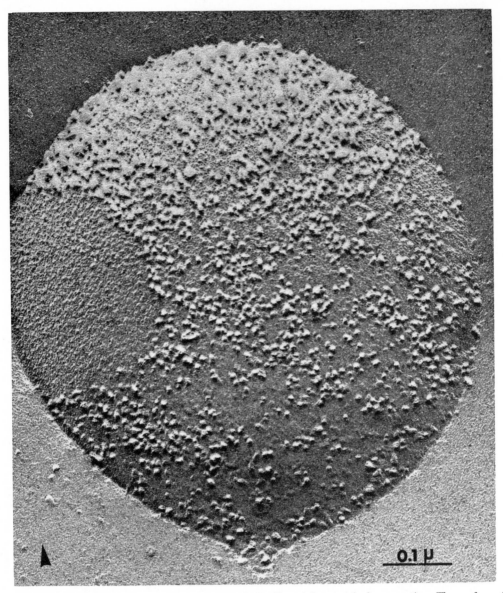

Figure 4.6. Isolated plasma membranes, untreated. Replica of freeze-etched preparation. The surface of the membrane sheet is dotted by globular repeating units.

contractile protein, showing ATPase activity in the presence of Mg^{2+} and Ca^{2+} ions, has been previously isolated from rat liver plasma membrane by Neifakh and Vasilets (78). This class of protein might be relevant to membrane contraction and relaxation, as well as to the determination of membrane pore sizes. Neville has recently isolated from rat liver plasma membrane an organ-specific protein and shown by ultraviolet circular dichroism that virtually all the residues in this protein are

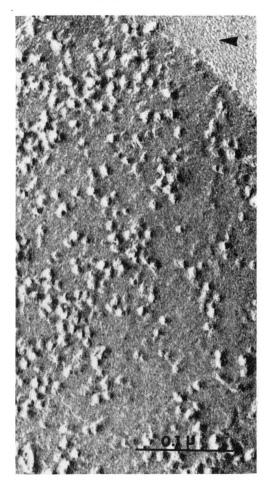

Figure 4.7. High magnification of Figure 4.6, showing the different shape of the surface subunits.

in the α-helix configuration. Furthermore, Neville (79) assigned to this specific protein a rod-like structure.

In some areas of the replica, true cross-fractures perpendicular to the plane of the membrane can be recognized. There, the cast of the membrane element consists of a triple-layered structure formed by two ridges separated by a linear depression (Fig. 4.10A). The surfaces of the ridges can be either smooth or dotted by protruding particles identical to those viewed on the membrane surfaces. The presence of particles associated with the triple-layered structure is also evident in cross-fractures

of vesicular elements. Not infrequently globular subunits are found spanning the triple-layered structure (Fig. 4.10B). This interesting feature is comparable with the observation of Weinstein (75) showing cylindrical particles across the membrane elements of freeze-cleaved red blood cells.

Several studies on artificial and natural

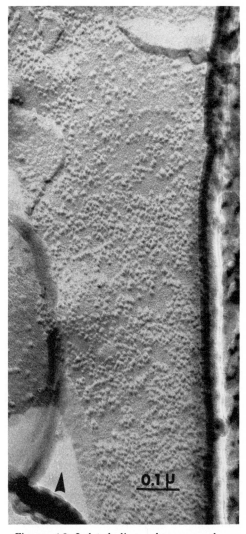

Figure 4.8. Isolated liver plasma membranes, treated with papain (CN-activated papain/membrane protein ratio, 1:200, 37° C for 15 minutes). Replica of freeze-etched preparation. The globular subunits are apparently unmodified.

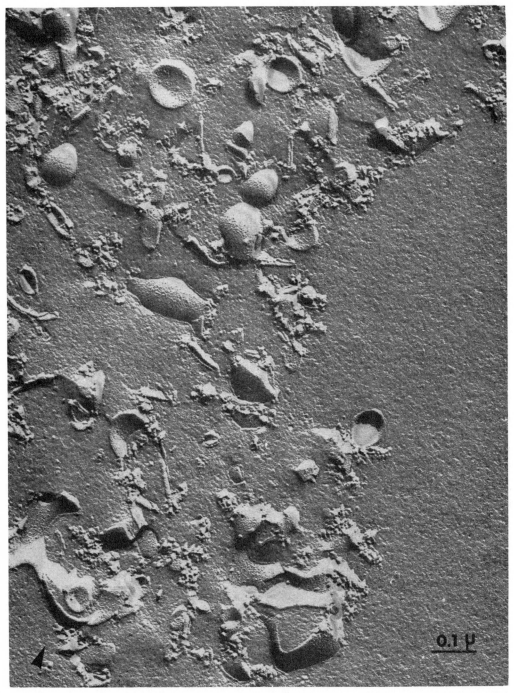

Figure 4.9. Reconstituted plasma membranes after solubilization with 1% DOC and dialysis against Tris pH 5.2–20 mM MgCl$_2$ for 24 hours. Replica of freeze-etched preparation. The replica shows small membrane fragments with surface devoid of 60- to 90-Å globular subunits.

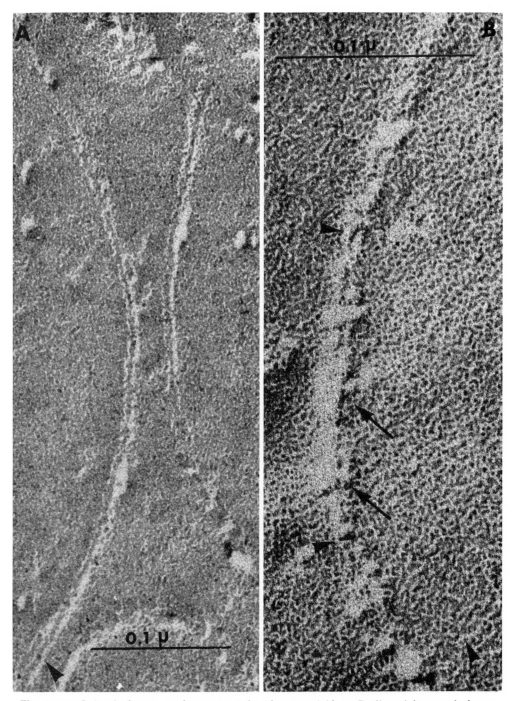

Figure 4.10. Isolated plasma membranes treated with neuraminidase. Replica of freeze-etched preparation. A, the triple-layer structure of the adjoining plasma membranes is visualized. B, globular subunits are shown attached to one surface (*arrows*) of the membrane or spanning it (*arrow heads*).

membranes show that the triple-layered structure remains unaltered by the rapid freezing. The present investigation confirms this view and extends the evidence for the preservation of the triple-layered structure in replica of freeze-etched isolated plasma membrane. Recently, Buckingham and Staehelin (80) have extensively studied, by freeze-etch and X-ray diffraction, the effect of glycerol on lecithin in water at the concentration utilized for preventing ice formation in biological specimens. According to these authors the glycerol may strengthen the cohesive forces in the surface layers of bilayer membranes by cross-linking the hydrophilic ends of lecithin molecules. The stabilization of each half of the bilayer would also favor the cleavage or splitting of it. Noteworthy is the fact that the splitting of the bilayer and plaque formation, due to the uncompleted and fragmentary separation of the two halves, are affected by the concentration of lecithin in the water-glycerol phases. The study of Buckingham and Staehelin in a way brings further support to Branton's hypothesis that frozen membranes may be fractured to expose hydrophobic faces. On the other hand, the demonstration that variation of the lecithin concentration may affect the process of cleavage of the bilayer may provide a basis for understanding the controversial results of several authors concerning membrane splitting by freeze-etch. Since biological membranes are characterized by a defined chemical composition, in particular with regard to lipid concentration, saturation or unsaturation of the fatty acids, and amount of cholesterol, it is conceivable that such variations, and glycerol concentration, are reflected in the fracture mechanism of frozen samples.*

Although some observations stress that the main cohesive forces in membrane conformation are probably hydrophobic, and according to Branton (71), those forces are of little relevance in frozen specimens, the possibility remains that other types of bonding may also exert a great influence on frozen membrane cohesion. Ionic requirements for membrane stability and reassociation (81, 82) and the solubility properties of membrane protein in low ionic (77) environment show the complexity of the cohesive forces and interactions between membrane constituents. The globular subunit and the rod-like structure are not affected by treatment with a chelating agent (EDTA), neuraminidase, or incubation in physiological saline at 37° C, suggesting that these structures are probably not linked to polar heads of phospholipids and proteins through divalent cations, nor by other weak ionic interactions.

Removal of calcium, however, affects the stability of the triple-layered structure which is no longer visible as such in replicas of EDTA-treated membranes. The membrane element, then, is found to consist of a row of globules rather than of two linear ridges (Fig. 4.11), as observed in thin sections of isolated plasma membrane submitted to the same treatment (19).

Membrane Structural Differentiation in Relation to Cell Contact and Cell-to-Cell Communication

Another type of structural differentiation in rat liver plasma membrane has been revealed in negative stained prepa-

---

* Recent studies of P. Pinto da Silva and D. Branton (*J. Cell Biol. 45:* 598, 1970), of T. W. Tillach and V. T. Marchesi (*J. Cell Biol. 45:* 649, 1970), and of R. S. Weinstein and N. S. Mc Nutt (*Seminars Hemat. 7:* 259, 1970) on the path of cleavage along

the red cell membrane are consistent with the hypothesis that the membrane is fractured along its inner matrix. Recently, we have also obtained some evidence that the same principle may be applicable to the mechanism of cleavages along isolated liver plasma membranes. However, a careful analysis is still required to interpret the fracture process in specialized regions of the plasma membranes, such as the junctional complexes, where the molecular architecture still needs further elucidation.

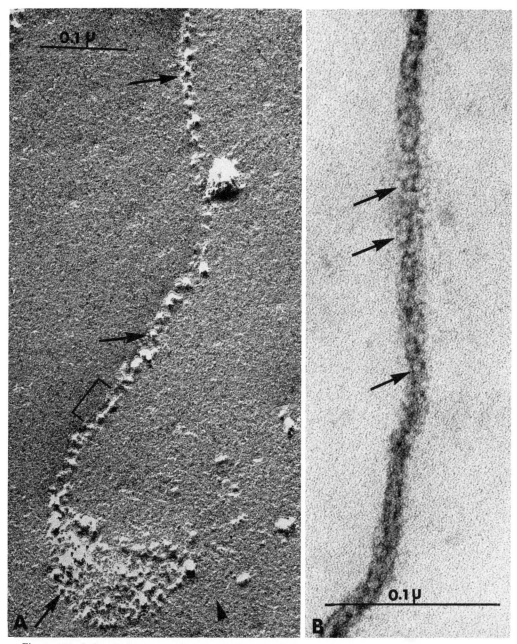

Figure 4.11. Isolated plasma membrane treated with EDTA. A, the replica of a freeze-etched preparation shows the membrane element as a row of globular subunits (*arrows*). Small segments of the membrane show a triple-layer structure (*square brackets*). B, thin section of the same preparation. The arrows point to globular subunits.

rations where a hexagonal array of subunits was found associated with certain
areas of the membrane. Solubilization by
a detergent, deoxycholate (DOC) of the
isolated plasma membrane and centrifugation yielded a fraction which was mainly
composed of membranous fragments consisting of a pentalayered structure having
morphological features very similar to
those of the "tight" junction (83). Negative staining either at 37° C or at lower
temperatures (Fig. 4.12) showed in the

same fraction a large amount of membranous sheets of hexagonal packed subunits
(83). It was then deduced that the hexagonal pattern was associated with that
type of intercellular junction. However,
the result of the negative staining and
the examination of thin-sectioned isolated junctions were not conclusive as to
whether the hexagonal array of subunits
was present as a single sheet or as a surface feature of the outer leaflets of the
two adjoining plasma membranes.

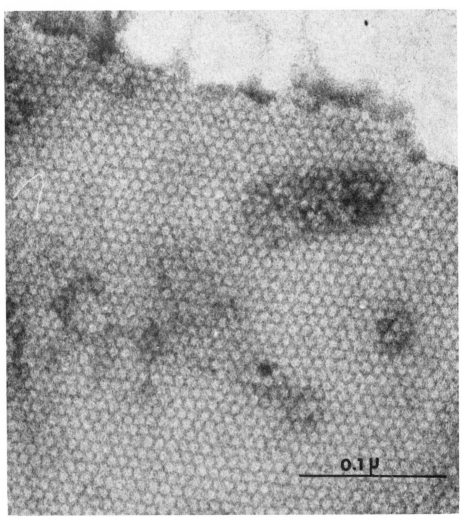

Figure 4.12. Close junctions isolated by DOC treatment. Hexagonal pattern negatively stained at low
temperature.

Further information concerning the fine structure of the "zonula occludens" or "tight" junction has been provided by Revel and Karnovsky (84), and more recently by Brightman and Reese (85), using uranyl acetate staining during the dehydration, and impregnation of tissue blocks by colloidal lanthanum. By these means two different types of intercellular junctions could be identified in many cell systems. One type corresponds to the true tight junction or zonula occludens, with complete obliteration of the intercellular space providing sufficient insulation and acting as a barrier to the inflow of matter through the clefts between the cells.

The other type, the gap or close junction, probably mediates humoral and electrical intercellular transmission (87, 88),

and is characterized by the presence between the two adjoining membranes of a 20-Å space where lanthanum penetration outlines a polygonal lattice of cylindrical subunits (84, 89).

In rat liver, the tight junctions are found in close approximation to the bile spaces, which are sealed off by these junctions from the lateral intercellular spaces (Fig. 4.13). Other structural features, which cannot be discussed extensively here, characterize the rat liver zonula occludens. A study in our laboratory is in progress in order to get more information on this type of junction during hepatocyte differentiation (90).

In rat liver, the shape that can be assigned to the gap junction is more like that of a plaque of limited extent rather

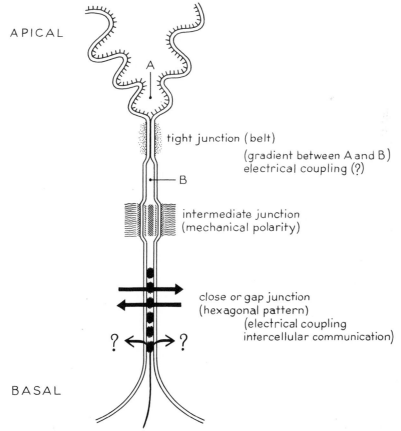

Figure 4.13. Diagram depicting different types of junctions in glandular epithelium, including liver cells.

than that of a continuous belt between the liver cells. Further details about the architecture of the gap junction in various cell systems have been provided by the study of freeze-cleaved and freeze-etched specimens. In isolated rat liver plasma membrane, the replica of freeze-etched close junctions exhibit multiple cleavages and fractured planes, which are not usually seen in other membrane regions. Incomplete membrane fracture at the level of the close junction reveals the presence of regular arrays of particles situated between and interlocking two faces (Fig. 4.14).

The face which supports the arrays of particles is continuous with one membrane face dotted by 60- to 90-Å particles (Fig. 4.14). On the other hand, the sheets formed by the regular arrays of particles are in some places covered by a plaque of variable extent which might correspond to a fragment of the other plasma membrane incompletely removed by the fracture (Fig. 4.14) or to the middle layer of the junction. In several replicas of rat liver plasma membrane, and in different regions of the same replica, these plaques show two distinct morphological features. In some junctions, the plaque surface is completely smooth and appears as a homogeneous layer (Fig. 4.15), whereas in other fractured junctions, the plaque surface consists of a regular hexagonal lattice formed by flat facets with a center-to-center space of 90 Å (Fig. 4.14). The centers of the hexagonally packed facets do not seem to be in register with the space between the rows of subunits. Mc Nutt and Weinstein (89) have observed similar structural features in nexus membranes in papillary muscles from mouse and pig hearts. However, they did not describe the existence of a smooth surface of junctional membrane in addition to the hexagonal pattern. We do not know whether these differences may be due to intrinsic variations existing within the same junction type, or whether these different features are related to one type of tissue, functional requirements, and species differences. This latter possibility is supported by the following observations. The uranyl acetate staining of rat liver blocks fails to show consistently, in the close junction, the 20-Å gap, and the hexagonal array of subunits is not outlined by lanthanum impregnation as found in the mouse liver gap junction (90). Differences between the liver plasma membrane of mouse and rat were already demonstrated with regard to the chemical composition and the temperature dependency of the hexagonal pattern visualized in negatively stained preparations (83, 86).

The application of freeze-etching to the study of the gap junction has revealed interesting structural features, but has also raised some as yet unresolved questions. It is not easy to determine whether the hexagonal pattern visualized in the negatively stained preparations corresponds to the interlocking arrays of particles or to the hexagonal lattice.* Preliminary observations using optical diffraction on micrographs of negatively stained preparations revealed that the pattern consists of one single bidimensional hexagonal lattice of subunits. It is difficult, therefore, to reconcile the results of the optical diffraction with a previous suggestion that the image of the hexagonal array of subunits, might arise from the projection pattern of two superimposed hexagonal lattices (83). An alternative explanation is that during negative staining the phosphotungstic acid penetrating between the interlocking array of particles would outline preferentially only this intermediate layer. Another possibility is that during negative staining the gap junction undergoes a partial or complete disintegration and that

---

* Recent observations in our laboratory suggest that a single hexagonal lattice may form the middle layer of the close junction. The arrays of particles are probably associated with the two adjoining plasma membranes, rather than forming the interlocking structure of the junction.

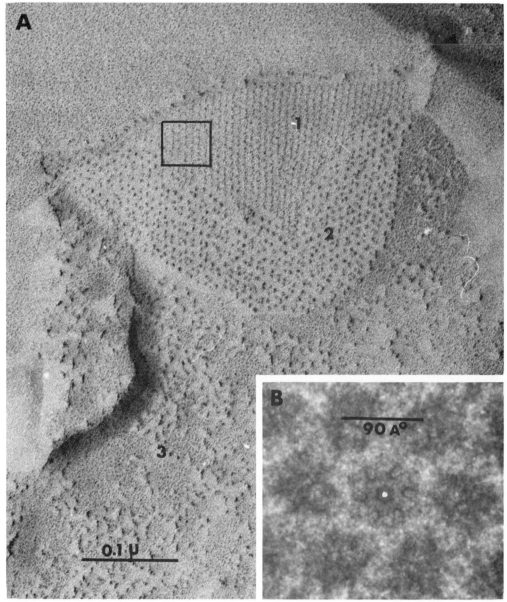

Figure 4.14. Close junction in isolated plasma membranes. Replica of freeze-etched preparation. Three fracture planes are visualized. Face 1 consists of a hexagonal lattice of regular facets. Face 2 is formed by arrays of subunits, and face 3 is dotted by irregularly shaped subunits. Face 1 may correspond to the middle surface of the junction and face 3 the outer surface of the plasma membrane. B, enhancement of the hexagonal lattice by means of the rotation technique ($n = 6$).

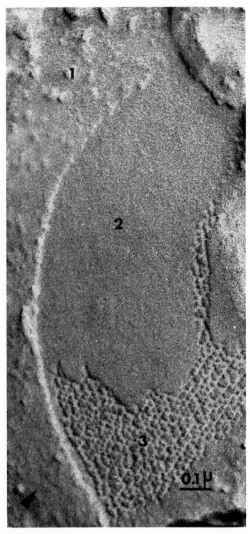

Figure 4.15. Close junctions in isolated plasma membranes. Replica of freeze-etched preparation showing different fracture planes. Surface 1 may correspond to eutectic ice layer. Face 2 shows the middle junctional surface having a smooth appearance. Face 3 shows the arrays of particles.

tating the penetration of the potassium phosphotungstate and the fragmentation of the junction. That partial solubilization of the lipids of the junctions occur, may be argued from the high specific density of the deoxycholate-treated gap junction which sediments at the bottom of a linear sucrose gradient of density, 1.16 to 1.22 (Fig. 4.16). Studies are in progress in our laboratory to determine the composition and enzymatic spectrum of these isolated close junctions.

In keeping with the cytochemical observations reported above showing the ATPase and AMPase end products localized on the inner surface of the gap junctions, significant specific activities for these two enzymes have been found in the gap junction rich fraction after DOC treatment. Independently, Bont *et al.* (91) have reported comparable results.

The complex structural differentiation in the gap junction and in particular the existence of regularly packed subunits does not explain *per se* the humoral and electrical transmission which occurs most probably at the level of this junction. A regular lattice of subunits has been described in specialized regions of plasma membranes in different organisms and tissues and it has been related to a variety of functions including some unrelated to intercellular communications (69, 70). For instance, Hicks and co-workers (92, 93) have shown the presence of a hexagonal lattice of subunits with center-to-center distance of 140 Å in luminal plasma membrane isolated from superficial squamous cells lining the rat urinary bladder. This type of epithelium acts as a barrier to the flow of water and ions between the underlining tissue fluids and the hyperosmotic urine.

That junctional permeability cannot be easily related to a particular and unique structural model is also demonstrated by the observation that artificial uncoupling is not followed by an obvious structural change of the junction as visualized by electron microscopy (94). Noteworthy are

the individual elements of the junction are visualized as membranous, independent sheets. The deoxycholate treatment that allows the separation of the junction from the rest of the plasma membrane (83) may also solubilize, at least partially, some junctional components, thus facili-

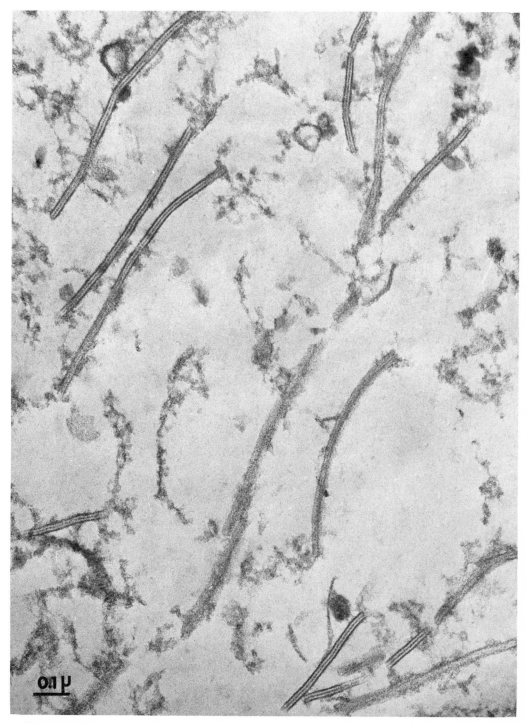

Figure 4.16. Close junctions isolated by DOC treatment and linear gradient centrifugation (density, 1.16–1.22). The junctions are found mainly in the bottom pellet.

77

the observations of Politoff *et al.* (95) indicating that ion permeability of the junctional membrane appears to depend on energy provided by oxidative phosphorylation. The presence of ATPase activity at the level of the gap junction and the essential role of calcium ion as a factor for both ATPase activities and junctional permeability may point to the existence of close dependency of the intercellular coupling to the utilization of energy sources. The hexagonal lattice of subunits is topologically the most favorable conformation to allow membrane function based on rapid cooperative membrane transition in response to the binding of regulatory ligands. By these means, a hexagonal lattice of subunits probably represents a suitable design for regulation of both permeability and/or uncoupling.

CONCLUSIONS

A line of evidence emerges from the present review and concerns the existence of multiple features of the liver plasma membrane which are consistently revealed by various technical means. The configuration of the membrane element results from the association of at least two main structural components: a triple-layered structure and small globular subunits. Other even more elaborate features have been found in relation to junctional complexes. The triple-layered structure appears to be the backbone of the membrane and the particulate component is either attached to the surfaces of the leaflet or spanning it. The association of these two components is probably dependent on strong chemical interactions. Calcium ions seem to have a preponderant role in the maintenance of the triple-layered structure rather than in the association of the subunit to the leaflet. The evidence that after withdrawal of divalent cations by chelating agents the triple-layered structure is no longer recognizable and the membrane element appears as a row of globules strengthens this view.

The transverse polarity, illustrated by the localization of charged groups and enzymatic end products, appears to be an intrinsic property of the plasma membrane since it is maintained throughout the entire isolation procedure. This structural property may be regarded as an important functional parameter, since it ensures vectorial enzymatic activity, transport across the plasma membrane and cell coat, and the exposure of ionic groups and antigenic determinants of the cell surfaces (96, 97). The specific localization of globular or rod-like subunits on the outer or inner membrane surfaces, respectively, can be considered as a structural expression of such a polarity. The postulate that biological membranes consist of lipoprotein subunits has favored the concept that membrane construction could be a self-assembling process governed by the same general design principle which has been applied to virus particles (98). The observations outlined in the present discussion are by no means conclusive evidence for a globular model. On the contrary, the principle of organization of the plasma membrane does not apparently follow a unique model, but rather a combination of multiple designs.

The triple-layered structure, the association of repeating units, and the hexagonal lattice of regular facets are hardly explained by means of a common design principle.

Several experimental studies on solubilization and reassociation of biological membranes did not succeed in proving the existence of a homogeneous class of subunits (81, 82), nor did they achieve a recombination of the membrane components resulting in membranous structures characterized by most of the properties of the original membrane (81, 82, 28).

According to Kellenberger (99), one can define a self-assembling system of *n* components as a system in which *n* components assemble into a shell which contains *all n* components. If one or more components operate only transiently or catalytically during the assembling process, and are not found in the reassociated structure, it is no longer possible to speak of self-assembly.

The biogenesis of a specific membrane type probably is characterized by a multi-step process (100), during which transient and catalytic, morphopoietic supplementary functions operate within a programmed pathway. Under these circumstances, the morphopoietic order will be higher than the number of components found in the final product and each single component would probably not recall the complete information for a correct self-assembly.

It is suggested that membrane development and differentiation are achieved following morphopoietic models of different orders. This postulate can be derived from the evidence of the complexity and degree of versatility of membrane structures and functions.

SUMMARY

Ultrastructural studies on biological membranes have often been oriented to prove the existence of a unique molecular model. However, such a model seems to be questionable if the multiple features of the cell membranes are taken into consideration. Examples of such diversity are presented. Some structural properties of the plasma membrane (transverse and tangential polarity) and of membrane constituents which are important parameters ensuring vectorial functions, specific surface recognition, and membrane coding are discussed. These properties are also investigated in relation to the process of membrane reaggregation after solubilization.

Acknowledgments. This article is dedicated by E. L. Benedetti to the memory of Dr. Nicole Granboulan. The authors wish to thank Dr. A. Kepes and Dr. J. McNary for their criticism and suggestions during the redaction of the present review. The authors gratefully acknowledge the technical assistance of Mrs. Diawara and Mr. Recouvreur.

REFERENCES

1. CHANGEUX, J. P. Remarks on the symmetry and cooperative properties of biological membranes. In *Symmetry and function of biological Systems at the Macromolecular Level*, edited by Engstrom, A., and Strandberg, B., p. 235. Stockholm, Almquist and Wiksell, 1969.

2. CHANGEUX, J. P., and THIERY, J. On the excitability and cooperativity of biological membranes. In *Regulatory Mechanisms in Excitable Membranes*, edited by Järnefelt, J., p. 116. New York, Elsevier Publishing Co., 1968.

3. KILKSON, R. Membrane structure and transitions, a molecular basis of regulation. In *Symmetry and Function of Biological systems at the Macromolecular Level*, edited by Engstrom, A., and Strandberg, B., p. 257. Stockholm, Almquist and Wiksell, 1969.

4. SJÖSTRAND, F. S. Ultrastructure and function of cellular membranes. In *The Membranes*, edited by Dalton, A. J., and Haguenau, F., p. 151. New York, Academic Press, 1968.

5. BLASIE, J. K., AND WORTHINGTON, C. R. Molecular localization of frog retinal receptor photopigment by electron microscopy and low-angle X-ray diffraction. *J. Molec. Biol. 39:* 407, 1969.

6. GLAUERT, A. M., AND LUCY, J. A. Globular micelles and the organization of membrane lipids. In *The Membranes*, edited by Dalton, A. J., and Haguenau, F., p. 1. New York, Academic Press, 1968.

7. ROBERTSON, J. D. Molecular structure of biological membranes. In *Handbook of Molecular Cytology*, edited by Lima de Faria, A., p. 1404. Amsterdam, North Holland Publishing Co., 1969.

8. FLEISCHER, S., FLEISCHER, B., AND STOECKENIUS, W. Fine structure of lipid-depleted mitochondria. *J. Cell Biol. 32:* 1967.

9. NAPOLITANO, L., LEBARON, F., AND SCALETTI, J. Preservation of myelin lamellar structure in the absence of lipid. *J. Cell Biol. 34:* 817, 1967.

10. LUZZATTI, V., GULIK-KRZYWICKI, T., AND TARDIEU, A. Polymorphism of lecithins. *Nature (London) 218:* 1031, 1968.

11. LUZZATI, V. X-ray diffraction studies of lipid-water systems. In *Biological Membranes*,

Physical Fact and Function, edited by Chapman, D., p. 71. New York, Academic Press, 1968.

12. LUZZATI, V., TARDIEU, A., AND GULIK-KRZYWICKI, T. Polymorphism of lipids. *Nature (London)* 217: 1028, 1968.

13. GULIK-KRZYWICKI, T., SHECHTER, E., LUZZATI, V., AND FAURE, M. Interactions of proteins and lipids: Structure and polymorphism of protein-lipid-water phases. *Nature (London)* 223: 1116, 1969.

14. CHAPMAN, D., AND WALLACH, D. F. H. Recent physical studies of phospholipids and natural membranes. In *Biological Membranes, Physical Fact and Function*, edited by Chapman, D., p. 125. New York, Academic Press, 1968.

15. WALLACH, D. F. H., AND GORDON, A. Lipid protein interactions in cellular membranes. *Fed. Proc. 27:* 1263, 1968.

16. WALLACH, D. F. H., AND ZAHLER, P. H. Infrared spectra of plasma membrane and endoplasmic reticulum of Ehrlich ascites carcinoma. *Biochim. Biophys, Acta 150:* 186, 1968.

17. WALLACH, D. F. H. Membrane lipids and the conformations of membrane proteins. *J. Gen. Physiol. 54:* 3s, 1969.

18. LENARD, J., AND SINGER, S. J. Protein conformation in cell membrane preparations as studied by optical rotatory dispersion and circular dichroism. *Proc. Nat. Acad. Sci. U.S.A. 56:* 1828, 1966.

19. BENEDETTI, E. L., AND EMMELOT, P. Structure and function of plasma membranes isolated from liver. In *The Membranes*, edited by Dalton, A. J., and Haguenau, F., p. 33. New York, Academic Press, 1968.

20. EMMELOT, P., AND BENEDETTI, E. L. On the possible involvement of the plasma membrane in the carcinogenic process. In *Carcinogenesis: A broad critique*. Presented at the Twentieth Annual Symposium on Fundamental Cancer Research, 1966. Published for the University of Texas M. D. Anderson Hospital and Tumor Institute, Houston, Texas, p. 471. Baltimore, The Williams and Wilkins Co., 1967.

21. BLAT, C., AND HAREL, L. Phosphoprotéines des membranes plasmiques isolées du foie de rat. Incorporation du ³²P dans ces phosphoprotéines. *Biochim. Biophys. Acta 173:* 23, 1969.

22. DOD, B. J., AND GRAY, G. M. The lipid composition of rat-liver plasma membranes. *Biochim. Biophys. Acta 150:* 397, 1968.

23. SKIPSKI, V. P., BARCLAY, M., ARCHIBALD, F. M., TEREBUS-KEKISH, O., REICHMAN, E. S., AND GOOD, J. J. Lipid composition of rat-liver cell membranes. *Life Sci. 4:* 1673, 1965.

24. TRIA, E., AND BARNABEI, O. Presence of a phosphatide-peptide fraction in liver cell membranes and its possible role in active transport. *Nature (London) 197:* 598, 1963.

25. COLEMAN, R., AND FINEAN, J. B. Preparation and properties of isolated plasma membranes from guinea-pig tissues. *Biochim. Biophys. Acta 125:* 197, 1966.

26. EMMELOT, P., VISSER, A., AND BENEDETTI, E. L. Studies on plasma membranes. VII. A leucyl-β-naphtylamidase-containing repeating unit on the surface of isolated liver and hepatoma plasma membranes. *Biochim Biophys. Acta 150:* 364, 1968.

27. EMMELOT, P., AND BOS, C. J. Studies on plasma membranes. V. On the lipid dependence of some phosphohydrolases of isolated rat-liver plasma membranes. *Biochim. Biophys. Acta 150:* 341, 1968.

28. EMMELOT, P., AND BENEDETTI, E. L. Structure and function of isolated plasma membranes from liver. In *Protides of the Biological Fluids, Proceedings of the Fifteenth Colloquium Bruges 1967*, edited by Peeters, H., p. 315. New York, Elsevier Publishing Co., 1968.

29. COLEMAN, R. Phosphatidate phosphohydrolase activity in liver cell surface membranes. *Biochim. Biophys. Acta 163:* 111, 1968.

30. FLEISCHER, B., AND FLEISCHER, S. Glycosidase activity of bovine liver plasma membranes. *Biochim. Biophys. Acta 183:* 265, 1969.

31. WIDNELL, C. Personal communication.

32. ORRENIUS, S., AND ERICSSON, J. L. E. On the relationship of liver glucose-6 phosphatase to the proliferation of endoplasmic reticulum in phenobarbital induction. *J. Cell Biol. 31:* 243, 1966.

33. PARSONS, D. F. Recent advances correlating structure and function in mitochondria. *Int. Rev. Exp. Path. 4:* 1, 1965.

34. LEHNINGER, A. L. The neuronal membrane. *Proc. Nat. Acad. Sci. U.S.A. 60:* 1069, 1968.

35. DEL CASTILO, J., AND KATZ, B. Identity of intrinsic and extrinsic acetyl-choline receptors in the motor end-plate. *Proc. Roy. Soc. (London) [Biol.] 146:* 357, 1957.

36. NARAHASHI, T., AND MOORE, J. W. Neuroactive agents and nerve membrane conductances. *J. Gen. Physiol. 51:* 93s, 1968.

37. BENNETT, H. S. The cell surface: Components

and configurations. In *Handbook of Molecular Cytology*, edited by Lima de Faria, A., p. 1261. Amsterdam, North Holland Publishing Co., 1969.

38. STOECKENIUS, W., AND ENGELMAN, D. M. Current models for the structure of biological membranes. *J. Cell Biol. 42:* 613, 1969.

39. MARTINEZ-PALOMO, A., BRAISLOVSKY, C., AND BERNHARD, W. Ultrastructural modifications of the cell surface and intercellular contacts of some transformed cell strains. *Cancer Res. 29:* 925, 1969.

40. RAMBOURG, A. Localisation ultrastructurale et nature du matériel coloré au niveau de la surface cellulaire par le mélange chromique-phosphotungstique. *J. Micr. 8:* 325, 1969.

41. REVEL, J. P., AND ITO, S. The surface components of cells. In *The Specificity of Cell Surfaces*, edited by B. D. Davis, and L. Warren, p. 213. Englewood Cliffs, New Jersey, Prentice-Hall, Inc., 1967.

42. BENEDETTI, E. L., AND EMMELOT, P. Studies on plasma membranes. IV. The ultrastructural localization and content of sialic acid in plasma membranes isolated from rat liver and hepatoma. *J. Cell Sci. 2:* 499, 1967.

43. GASIC, G. J., BERWICK, L., AND SORRENTINO, M., Positive and negative colloidal iron as cell surface electron stains. *Lab. Invest. 18:* 63, 1968.

44. MADDY, A. H. The chemical organization of the plasma membrane of animal cells. *Int. Rev. Cytol. 20:* 1, 1966.

45. COOK, G. M. W. Glycoproteins in membranes. *Biol. Rev. 43:* 363, 1968.

46. WARD, P. D., AND AMBROSE, E. J. Electrophoretic and chemical characterization of the charged groups at the surface of murine CL3 ascites leukaemia cells. *J. Cell Sci. 4:* 289, 1969.

47. CURRIE, G. A., AND BAGSHAWE, K. D. The role of sialic acid in antigenic expression: Further studies of the Landschütz ascites tumour. *Brit. J. Cancer 22:* 843, 1968.

48. GOLDFISCHER, S., ESSNER, E., AND NOVIKOFF, A. B. The localization of phosphatase activities at the level of ultrastructure. *J. Histochem. Cytochem. 12:* 72, 1964.

49. BENEDETTI, E. L., AND DELBAUFFE, E. D. The localization of phosphatase activities in isolated liver plasma membranes. In preparation.

50. GANOTE, C. E., ROSENTHAL, A. S., MOSES, H. L., AND TICE, L. W. Lead and phosphate as sources of artifact in nucleoside phosphatase

histochemistry. *J. Histochem. Cytochem. 17:* 641, 1969.

51. JACOBSEN, N. O., AND JORGENSEN, P. O. A quantitative biochemical and histochemical study of the lead method for localization of adenosine triphosphate-hydrolyzing enzymes. *J. Histochem. Cytochem. 17:* 443, 1969.

52. TICE, L. W. Lead-adenosine triphosphate complexes in adenosine triphosphatase histochemistry. *J. Histochem. Cytochem. 17:* 85, 1969.

53. MARCHESI, V. T., AND PALADE, G. E. The localization of Mg-Na-K-activated adenosine triphosphatase on red cell ghost membranes. *J. Cell Biol. 35:* 385, 1967.

54. WATTIAUX DE CONINCK, S., AND WATTIAUX, R. Nucleoside diphosphatase activity in plasma membrane of rat liver. *Biochim. Biophys. Acta 183:* 118, 1969.

55. DELBAUFFE, D., PELLETIER, C., AND OLIVE, J. Etude du processus de réagrégation des membranes plasmiques isolées, solubilisées par des détergents. In *Septième Congrès International de Microscopie Electronique*, Grenoble, Switzerland, edited by P. Favard, Vol. 3, p. 19. Paris, France, Société Française de Microscopie Electronique, 1970.

56. FINEAN, J. B. Biophysical contributions to membrane structure. *Quart. Rev. Biophys. 2:* 1, 1969.

57. KORN, E. D. Cell membranes: Structure and synthesis. *Ann. Rev. Biochem. 38:* 694, 1969.

58. KORN, E. D. Structure and function of the plasma membrane: A biochemical perspective. *J. Gen. Physiol. 52:* 257, 1968.

59. BENEDETTI, E. L., AND EMMELOT, P. Electron microscopic observations on negatively stained plasma membranes isolated from rat liver. *J. Cell Biol. 26:* 299, 1965.

60. OVERTON, J., EICHHOLZ, A., AND CRANE, R.K. Studies on the organization of the brush border in intestinal epithelium cells. II. Fine structure of fractions of Tris-disrupted hamster brush borders. *J. Cell Biol. 26:* 693, 1965.

61. CUNNINGHAM, N. P., AND CRANE, F. L. Variation in membrane structure as revealed by negative staining technique. *Exp. Cell Res. 44:* 31, 1966.

62. ODA, T., IWATA, S., OMURA, S., SEKI, S., YAMAMOTO, G., HATASE, O., HAYASHI, H., WAKABAYASHI, A. Isolation and characterization of plasma membranes from AH-130 strain cancer cells and liver cells of rats. Proceedings of the 9th International Cancer Congress, Tokyo, Abstract S0236, p. 154, 1966.

63. Johnson, C. F. Intestinal invertase activity and a macromolecular repeating unit of hamster brush border plasma membranes. Proceedings of the 6th International Congress on Electron Microscopy, Kyoto, p. 389, 1965.

64. Eichholz, A. Studies on the organization of the brush border in intestinal epithelial cells. V. Subfractionation of enzymatic activities of the microvillus membrane. Biochim. Biophys. Acta 163: 101, 1968.

65. Parsons, D. F. Ultrastructural and molecular aspects of cell membranes. Canad. Cancer Conf. 7: 193, 1967.

66. Martonosi, A. Sarcoplasmic reticulum. V. The structure of sarcoplasmic reticulum membranes. Biochim. Biophys. Acta 150: 694, 1968.

67. Koehler, J. K. The technique and application of freeze-etching in ultrastructure research. Int. Rev. Cytol. 62: 1, 1969.

68. Moor, H. Use of freeze-etching in the study of biological ultrastructure. Int. Rev. Cytol. 63: 179, 1969.

69. Staehelin, L. A. Ultrastructural changes of the plasmalemma and the cell wall during the life cycle of cyanidium caldarium. Proc. Roy. Soc. (London) 171: 249, 1968.

70. Staehelin, L. A. The interpretation of freeze-etched artificial and biological membranes. J. Ultrastruct. Res. 22: 326, 1968.

71. Branton, D. Membrane structure. Ann. Rev. Plant Physiol. 20: 209, 1969.

72. Park, R. B., and Pfeifhofer, A. O. Ultrastructural observations on deep-etched thylakoids. J. Cell Sci. 5: 299, 1969.

73. Park, R. B., and Pfeifhofer, A. O. The effect of ethylenediamine tetracetate washing on the structure of spinach thylakoids. J. Cell Sci. 5: 313, 1969.

74. Clark, A. W., and Branton, D. Fracture faces in frozen outer segments from the guinea-pig retina. Z. Zellforsch. 91: 586, 1968.

75. Weinstein, R. S. Electron microscopy of surfaces of red cell membranes. In Red Cell Membrane Structure and Function, edited by Jamicson, G. A., and Greenwalt, T. J., The American National Red Cross Second Annual Scientific Symposium. Philadelphia, J. B. Lippincott Company, 1969.

76. Steers, E., and Marchesi, V. T. Studies on a protein component of guinea-pig erythrocyte membranes. J. Gen. Physiol. 54: 65s, 1969.

77. Mazia, D., and Ruby, A. Dissolution of erythrocyte membranes in water and comparison of the membrane protein with other structural proteins. Proc. Nat. Acad. Sci. U.S.A. 61: 1005, 1968.

78. Neifakh, S. A., and Vasilets, I. M. Actomyosin-like protein in outer membrane of liver cells (translated from the Russian). Fed. Proc. 24: No. 3, Part I, T561, 1965.

79. Neville, D. M. Circular dichroism of liver cell membrane organ specific protein. Biochem. Biophys. Res. Commun. 34: 60, 1969.

80. Buckingham, J. H., and Staehelin, L. A. The effect of glycerol on the structure of lecithin membranes, a study by freeze-etching and X-ray diffraction. J. Micr. 90: 83, 1969.

81. Engelman, D. M., and Morowitz, H. J. Characterization of the plasma membrane of mycoplasma laidlawii. IV. Structure and composition of membrane and aggregated components. Biochim. Biophys. Acta 150: 385, 1968.

82. Razin, S., Neeman, Z., and Ohad, I. Selective reaggregation of solubilized mycoplasma membrane proteins and the kinetics of membrane reformation. Biochim. Biophys. Acta 193: 277, 1969.

83. Benedetti, E. L., and Emmelot, P. Hexagonal array of subunits in tight junctions separated from isolated rat liver plasma membrane. J. Cell Biol. 38: 15, 1963.

84. Revel, J. P., and Karnovsky, M. J. Hexagonal array of subunits in intercellular junctions of the mouse heart and liver. J. Cell Biol. 33: C7, 1967.

85. Brightman, M. W., and Reese, T. S. Junctions between intimately apposed cell membranes in the vertebrate brain. J. Cell Biol. 40: 648, 1969.

86. Emmelot, P., and Bos, C. J. Studies on plasma membranes. X. A survey of enzyme activities displayed by plasma membranes isolated from mouse liver and three mouse hepatoma strains. Int. J. Cancer 4: 723, 1969.

87. Loewenstein, W. R., and Kanno, Y. Intercellular communication and tissue growth. I. Cancerous growth. J. Cell Biol. 33: 225, 1967.

88. Borek, C., Higashino, S., and Loewenstein, W. R. Intercellular communication and tissue growth. IV. Conductance of membrane junctions of normal and cancerous cells in culture. J. Membrane Biol. 1: 274, 1969.

89. Mc Nutt, N. S., and Weinstein, R. S. Interlocking subunit arrays forming nexus membranes. In 27th Annual Proceedings of the Electron Microscope Society of America, edited by

C. J. Arceneaux. Baton Rouge, Louisiana, Claitor's Publishing Division, 1969.

90. DUNIA DE GONZALEZ, I., AND BENEDETTI, E. L. Comparative morphology of junctional complexes in rat and mouse liver. In *Septième Congrès International de Microscopie Electronique*, Grenoble, Switzerland, edited by P. Favard, Vol. 3, p. 1. Paris, France, Société Française de Microscopie Electronique, 1970.

91. BONT, W. S., EMMELOT, P., AND VAZ DIAS, H. Studies on plasma membranes. VIII. The effects of sodium deoxycholate and dodecyl sulfate on isolated rat-liver plasma membranes. *Biochim. Biophys. Acta 173:* 389, 1969.

92. HICKS, R. M., KETTERER, B., AND BEALE, D. The isolation and analysis of the plasma membrane lining the lumen of the rat bladder. *Biochem. J. 109:* 418, 1968.

93. HICKS, R. M., AND KETTERER, B. Hexagonal lattice of subunits in the thick luminal membrane of the rat urinary bladder. *Nature (London) 224:* 1304, 1969.

94. BULLIVANT, S., AND LOEWENSTEIN, W. R. Structure of coupled and uncoupled cell junctions. *J. Cell Biol. 37:* 621, 1968.

95. POLITOFF, A. L., SOCOLAR, S. J., AND LOEWENSTEIN, W. R. Permeability of cell membrane

junction. Dependence on energy metabolism. *J. Gen. Physiol. 53:* 498, 1969.

96. INBAR, M., AND SACHS, L. Structural difference in sites on the surface membrane of normal and transformed cells. *Nature (London) 223:* 710, 1969.

97. AOKI, T., HAMMERLING, U., DE HARVEN, E., BOYSE, E. A., AND OLD, L. J. Antigenic structure of cell surfaces. An immunoferritin study of the occurence and topography of H-2, and TL alloantigens on mouse cells. *J. Exp. Med. 130:* 979, 1969.

98. CASPAR, D. L. D. Design and Assembly of organized biological structures. In *Molecular Architecture in Cell Physiology*, edited by Hayashi, T., and Szent-Györgyi, A. G., p. 191. Englewood Cliffs, New Jersey, Prentice-Hall, Inc., 1966.

99. KELLENBERGER, E. Polymorphic assemblies of the same major virus protein subunit. In *Symmetry and Function of Biological Systems at the Macromolecular Level*, edited by Engström. A., and Strandberg, B., p. 349. Stockholm, Almquist and Wiksell, 1968.

100. DALLNER, G., SIEKEVITZ, P., AND PALADE, G. E. Biogenesis of endoplasmic reticulum membranes. II. Synthesis of constitutive microsomal enzymes in developing rat hepatocyte. *J. Cell Biol. 30:* 97, 1966.

5

THE ROLE OF ENERGY METABOLISM, ION, AND WATER SHIFTS IN THE PATHOGENESIS OF CELL INJURY

Benjamin F. Trump, Byron P. Croker, Jr., and Wolfgang J. Mergner

SEQUENCE OF ULTRASTRUC- TURAL CHANGE IN LETHALLY ALTERED CELLS

Review of the numerous publications dealing with ultrastructural aspects of disease and cell injury that have been published during the past two decades reveals a variety of ultrastructural alterations (see reviews 1–3) which, with relatively few exceptions, have been viewed only at the descriptive level. At first acquaintance, such a perusal of the literature reveals a somewhat bewildering array of ultrastructural changes, however, further examination shows a limited number of ultrastructural patterns which are common to many types of injury and many types of disease processes. In some instances, it has been possible to classify or categorize changes as being characteristic of sublethal as opposed to lethal injury, though in many instances the former represent stages en route to the latter. In our laboratory we have examined the sequence of ultrastructural changes following acute lethal injuries of diverse

Department of Pathology, Duke University, Durham, North Carolina 27706, and the Duke Marine Laboratory, Beaufort North Carolina 28516.

Supported by National Institutes of Health Grant AM 10698 and Training Grant GM-00726.

type to a variety of different cell systems in both plants and animals, and have been impressed with the similarity of progression (2–28); indeed, the concept of a final common pathway of changes following lethal injury becomes quite compelling. Examples of such similarities in diverse systems following various types of injury might include ultrastructural changes in experimental myocardial infarction (29), changes in the centrilobular cells of the liver following carbon tetrachloride administration (1, 71), progression of changes in the kidney tubule after injection of mercuric chloride (30), the changes in HeLa cells infected with polio virus (31), and the changes in an ascites tumor cell treated with cytolytic antibody and complement (26). In all of these examples the types of changes are similar; the chief differences involve the rate of progression. In part this can be explained by differences in the specific pathogenetic mechanisms as given in detail below.

For our present purposes, an injury is considered as any perturbation which alters cellular homeostasis. Injury may also be thought of as a process which changes the entropy (disorganization) level of the steady-state cell either by decreasing the rate of dissipation of entropy relative to production or conversely, increasing production relative to dissipation (32). Injury may result in (a) a new steady state or (b) a perturbation which returns to the original state; both (a) and (b) can be classed as sublethal. Injury may also result in (c) a change which is incompatible with any "steady state" other than equilibrium and would therefore be a lethal injury. Injury may affect one or more of the following.

1. Rate of production and utilization of energy or chemical constituents such as proteins, carbohydrates, lipids, or nucleic acids.

2. Ion and water movements.

3. Molecular and supramolecular arrangement.

4. The genetic material.

Effects involving genetic material do not seem important in acute injury except when cells are in the mitotic cycle. Although with prolonged sublethal injuries or in the case of rapidly turning over mRNA, if such exists, such effects could be important in interphase cells. A conceptualization of the events following lethal or sublethal injury is shown in Figure 5.1.

Studies performed in our laboratory suggest that following acute lethal injury cells pass in a sequential fashion through the following stages (6, 12, 33) (Fig. 5.2). It should be emphasized that the rate of passage through these stages varies considerably, particularly in the case of stage 3. A review of the literature, as well as of our work however, substantiates that identical stages can be identified in a variety of injuries in plant and animal cells (1–3, 12, 33, 70).

Stage 1

This is the normal *in vivo* state. The cell membrane has the normal configuration for the particular cell type and exhibits the typical trilaminar structure at high resolution. The endoplasmic reticulum is either collapsed with a very small lumen or is slightly enlarged containing flocculent material presumed to represent secretory protein in some cells. The mitochon-

dria have an orthodox appearance with closely apposed inner and outer membranes and a moderately dense matrix compartment containing mitochondrial granules and the granulofibrillar matrix proteins. The cell sap contains flocculent material of moderate density, and occasional clusters of free ribosomes. Nuclear chromatin is diffuse except for occasional regions of heterochromatin. Lysosomes have intact membranes and a matrix of moderate density.

Stage 2

Cells in this stage exhibit dilation, sometimes massive, of the endoplasmic reticulum giving rise to so-called hydropic degeneration (Figs. 5.3A and 5.10A). More often the cisternae are moderately dis-

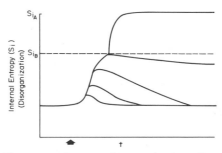

Figure 5.1. Conceptualization showing effects of injury in terms of change in internal entropy (Si) or disorganization. When a cell in a normal steady state with "normal" level of internal entropy is injured (*arrow*) we postulate that the entropy level increases. In the case of sublethal injuries, removal of the injurious stimulus permits return of the internal entropy to normal levels, that is, the homeostasis is restored. In the case of lethal injuries, however, entropy increases to a point Si_B which represents the maximum internal entropy that can be tolerated by the cell. This "point-of-no-return" can also be referred to as the point of cell death. After this time the cell enters a degradative series of reactions with increase of internal entropy to thermodynamic equilibrium. This phase from Si_B to Si_A is often referred to as the phase of necrosis. Some injuries, even if prolonged, are sublethal; that is, the cell is able to adapt to the presence of continued injurious stimuli by taking some new steady state with higher levels of internal entropy Si. t time.

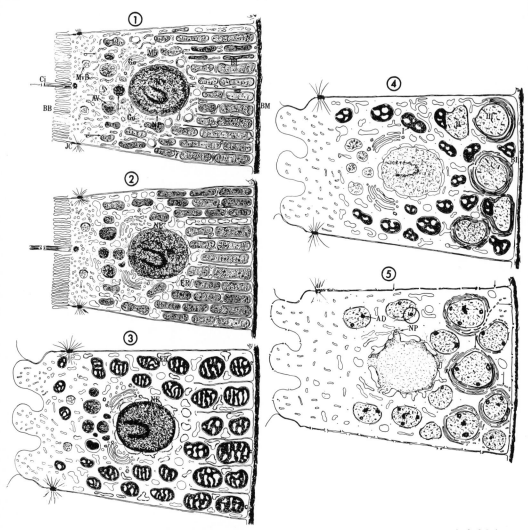

Figure 5.2. Stages of morphological change indicating the progressive cellular response to a lethal injury. Stage 1 represents the normal appearance of the cell. In stage 2, changes consist only of dilation of the endoplasmic reticulum. In stage 3, additional changes include contraction of the inner compartment of mitochondria and enlargement of the cell sap. Plasma membrane contours are simplified with membrane blebs as seen at the left. In stage 4, additional changes include high amplitude swelling of some mitochondria (III) and some mitochondria in which a portion of the inner compartment is contracted and other portions expanded (II). Basilar infoldings are wrapped around organelles and polysomes are lost from the endoplasmic reticulum. In stage 5, all mitochondria show high amplitude swelling plus flocculent (AD) and/or microcrystalline deposits (*circled*). The nucleus shows karyolysis, the plasma membrane shows points of interruption, and lysosomes cannot be distinguished. Explanation of abbreviations: BB, brush border; Ci, cilium; MvB, multivesicular body; JC, junctional complexes; AV, autophagic vacuole; L, lysosome; Go, Golgi apparatus; Mb, microbody; NP, nuclear pore; ER, endoplasmic reticulum; BI, basilar infoldings; BM, basement membrane. (From Ginn, F. L., Shelburne, J. D., and Trump, B. F., *Amer. J. Path. 53:* 1041, 1968.)

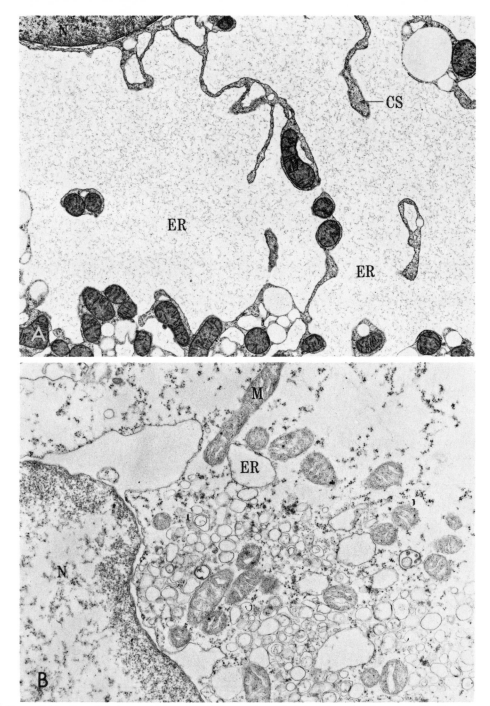

Figure 5.3A. Centrilobular rat hepatocyte 12 hours after administration of carbon tetrachloride. Note the massive dilation of the endoplasmic reticulum (ER), with small intervening areas of cell sap (CS). This represents stage 2 and has been classically termed hydropic change. Part of the nucleus (N) appears at the top. ×24,000.

Figure 5.3B. HeLa cell 6 hours after inoculation with polio virus showing typical stage 3 changes with dilation of endoplasmic reticulum (ER), and contraction of mitochondria (M). The nucleus (N) shows clumping of chromatin. ×24,000.

tended and appear to break up into discontinuous vesicles. The ribosomes may or may not be attached to the surface of the endoplasmic reticulum membrane. Nuclear chromatin is usually clumped and the plasma membrane may show irregularities such as blebs or protrusions.

Stage 3

These cells have in addition to the changes of stage 2, enlargement of the cell sap which becomes of low density, and condensation of the mitochondrial inner compartment which may be striking (Figs. 5.3B, 5.10B, 5.13B and C, 5.16B, 5.17, and 5.20A). The inner compartment change in mitochondria results in a relative increase in volume of the outer compartment. The inner compartment is quite dense, consisting of closely packed filamentous or granular images. The mitochondrial granules may or may not be present.

Stage 4

This is an intermediate stage where some mitochondria show high amplitude swelling while others show maintenance of the condensed configuration (Figs. 5.4A and 5.11A). A few mitochondria show both types of change in two divisions of the inner compartment, one side being markedly swollen and the other condensed. The mitochondria showing the high amplitude change may resemble those of stage 5. Clumping and margination of nuclear chromatin is extreme in this stage.

Stage 5

In this phase the mitochondria all show high amplitude swelling (Figs. 5.4B, 5.11B, 5.20B, and 5.34B–D). This is ordinarily accompanied by interruption of the continuity of the outer membrane and simplification of the inner membrane. In later stages, tubular profiles appear to grow from the inner membrane into the matrix compartment. The matrix may show one or both of the following types of densities. The first type is a flocculent or fluffy aggregate which appears to represent coagulated matrix proteins. These often seem to form near cristae and may envelope them. The mitochondria showing these matrix densities do not contain increased levels of calcium and this type of change may be observed in mitochondria in which calcium uptake is completely blocked. The second type of density is composed of particulate aggregates of material which occur in circular distributions forming annular images; ultimately these become multilaminated. In some instances long needle-like crystals are observed (Fig. 5.4B). These represent calcifications within the mitochondrion. Changes in other organelles include interruptions in the continuity of the cell membrane; elaborate formations resulting from winding of complex membranes, such as those at the base of a kidney tubule, around organelles such as mitochondria; disappearance of lysosomes; beginning karyolysis; and often disappearance of polysomes from the cytoplasm.

As discussed below, stages 2 and 3 appear to be compatible with cell survival whereas stages 4 and 5 represent irreversibly altered cells in the necrotic phase.

As will be developed in detail below, our experimental results to date favor the hypothesis that progression of cells through these stages both in selected situations *in vitro* as well as in complex injury *in vivo* results from modification of cell membrane function and/or modification of cell energy metabolism. It has recently become evident that both of these parameters involve membrane function; often this results from the concerted action of highly integrated membrane-bound enzyme systems. It has also become evident that the relationship between structure and function in membranes is a very close one; indeed at the molecular level the concepts of structure and function become virtually inseparable. This idea is shown in diagrammatic fashion in Figure 5.5.

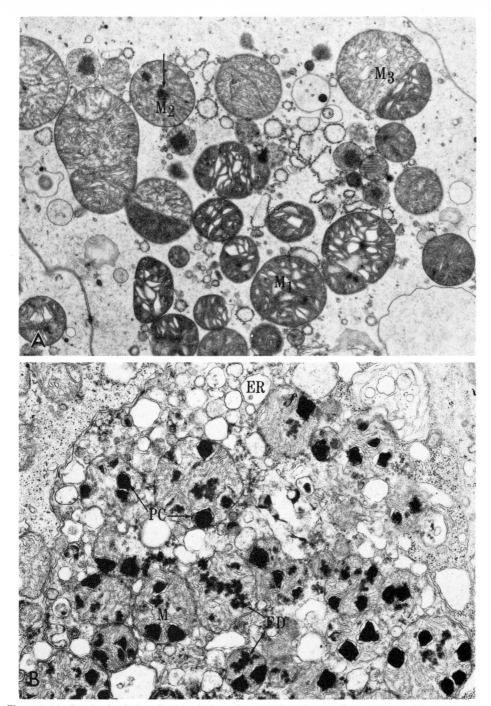

Figure 5.4A. Proximal tubule cell of rat kidney slices incubated at 4° C for 48 hours. There is a mixture of contracted (M_1) and moderately swollen mitochondrià (M_2) which also contain amorphous densities. M_3 demonstrates compartmentation of the mitochondrial matrix; the lower segment appears dense and contracted while the upper portion is swollen. ×24,000.

Figure 5.4B. Pars recta of rat kidney 24 hours after injection of mercuric chloride (16 mg/kg). This figure displays the typical characteristics of stage 5. The endoplasmic reticulum (ER) is dilated, the cell sap is swollen, and the mitochondria (M) contain two types of densities: flocculent densities (FD) and crystalline densities (PC). Previously these were referred to as paracrystalline accumulations. These crystalline densities presumably represent accumulations of complex forms of calcium phosphate. These aggregates represent accumulations of microcrystals. This calcium accumulation presumably represents the effects of secondary leak of calcium through the damaged plasma membrane with accumulation by the mitochondria (see Fig. 5.6). ×21,000.

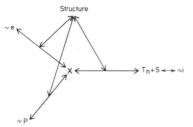

Figure 5.5. Diagram of energy conserving and transducing properties of membranes. The relationship between the three main forms of energy is shown: $\sim e$, electron transport energy; $\sim P$, chemical bond energy; $\sim i$, ion gradient energy which is interconnected by a specific translocator (T_n) and a selector S. X indicates an unknown but postulated intermediate. The pyramid created by connection of each symbol of transduction with structure symbolizes the inter-relationship of energy transduction and structure. (Modified from Mueller, P., and Rudin, D. O. Translocators in bimolecular lipid membrane; their role in dissipative and conservative bioenergy transduction. In *Current Topics in Bioenergetics*, edited by Sanadi, D. R., Vol. 3, p. 157. New York, Academic Press, Inc., 1969.)

ION AND WATER MOVEMENTS: CELL VOLUME REGULATION

The above stages can be characterized as chiefly involving differential expansion of various intracellular compartments as a function of time. Based on current concepts of cell ion and water regulation, these changes imply a redistribution of ions and water which, it has been found, can occur either with or without an increase in total cell volume. Measurements of ion and water contents of cells following injurious stimuli *in vivo* results in general, in an increased level of sodium, water, and chloride with roughly corresponding decreases in content of potassium (Fig. 5.6). Such studies imply that changes in ion and water content are common accompaniments of cell injury, indicating the possible importance of these redistributions in the pathogenesis of cell change. At the same time, since the volume of membrane compartments is changing, the entire sequence can be characterized as involving major altera-

tions in cellular and intracellular compartment volume regulation.

For this reason we were prompted to examine systematically the effects of modifying cell volume regulation to determine the similarities or differences with regard to the sequence of changes observed following complex injuries *in vivo*. In mammalian cells the control of cell volume is a consequence of control of intracellular water content. This water content, however, results from primary modification of electrolyte composition; water movement being generally regarded as passive (34). Factors that can affect the distribution of water between cells and their environment include differences in hydrostatic pressure, differences in electrical potential, differences in chemical activity, and differences in temperature. It has, however, been shown that the activity of water within the cell and the hydrostatic pressure within the cell are essentially equal to those same parameters outside the cell.

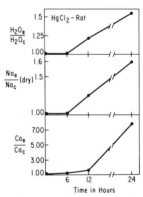

Figure 5.6. The water, sodium, and calcium content of outer strip of outer medulla of rat kidney as a function of time following injection of mercuric chloride. In each case the ratio of experimental (e) to control (c) is shown. Note the roughly parallel increases of water and sodium beginning by 6 hours and the beginning accumulation of calcium by 12 hours. This delay suggests that a secondary leak, possibly related to prior swelling and stretching of the plasma membrane, promotes calcium intake with active sequestration by mitochondria, accounting for the much higher ratios observed with calcium than with sodium.

It has also been shown that the cell membrane is permeable to sodium, potassium, and chloride. Permeability also exists for calcium and magnesium but permeability characteristics of these ions are less well understood. Because of the presence of a relatively high concentration of negatively charged intracellular protein as compared with that of the extracellular space and the presence of diffusible ions there is the possibility that the cells might exist at Gibbs-Donnan equilibrium. It can, however, be established that this cannot be the case since if the cells were at Gibbs-Donnan equilibrium, the osmolality and intracellular hydrostatic pressure would exceed those in the extracellular fluid. Some cells, notably plants, solve this problem by accepting high hydrostatic pressures, surrounding the cell membrane with a thick cell wall of cellulose, which however restricts movement while regulating cell volume. It appears that the key to intracellular volume regulation in mammalian cells resides within vectorial ion pumps especially those for sodium and potassium. These pumps must resist the tendency toward Gibbs-Donnan equilibrium by regulating intracellular ion content. Cell volume regulation can thus be regarded as representing a balance between leak of these ions into the cells and active transport out of the cell. If leak of sodium increases, then the pump must increase lest cell volume control be lost. On the other hand, if leak into the cell is retarded or decreased, pump activity may also decrease. It furthermore seems evident that cells can be regarded as a series of membrane-bound compartments. Each compartment therefore may lose volume control independently of other compartments. The understanding of each of these will require knowledge concerning contents of ion, ion permeabilities, and vectorial ion pumps. So far clear ultrastructural differences between these various membrane systems have been observed (35–37).

Since it is difficult to obtain data bearing on these hypotheses in intact cell systems, that is, measurements of electrical potential, ion movements, and cell volume are extremely difficult, it has been our plan to employ various model systems with which data can be accumulated more readily. This strategy involves a rather systematic exploration of the effects of modifying cell volume regulation in these model systems.

Reference to the diagram, Figure 5.7, which summarizes the important characteristics of volume regulation in the mammalian cell, makes it evident that cell volume regulation can be modified in two major ways. Membrane permeability can be modified or the energy supply for the pump can be increased or decreased. Further insight into the relationship of volume regulation to other metabolic processes is illustrated in Figure 5.8 which is a bar-type metabolic control diagram (38). In that diagram the inter-relationships between the pump, leak, and energy metabolism should be evident. It should be pointed out that the sodium pump at the cell membrane provides an important control step in mitochondrial metabolism. Increased pumping activity often prompts an increase in intracellular sodium levels, releasing more ADP which, in turn, stimulates mitochondrial phosphorylation in turn creating more ATP. This important feedback type control mechanism may apply to all parts of this system.

Effects of Inhibition of Na Extrusion Mechanisms

Decreased Na extrusion

In order to explore the specific effects on cell ultrastructure of interfering with sodium transport, we studied the effects of the cardiac glycoside ouabain (6) on the ultrastructure and function of isolated nephrons of the marine flounder, *Paralichthys lethostigma*. This compound specifically inhibits the sodium-potassium ATP-ase of the plasma membrane, (Fig. 5.9). Active transport of Diodrast and chlor-

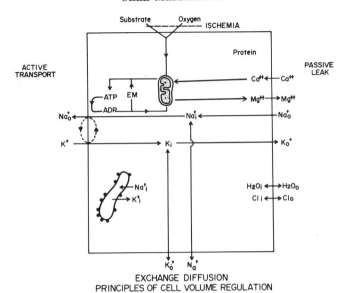

Figure 5.7. Diagram showing factors considered important in cell volume regulation in mammalian cells. Because of the presence of intracellular protein, active control mechanisms for sodium and potassium must balance effects of passive leak and exchange diffusion. Active extrusion mechanisms require energy, often in the form of ATP, which can be supplied by the Embden-Meyerhoff pathway or by the mitochondria. In the absence of substrate and oxygen, that is in ischemia, inhibition of the extrusion mechanism occurs. Mechanisms for active accumulation and extrusion of magnesium and calcium, respectively, are poorly understood. However, when calcium leaks into the cell, it is often rapidly accumulated in the mitochondria. Active pumps for sodium and potassium may exist within the endoplasmic reticulum, though the nature of such mechanisms is not clear presently. Water is assumed to be distributed according to the osmotic gradient and chloride according to the electrochemical gradient.

phenol red by the tubule and protein synthesis are also inhibited. The protein synthesis inhibition is probably the result of decreased intracellular potassium (39). Studies of ions and water show a progressive increase in sodium and water content which is accompanied by cell swelling. Electron microscopic studies reveal a progression of morphologic change from stage 2 through stage 5 (Figs. 5.10A–5.11B). In stages 4 and 5 intramitochondrial calcification was prominent. Since ouabain is not known to affect calcium transport at the cell membrane it is our impression that leak of calcium into the cell was abetted by the swelling and stretching of the plasma membrane. The latter probably results in a secondary leak as described below. These experiments also illustrate the effects of modifying ion content on complex cell functions such as active ion transport.

Effects of decreased ATP levels

Treatment of flounder tubules with agents depressing ATP levels such as potassium cyanide (15, 16) also resulted in rapid progression through stages 2 to 5 (Fig. 5.12). Stages 3 and 4 were short-lived under these conditions, probably because at the temperature of incubation used, the contracted state of mitochondria cannot be maintained for prolonged periods. The changes are accompanied by rapid cell swelling, influx of sodium, and loss of potassium.

Similar results have been obtained by incubation of rat kidney cortex slices at 0–4° C in Robinson's balanced salt solution (13) (Fig. 5.4A). These conditions result in swelling because of failure of sodium extrusion resulting from decreased ATP synthesis at the reduced temperature. Cells

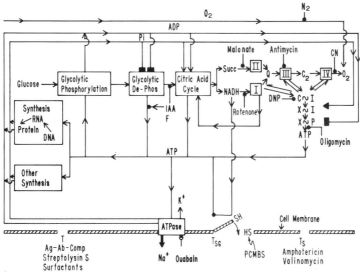

Figure 5.8. Control bar diagram showing relationship between cell membrane and energy metabolism. Along the lower portion of the picture are several conditions listed which modify membrane permeability and/or transport systems. Treatment of cells with antigen-antibody and complement (Ag-Ab-Comp), strepto-lysin S, or surfactant apparently produces rather non-specific leaks in the membrane. Membrane sulfhydryl compounds may participate in redox gating mechanisms ($T_{SG} + T_s$). Such redox gates may be modified by sulfhydryl compounds such as *p*-chloromercuribenzenesulfonic acid (PCMBS) which, in general, promote leakiness of the membrane. In certain circumstances such as the anoxic toad bladder, closing of redox gates may occur as produced by reduced components, possibly including NADH. Membrane permeability can also be modified by more specific translocator or translocator-selector compounds such as amphotericin B or valin-omycin. In each of these cases, when sodium enters the cell, the sodium-potassium pump (ATPase) is pre-sumably stimulated. This utilizes ATP and generates ADP and P_i which, in turn, stimulate mitochondrial phosphorylation or particularly in the absence of oxygen, glycolysis is stimulated. ATP can also be utilized for synthesis of proteins and nucleotides as well as other compounds within the cell; however, in the case of acute lethal injury, alterations in these pathways seem to be relatively unimportant in determining the changes seen. Also shown are the effects of inhibitors of glycolysis, such as iodoacetate (IAA) and fluoride, the electron transport complexes (I–IV), and inhibitors of this pathway, such as malonate, rotenone, antimy-cin, and cyanide. The action of dinitrophenol as an uncoupler is diagrammed according to the chemical inter-mediate theory and oligomycin, an inhibitor of phosphorylation, is shown producing a terminal block of ATP synthesis. (Modified from Jobsis, F. F. Basic processes in cellular respiration. In *Handbook of Physiology, Respiration Section*, edited by Finn, W. O., and Rahn, H., Vol. 1, p. 117. Washington, D.C., American Physiological Society, 1964.)

can be maintained in stage 3 for as long as 24 hours. These studies provide evidence of the reversibility of stage 3, since when such cold-incubated slices are warmed and oxygenated, sodium and water extrusion rapidly occur.

Conditions Associated with Increased Rates of Influx of Sodium and Water into the Cell

Such conditions include treatment of cells with specific antibody plus comple-ment or treatment with agents binding sulfhydryl groups such as *p*-chloromercuri-benzenesulfonate (PCMBS) (Fig. 5.13A–C). Studies with PCMBS have been con-ducted on isolated flounder kidney tubules and Ehrlich ascites cells (8, 11). In both cases extremely rapid increases in volume occur accompanied by influx of sodium and water (Fig. 5.14). Cells rapidly enter stage 3 which is transient under these conditions. Calcium presumably enters soon there-after and is accumulated by mitochon-

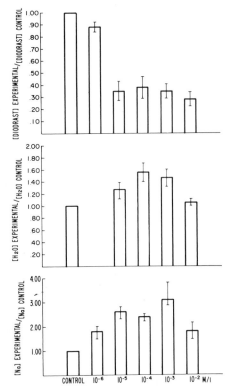

Figure 5.9. Effects of ouabain in various concentrations on sodium content, water content, and Diodrast transport by isolated flounder kidney tubule preparations. (From Ginn, F. L., Shelburne, J. D., and Trump, B. F., *Amer. J. Path. 53:* 1041, 1968.)

dria, though with higher concentration of PCMBS, calcification does not occur probably because these agents inhibit the accumulation system when they enter the cell. Treatment of ascites cells with specific antibody in the presence of complement is also followed by a similar progression, cells rapidly entering stage 3 and passing to stages 4 and 5. Using this system it can be observed that stage 4 or 5 cells stain with dyes such as trypan blue, nigrosin, or erythrosin B (Fig. 5.14).

PATHOGENESIS OF CHANGES; MODEL SYSTEMS

The hypothesis that changes, described as stages 2 to 5 above, can result from conditions associated with loss of cell volume regulation suggests the possibility of close correlations between ion and water movements and pathogenesis of these types of changes (10, 33). Accordingly, studies have been performed with two systems which are particularly suitable for correlation between ion movements and altered cell ultrastructure.

The Isolated Toad Bladder Preparation

The use of isolated transporting epithelial cell preparations has become widespread in physiology since the introduction of this technique by Ussing for the study of sodium and water transport by amphibian skin (40). The principle of this preparation is that the epithelial cells of the mucosal lining are capable of vectorial sodium transport which gives rise to a potential difference of 40 to 50 mV (mucosal side negative) when incubated in a chamber where the bladder separates two compartments containing oxygenated balanced salt solution (Fig. 5.15). The potential difference can be nulled by an external voltage source; the amount of current required to reduce the potential to zero is referred to as the "short-circuit current" and it has been shown that this can be taken as a measure of net sodium transport from the mucosal to the serosal compartments. Such a preparation is also useful for measurements of membrane resistance, which is defined in this case as the change in potential produced by a step increase in current. With this preparation it is possible to easily record changes in membrane permeability and net sodium transport. According to the modified Koefoed-Johnson-Ussing hypothesis (40), net sodium flux from mucosal to serosal compartments in the toad bladder preparations, results from vectorial pumps localized near the basilar or serosal surface of the epithelium. Sodium is presumed to enter passively along the mucosal surface by means of simple or facilitated diffusion. Another advantage of this preparation is that excellent ultrastructure and function can be maintained

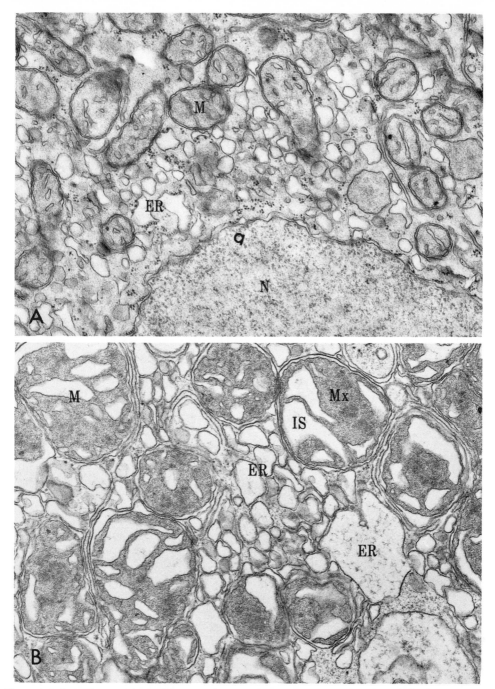

Figure 5.10A. Early stage of alteration following ouabain treatment of flounder tubule showing stage 2. N, nucleus; M, mitochondria. ×40,000. (Modified from Ginn, F. L., Shelburne, J. D., and Trump, B. F., *Amer. J. Path. 53:* 1041, 1968.)

Figure 5.10B. Later stage of alteration following ouabain treatment of flounder kidney tubule showing typical stage 3. Note contraction of mitochondrial matrix (Mx), dilated intracristal space (IS), and dilated endoplasmic reticulum (ER). ×50,000. (Modified from Ginn, F. L., Shelburne, J. D., and Trump, B. F., *Amer. J. Path. 53:* 1041, 1968.)

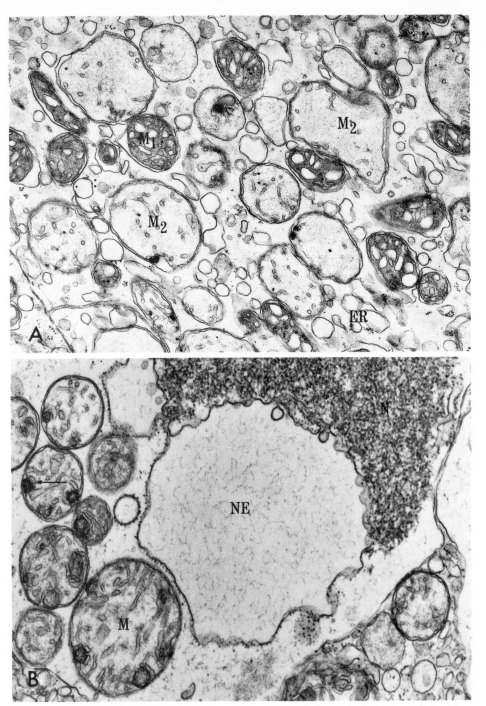

Figure 5.11A. Stage 4 change following treatment of flounder kidney tubules with ouabain. Note contracted mitochondria (M_1) and mitochondria showing high amplitude swelling (M_2). ER, endoplasmic reticulum. $\times 40,000$.

Figure 5.11B. Stage 5 changes in flounder kidney tubules treated with ouabain showing dilated nuclear envelope (NE), dilated endoplasmic reticulum, and mitochondria (M) showing high amplitude swelling and microcrystalline aggregates (*arrow along the inner membrane*). Again the mitochondrial accumulation of calcium is thought to represent secondary leak of calcium through the damaged membrane rather than a primary effect of ouabain on a calcium transport system. Similar mitochondrial calcification is seen in flounder kidney tubules after brief treatment with the sulfhydryl agent PCMBS, and similar increases of calcium flux may be promoted by parathormone. N, nucleus. $\times 50,000$.

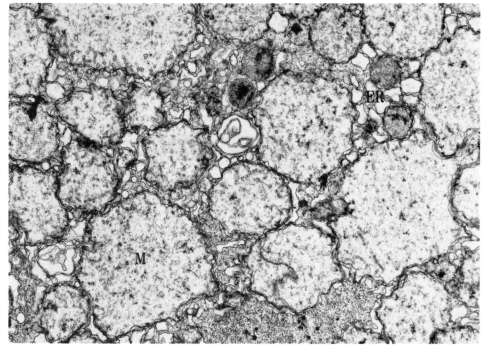

Figure 5.12. Stage 5 changes in flounder tubule 1 hour after treatment with 10^{-3} M potassium cyanide. Note the high amplitude swelling in mitochondria (M) with flocculent densities and dilated endoplasmic reticulum (ER). Note also lack of intramitochondrial calcification which in this case, as in complete ischemia, is inhibited by the inhibition of electron transport and the absence of ATP. ×25,000.

in vitro for many hours when glucose is added to the Ringer's solution (Fig. 5.16A).

Effects of increased sodium influx on ultrastructure and function of the toad bladder preparation

In these experiments, toad bladders were treated with the antibiotic amphotericin B, a polyene compound which acts on high cholesterol membranes to greatly increase sodium permeability. When this is added to the mucosal surface, the short-circuit current is stimulated; however, even though net transepithelial sodium transport increases following addition of amphotericin B, the cells markedly increase in volume (10) (Figs. 5.16B, 5.17, and 5.18).

Presumably this occurs because sodium enters the cells at the mucosal border faster than it can be pumped out the serosal side. In addition, the mitochondria become markedly contracted within 8 minutes thus constituting stage 3 (Fig. 5.16B). At later intervals the cells transform to stages 4 and 5 with intramitochondrial calcification, possibly again the result of secondary calcium leak through the stretched, ATP-deficient cell membranes. These studies strongly indicate that increased leak of sodium through the cell membrane is a sufficient condition to rapidly transform the cell to stage 3. Mitochondrial contraction is thought to be related to an ADP-induced transformation since respiration is stimulated (Fig. 5.18) and there is probably an increase in the ADP/ATP ratio. This is described further below.

Studies of anoxia in the isolated toad bladder preparation (33)

These studies were initiated to correlate

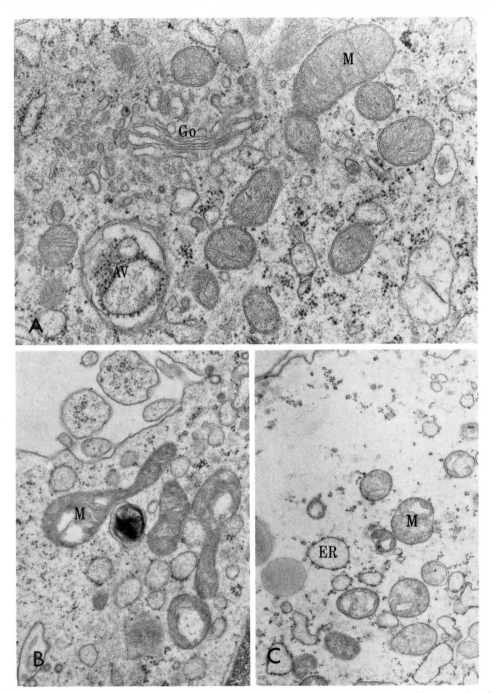

Figure 5.13A. Control Ehrlich ascites tumor cells showing appearance of cytoplasm. Note mitochondria (M), Golgi apparatus (Go), and autophagic vacuole (AV). ×25,000. (Courtesy of Dr. Kauno Laiho.)

Figure 5.13B. Portion of Ehrlich ascites tumor cell 5 minutes after treatment with 10^{-4} M PCMBS. Note contraction of inner compartment of mitochondria (M). This is thought to be related to influx of sodium, stimulation of ATPase, and increased ADP/ATP ratio. ×25,000. (Courtesy of Dr. Kauno Laiho.)

Figure 5.13C. Same conditions after 15 minutes showing more massive enlargement of cell sap. ER, endoplasmic reticulum. ×25,000. (Courtesy of Dr. Kauno Laiho.)

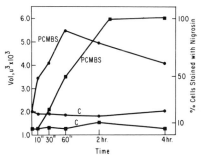

Figure 5.14. Plot of mean cell volume and percent of cells stained with the vital dye, nigrosin, as a function of time during incubation of Ehrlich ascites cells with PCMBS. Note the rapid increase in volume by 10 minutes and the lag in staining of cells with nigrosin. Again, this is thought to be explained by a secondary leak promoted by swelling which permits access of nigrosin to the interior of the cell. ●, cell volume in control (C) and PCMBS-treated cells; ■, nigrosin staining.

the effects of anoxia on nucleotide concentration, short-circuit current, membrane resistance, and cellular ultrastructure (Fig. 5.19). To our surprise, in the initial experiments the bladders maintained normal ultrastructure for as long as 24 hours of anoxia even though the short-circuit current

rapidly fell to 10 to 20% of the control level (Fig. 5.19). Measurements of the resistance, however, showed a marked increase and measurements of ATP showed essentially unchanged levels for 10 hours (Table 5.1). Thus a good correlation between ultrastructure and cell ATP was observed and it was inferred that the decreased short-circuit current might be related to the increased resistance, the latter indicating a limitation on entry of sodium into the cell. Stimulation of anaerobic glycolysis, as measured by increased lactate levels, appeared to be responsible, at least in part, for the maintenance of ATP levels. Further studies have corroborated this general scheme. Addition of amphotericin B to anoxic bladders was followed by a rapid increase in short-circuit current and a drop in resistance even after prolonged anoxia. However, this burst of sodium transport was of considerably shorter duration than in control preparations presumably since anaerobic glycolysis cannot supply ATP at sufficient rates to maintain the stimulated sodium transport. Addition of iodoacetate or 2-deoxyglucose (2-DG) to in-

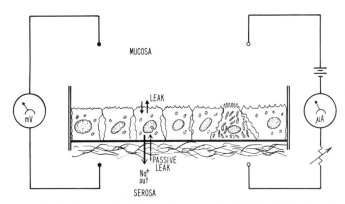

Figure 5.15. Diagram of circuitry employed in studies using isolated toad bladder. Toad bladder epithelium consists of a polarized cell population which actively pumps sodium from the mucosal to the serosal compartments. It appears that passive leak occurs across the mucosal membrane, and that the active pumps are concentrated along the serosal side. The resulting potential difference can be measured by attaching a millivoltmeter across the preparation and a parameter known as the short-circuit current is measured with a circuit including a source of potential connected to oppose the potential difference in series with a microammeter and a variable resistor. The amount of current required to neutralize the potential difference is termed the short-circuit current and has been shown to equal the net flux of sodium, under most conditions. (Courtesy of Mr. Hal K. Hawkins.)

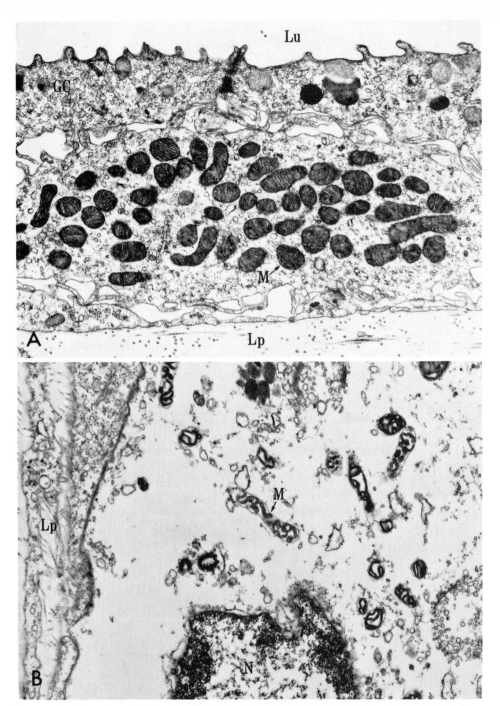

Figure 5.16A. Control toad bladder incubated 1 to 2 hours in Ussing chamber in oxygenated Ringer's solution. The lumen (Lu) can be seen toward the top, and the lamina propria (Lp) toward the bottom. Granulated cells (GC) are seen along the top of the picture, and the mitochondria-rich cell, which does not reach the surface in this plane of section, contains numerous mitochondria (M). Note slight enlargement of intercellular spaces. Note also appearance of mitochondria. ×12,000.

Figure 5.16B. Mitochondria-rich cell 8 minutes after addition of 1.3×10^{-5} M amphotericin B to the mucosal medium. Cells are rapidly converted to stage 3, with contraction of mitochondria (M), dilation of endoplasmic reticulum, and enlargement of cell sap. Lp, lamina propria. ×12,000. (Courtesy of Dr. A. J. Saladino.)

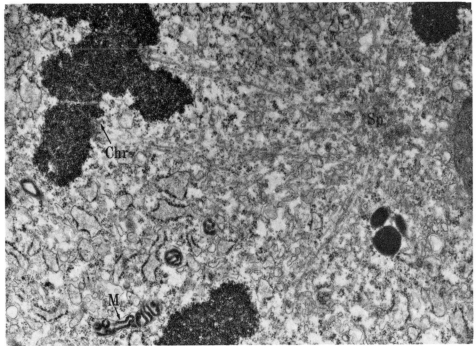

Figure 5.17. Dividing cell from bladder 8 minutes after treatment with amphotericin, showing contracted mitochondria (M) and dilated endoplasmic reticulum. The chromosomes (Chr) and spindle fibers (Sp) can be readily discerned. ×12,000. (Courtesy of Dr. A. J. Saladino.)

hibit anaerobic glycolysis was followed by rapid reduction of ATP levels, decreased membrane resistance, and transformation to stages 3, 4, and 5 (Fig. 5.20A and B). Many additional experiments involving inhibitors of electron transport such as rotenone, oligomycin, and 2,4-dinitrophenol (2,4-DNP) indicate that reduction of a component early in the electron transport chain possibly involving NADH is related to the increased resistance following anoxia. It also appears that normal levels of ATP are an additional necessary condition. The participation of cellular reducing potential, resulting from reduction of the electron transport chain, in a change in cell membrane permeability suggests an oxidation-reduction type gate, or so-called redox gate, for which sulfhydryl groups in membrane proteins are important candidates (41). The role of sulfhydryl groups in membrane permeability has long been estab-

lished; compounds that bind sulfhydryl groups such as mercurials often produce striking increases in membrane permeability. In the case of the anoxic toad bladder, the decreased permeability may well involve the closing of a redox gate (Fig. 5.8). In the anoxic toad bladder this has a great protective significance. It is interesting to speculate that compounds might be found which modify the membrane permeability of injured mammalian cells and thus protect against otherwise lethal injury.

Mitochondrial Changes

Mitochondrial changes are quite conspicuous in the stages described above. They involve contraction of the inner compartment to form the condensed conformation, disappearance of the normal matrical granules, transition from condensed conformation to high amplitude swelling, appearance of flocculent densities within the ma-

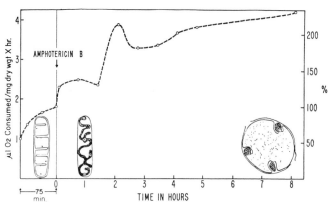

Figure 5.18. Diagram showing relationship between mitochondrial conformation and respiration following treatment with amphotericin B of the toad bladder. In the resting steady state, mitochondria have the orthodox conformation. Immediately following addition of amphotericin B, the mitochondria assume a condensed conformation. This is accompanied by stimulation of respiration which reaches still higher values at later intervals, at which time the mitochondria show high amplitude swelling and calcification. The latter is again believed to represent secondary leak of calcium through the stretched or modified plasma membrane. Stimulation of respiration at this stage is believed to represent the effects of calcium. ×30,000. (From Saladino, A. J., Bentley, P. J., and Trump, B. F., *Amer. J. Path. 54:* 421, 1969.)

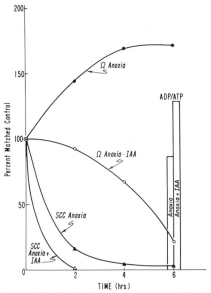

Figure 5.19. Graph showing resistance (Ω), short-circuit current (SCC), and ADP/ATP ratios in toad bladders during anoxia or during anoxia in the presence of iodoacetic acid. Higher ADP/ATP ratios are noted in the presence of anoxia and iodoacetic acid; though this correlates with the appearance of contracted mitochondria, a cause and effect relationship has not been proven in the intact cell.

trix, and appearance of crystalline aggregates which represent forms of calcium phosphate (2, 6, 11, 15, 17, 22, 33, 42) (Fig. 5.21).

Contraction

In the test tube, rapid contraction of mitochondria accompanies states associated with increased ADP/ATP ratios (43–45). In the toad bladder treated with iodoacetate and nitrogen, contraction of the mitochondria is extensive (33). Contraction of mitochondria in amphotericin B-treated bladders (10) is associated with the stimulation of respiration presumed to be the result of increased ADP concentration secondary to increased sodium influx and stimulation of the sodium transport system with hydrolysis of ATP. The duration of contraction in injured cells seems to depend on many conditions including temperature of incubation and the type of inhibition. For example, in ischemic rat kidney or mouse liver, contraction is not seen, the mitochondria proceeding directly from orthodox to high amplitude swelling (Figs. 5.33 and 5.34). On the other hand, rat kidney slices kept immersed for 8 to 20 hours at 0–4° C in Robinson's buffer show sustained contraction of the inner compartment (13) (Fig. 5.4A). It seems reasonable to suppose that contraction may only be maintained for as long as the permeability characteristics of the inner membrane remain intact. Following loss of integrity of the inner membrane, rapid high amplitude swelling occurs. This is not to say that changes in ion permeability are the cause of contraction, since many characteristics of this phenomenon could result from active contraction of the membrane (69) or of matrix proteins. Similar appearing contraction occurs when mitochondria are isolated by homogenization in 0.25 M sucrose (Fig. 5.23) or when mitochondria swollen to high amplitude levels are contracted by addition of ATP. The reason for this is not known. As shown in Table 5.2, many conditions studied in our laboratory have been associated with mitochondrial contraction in the intact cell. While all of these may share an increase in ADP/ATP ratios, it should be pointed out that it is also associated with sodium influx into the cell. Exactly which factors are responsible, cannot be stated presently. It is also not clear whether the response of mitochondria within the intact cell exactly corresponds to the response observed in isolated mitochondria when they are placed in the various respiratory steady states (46). For example, treatment of intact cells with 2, 4-DNP only modifies but does not prevent onset of contraction and in our experiments involving incubation of rat kidney slices in solutions containing 2,4-DNP, partial contraction of the inner compartment occurs. In other respects tested thus far, however, the behavior can be accounted for on the basis of theory developed for mitochondria *in vitro*. It is most interesting that mitochondria may possess more than one inner compartment, each compartment being surrounded by an inner membrane; the junction between two being represented by a double walled

TABLE 5.1

Effects of Anoxia on ATP Content of Toad Bladder

Condition	ATP
	% matched control
Anoxia	
3 hr	92
10 hr	89
Anoxia + 10^{-4} M iodoacetate	
3 hr	36
6 hr	17

septum. One can be contracted while the other is expanded. Preliminary studies with effects of polio virus on HeLa strongly suggest that non-membrane associated compartmentation may also exist and that focal regions of inner compartment can undergo contraction (31).

Disappearance of the normal matrix granules

These structures found within the matrix of normal mitochondria have still defied exact analysis. At high magnification they possess some filamentous fine structure and do not seem to represent ion accumulations as originally suggested. Furthermore, the normal mitochondrial granules appear as negative images in material prepared by aldehyde fixation without postosmification or by freeze sustitution. Thus, some of their density, if not all of it, in conventional preparations results from osmium binding, a situation compatible with a lipid or phospholipid composition.

The disappearance of these granules following cell injury (20) (Fig. 5.34A) is probably associated with decreased ATP levels in the cell though exact measurements of mitochondrial ATP have thus far not been in relation to this effect. Their disappearance is most likely reversible as suggested by the occurrence of this phenomenon at reversible phases following cell injury.

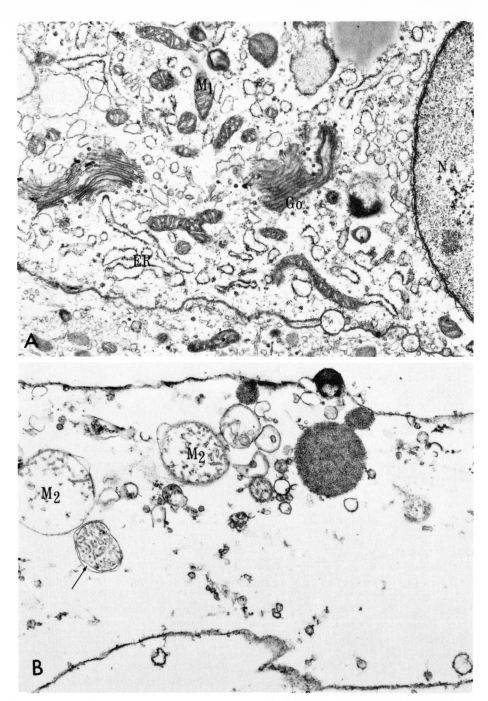

Figure 5.20A. Toad bladder epithelium 4 hours after incubation with 10^{-4} M iodoacetic acid and nitrogen. Note the stage 3 changes with contraction of the mitochondria (M_1), dilation of the endoplasmic reticulum (ER), and cell sap. The Golgi apparatus (Go) shows collapse and stacking of cisternae, and the nucleus (N) shows slight clumping of chromatin. $\times 12,000$.

Figure 5.20B. Toad bladder incubated for 24 hours under the conditions of Figure 5.20A, showing stage 5 changes with high amplitude swelling of mitochondria (M_2). The arrow indicates a mitochondrial profile containing tubular derivatives from the inner membrane. $\times 12,000$.

High amplitude swelling

High amplitude swelling of mitochondria in the cell resembles high amplitude swelling in the test tube in that the outer membrane often becomes interrupted (Fig. 5.23B) and the inner membrane appears to unfold (20, 47). The matrix becomes pale; much of this probably results from dilution. The matrix compartment contains sparse flocculent material which is thought to represent matrix protein. Often the cristae remain more or less localized at one pole. Conditions which frequently result in mitochondrial swelling *in vitro* include increased activity of water in the suspending solution, energy-dependent dysfunction of the inner membrane permitting entry of ions normally without net influx such as potassium chloride, facilitated uptake of ion in the carrier system, especially anions such as malate, acetate, succinate, and propionate (47).

Experiments on rates of swelling of mitochondria isolated from ischemic cells at serial time intervals reveal increased rates of swelling even without substrate in 0.15 M potassium chloride medium *in vitro* (Fig. 5.37). Examination of these mitochondria reveals massive high amplitude swelling. Initially these changes can be reversed by addition of ATP and magnesium to the medium. Four hours after ischemic injury, however, the mitochondria tend to disintegrate. Furthermore these high amplitude swelling changes are essentially similar in mitochondria placed in hypotonic solutions or even in distilled water indicating that water movements are responsible either because of a higher activity of extramitochondrial water or because of the presence of the penetrating solute. Since mitochondria are not normally permeable to chloride, this indicates that in injured cells the membrane becomes leaky to this anion.

Although volume changes are herein described as largely related to membrane activities, it should be pointed out that there are indications of order within the

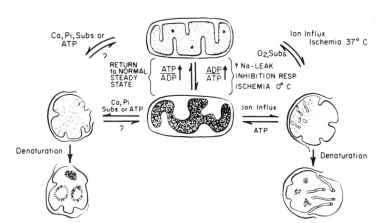

Figure 5.21. Diagram summarizing known relationships of mitochondrial conformational changes in intact cells following cell injury. The following points are particularly to be noted. On the left side are shown the effects of calcium accumulation in the presence of calcium or ATP. This results in two types of densities. One is an annular deposit of microcrystals, and the other is a flocculent deposit. On the right side, swelling and flocculent densities are shown, without the presence of calcification, since under these conditions substrate and ATP are lacking. These conditions are believed to explain calcification at the edges of an infarct but not at the center, *i.e.*, substrate and oxygen diffuse in at the edge and provide energy for the active accumulation of calcium by the mitochondria of swollen cells with damaged plasma membranes; the cells at the center do not have an adequate energy supply.

TABLE 5.2

Mitochondrial Changes in Injured Cells

At present a large volume of data has been collected about morphological alterations of mitochondria in a variety of conditions. Several patterns of change are clearly apparent, others are not. (1) In all cases, so far observed, where the injury is severe (duration times intensity) the end stage mitochondria take the typical appearance shown in stage 5. There are two subclasses: (a) microcrystalline deposits of calcium salt and (b) flocculent densities. (2) The earlier change $O \rightarrow C$ is more difficult to associate on a one-to-one basis with a specific pathophysiological state. Contracted mitochondria are seen in conditions where a raked influx of Na + H_2O has been measured. However, this generalization may be open to question and at least one possible exception to this last statement is known: ouabain-treated flounder tubules (6, 7). Contracted mitochondria are also not seen in rat kidney slices at 37° C. In explanation it is suggested that the mitochondria swell faster at this temperature. In several cases uncouplers modify the mitochondrial response to a contraction stimulus but this is not uniformly true. Thus mitochondrial contraction is a mitochondrial water shift in response to two related phenomena namely H_2O and Na influx into the cell and decreased cellular ATP levels. The question seems to be, what is the primary stimulus for contraction.

	System	Reference	Appearance*
Ischemia, 37° C	Rat kidney proximal tubule	(17)	$O \rightarrow S \rightarrow FD$
Ischemia, 0–4° C	Rat kidney proximal tubule	(13)	$O \rightarrow C \rightarrow S \rightarrow FD$
Cyanide, 10^{-3} M, 37° C	Rat kidney proximal tubule	(13), (16)	$O \rightarrow C \rightarrow FD \rightarrow S$
2,4-DNP, 10^{-4} M, 37° C	Rat kidney proximal tubule	(13)	$O \rightarrow PC \rightarrow FD \rightarrow S$
Antibody + complement	Ehrlich ascites cells	(26)	$O \rightarrow C \rightarrow S \rightarrow Ca + FD$
PCMBS, 10^{-4} M	Ehrlich ascites cells	(8)	$O \rightarrow C \rightarrow S \rightarrow Ca + FD$
Polio virus	HeLa cells	(31)	$O \rightarrow C \rightarrow S \rightarrow Ca + FD$
Amphotericin	Toad bladder	(10)	$O \rightarrow C \rightarrow S \rightarrow Ca$
N_2 + glucose	Toad bladder	(33)	$O \rightarrow RF$
N_2 + iodoacetate + glucose	Toad bladder	(33)	$O \rightarrow C \rightarrow S \rightarrow FD$
$HgCl_2$	Rat pars recta	(30)	$O \rightarrow C \rightarrow S \rightarrow FD + Ca$
2-DG	Ehrlich ascites cells	(72)	$O \rightarrow C$
Uncouplers $\rightarrow$ 2-DG	Ehrlich ascites cells	(72)	$O \rightarrow C$

* Abbreviations used are: O, orthodox; S, high amplitude swelling; FD, flocculent densities in matrix; Ca, microcrystalline aggregates (calcium phosphate in complex form) along inner membrane and cristae; PC, partially contracted; C, contracted; and RF, ring forms.

mitochondrial matrix, and it is conceivable that certain volume changes may be related to active contraction or expansion of matrix proteins. The existence of this is however unknown presently.

Flocculent densities in mitochondria (16, 17, 20, 27, 42)

These densities arise in mitochondria showing high amplitude swelling (Figs. 5.4A and 4B, 5.12, and 5.34B–D). At the time they appear, oxidative phosphorylation is depressed and when they become well developed no oxidative phosphorylation can be measured. We suspect them to be aggregates of matrix protein. These densities can be reproduced by aging mitochondria in sucrose (42) where they are not associated with increased calcification and in mitochondria isolated from ischemic kidneys. Furthermore, these densities show no crystalline or paracrystalline fine structure and do not resemble calcifications or other accumulations of divalent cations. We have observed that these densities are still present if osmium is omitted as a postfixative. This is also supported by studies using protein denaturants such as mercury (11, 12, 30), or heat denaturation (12). These flocculent densities rapidly appear within the matrix under these conditions (12). Although the earliest densities appear at a time when the changes are thought to be reversible, the well developed densities seem to indicate loss of reversibility.

Uptake of calcium

In the test tube accumulation of calcium is an energy-requiring process which can be energized either by oxidation of substrate or by hydrolysis of exogenous ATP (Fig. 5.22). The initial stages may involve both a low and a high affinity binding step (48). The low affinity step is insensitive to inhibition of respiration but is damaged by uncouplers. The high affinity site is sensitive to neither. In our studies, mitochondria in ischemic cells do not undergo calcification even up to 72 hours (see below). If mitochondria from cells ischemic for 2 hours are isolated and incubated in calcium-loading media, uptake does occur with typical intramitochondrial precipitation though at a slower rate than in normal mitochondria (Figs. 5.22 and 5.23). This indicates some integrity of the ion-accumulating systems in these mitochondria and suggests that the lack of calcification in the intact cell is due to lack of substrate, oxygen or ATP though small amounts of calcium might be accumulated without discernible precipitates along the inner membrane. Calcification of mitochondria is commonly observed in injured cells *in vivo* where blood supplies are intact, for example, after treatment with carbon tetrachloride in the liver (49) or mercuric chloride (30) in the kidney (Figs. 5.4B, and 5.39). Calcification is also observed in cells at the edges of infarcts and probably in ischemic cells after reflow of blood, even if the cells are necrotic. In a sense, then, calcification of mitochondria indicates at least partial integrity of ion-transporting systems within the mitochondria. In normal cells the mitochondria presumably do not "see" calcium in sufficient quantities to be accumulated. However,

following injury that results in direct damage to the integrity of the cell membrane or indirectly affects the membrane through loss of ATP production and "secondary" leak, calcium influx into the cell occurs. This is reflected by rapid mitochondrial calcium accumulation which promotes mitochondrial swelling and competes with oxidative phosphorylation. Thus, influx of calcium may well be an important late manifestation of cell swelling resulting in inhibition of mitochondrial ATP production.

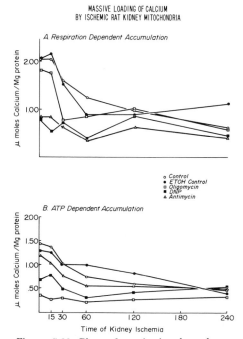

Figure 5.22. Plots of respiration-dependent and ATP-dependent accumulation of mitochondria *in vitro* during a 20-minute loading by mitochondria isolated from ischemic rat kidneys at zero time and after 15, 30, 60, 120, and 240 minutes of ischemia. While these mitochondria do not show calcium accumulations in the intact ischemic cell, when placed *in vitro* in calcium-loading media, they show low though definite accumulations with greater levels of calcium in the respiration-dependent situation in the absence of DNP or antimycin or in the ATP-supported situation by the lower values seen in the presence of oligomycin.

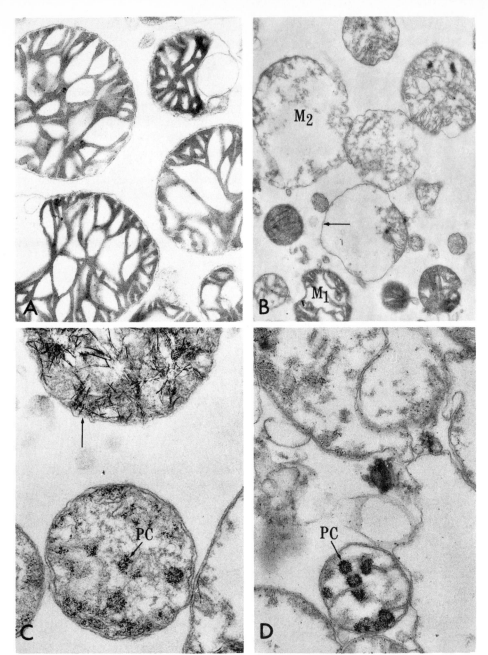

Figure 5.23A. Mitochondria from control rat isolated in 0.25 M sucrose. Note contracted profiles. ×40,000.

Figure 5.23B. Isolated mitochondria swollen in isosmotic potassium chloride containing 10^{-4} M calcium chloride showing high amplitude swelling (M_2) of most profiles. Note that the mitochondria are limited only by the inner membrane in most areas as indicated by the arrow and that cristal remnants as well as remnants of the outer membrane are often localized along one pole. These mitochondria that are swollen show no calcium accumulation because of the absence of phosphate and the absence of substrate and ATP. In this case calcium presumably acts to increase the permeability of the inner membrane to chloride. M_1, contracted mitochondrion. ×30,000.

Figure 5.23C. Control mitochondria incubated in calcium-loading media supported by substrate. Note two patterns of accumulation; in the lower, the accumulation consists of clusters or annular deposits of microcrystals (PC) whereas in the upper profile, long needle-like structures (*arrow*) appear to be growing out of the microcrystalline aggregates. ×40,000.

Figure 5.23D. Mitochondria from kidneys that have been ischemic for 2 hours incubated for 2 hours in calcium-loading medium supported by substrate. Although the rate of accumulation is much less after this period of ischemia, annular microcrystalline deposits (PC) can be seen. This indicates that in the intact cell, calcification does not occur during ischemia because of absence of ATP or substrate whereas if the mitochondria are placed in appropriate *in vitro* situations, accumulations can occur. ×40,000.

CORRELATION OF ALTERED STRUCTURE AND FUNCTION IN CELL MEMBRANES

It is evident from the foregoing that changes in the function of membrane systems are of importance in the understanding of the cellular reaction to injury. The accumulation of vast amounts of work in the literature indicates the key role of membranes in virtually every normal cell process such as ion transport, energy production, protein synthesis, nucleic acid synthesis, replication and cell division, and contact inhibition. These efforts are partially hampered at the present time by incomplete understanding of membrane structure.

In the case of acute lethal injury, cell membrane alterations are probably the most important determinants. It is generally accepted that most permeability properties of membranes can be produced by artificial lipid bilayers which have focal, specialized polar or other translocator regions that impart a heterogeneous character (41). The principal controversy regarding molecular structure of the membrane is involved with the extent of the hydrophilic or translocator regions. However, it seems likely that this may vary considerably in different membranes, being relatively sparse in myelin or in the plasma membrane of erythrocytes and being relatively numerous in membranes such as those of mitochondria or chloroplasts. In the mitochondrion, the membrane may be chiefly composed of the translocators and "structural" proteins, with the interstices being occupied by lipid. The topological configuration of the lipid domain within the membrane is still subject to some controversy though again most properties can be explained on the basis of bilayer arrangements. Recent studies employing electron spin resonance and nuclear magnetic resonance (50) suggest a rather high mobility of the fatty acids of the phospholipid and thus the center portion of the lipid domain may well be in a fluid or semifluid state (41). In membranes such as those of the mitochondrion, the lipid domains might exist as islands or as thin mortar in a continuous protein-rich mesh.

Similarly the precise conformation of the membrane protein is not fully understood. Although in the earlier models, the protein was often visualized as predominantly in β-configuration at the surface of the lipid bilayer, recent studies employing spectroscopic techniques suggest significant amounts of α-helix mixed with random coil (51, 52). Because of a red shift in the region of the Cotton effects, the importance of lipid-protein interactions in modifying signals from the α-helix has been suggested. The importance of protein-protein and protein-lipid interactions in membrane structure and function probably cannot be over emphasized (50, 53). For some purposes it is useful to consider membranes as made up of a series of lipoprotein units or protomers which have specific binding sites or ligands for many membrane-active materials including ions, drugs, and hormones (53). Many membranes respond *in vitro* or *in vivo* to ligand binding by a conformational change in the protomers, modifying their properties as well as their structure, probably indicating a conformational change in the protein (50, 53). In some instances amplification is obtained, that is with increasing stimulation or increased dose of the species to which the membrane is exposed, the membrane responds with a sigmoidal curve. Cooperativity phenomena are then suggested (54). This cooperativity can be thought of as resulting from the modification of neighboring protomers after specific binding to the ligands of one protomer. Thus a "domino"-type effect occurs, in which a small change in one type of protomer is rapidly reflected by conformational change of the membrane as a whole. (Compounds such as amphotericin or valinomycin can be thought of as modifying the protomeric composition, possibly through cooperative effects.) The initial interaction with the protomer can be thought of as a allosteric-type protein transformation. Membrane translocators may involve selector or permease components within the membrane that are related to their membrane-transforming effect. Some authors (41) have reported an additional concept of membrane phenomena called gating control which may involve translocators and/or selectors. Membrane gating, which can involve opening or closing of channels through the membrane, can depend on such factors as the redox state. Thus in the example given above, in which we studied the effects of anoxia on the toad bladder, it seems that increased reducing potential may effect the closing of a redox-type gate which in this case is protective to the cell since it maintains its cellular integrity (41).

The evidence available strongly suggests that some if not all biological membranes can act as reversible energy transducers of three equivalent energy forms (Fig. 5.24). These are (a) redox energy "∼e," (b) group or bond energy "∼P," and (c) ion gradient energy "∼i." As shown in the figure, these are interconvertible or potentially interconvertible and closely related to membrane conformation. It has been suggested for the case of the mitochondrion that conformational energy is an important initial step in the phosphorylation of ADP. The notation, ∼e. indicates the redox energy of electron or hydrogen atom as it lies in a higher energy state in a molecule or an electron transport carrier; ∼P represents a high energy phosphate as in ATP, relative to its energy in inorganic phosphate or water; ∼i represents the electrochemical gradient of an ion existing in concentration gradient relative to its energy in no gradient.

As shown above we can visualize the events occurring after cell injury as resulting in an increase in the internal entropy of the cell and since the potential free energy can be estimated for these three

types of energy as shown by the equations in the figure legend, real meaning can potentially be given to the type of curve mentioned above. For this purpose, it is necessary to know the $ATP/ADP \times P_i$ ratio, the state of reduction of adjacent electron transport carriers, and the ionic and electrical potential gradients. The energy diagram in Figure 5.5 shows the inter-relationship and interconversion between the three types of energy and structure. This concept emphasizes the intimate relationship of structure and function and in fact illustrates how both can be considered as different aspects of the same property. Thus the ancient dichotomy between structure and function must be discarded. Although this has become evident in the case of protein conformation, i.e., the change in the β relative to the α-chains in reduced versus oxidized hemoglobin (55); these ideas have not been fully developed in the realm of integrated macromolecular structures. As discussed below, the conformation or configuration of cell membranes is immediately affected by inter-related changes in protein conformation and in lipid domains affecting protein-lipid interactions. Conformational changes in the models presented below illustrate the effects of structure-function relationships and membrane enzyme proteins. It is inferred from these studies that similar conformational changes can affect membrane translocators or selectors through the allosteric, cooperative effects mentioned above.

Microsomes Treated with Phospholipase C (Figs. 5.25–5.27)

In order to explore these concepts at the ultrastructural level, we have studied the effects of modification of membrane structure and function in isolated microsomes from rat liver, employing treatment with phospholipase C or with peroxidation through the NADPH-dependent electron transport system (4, 18).

It has been observed that treatment of rat liver microsomes with phospho-

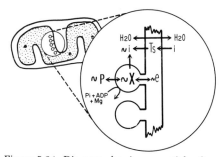

Figure 5.24. Diagram showing essentials of energy transduction in mitochondria. The inner membrane contains the electron transport change shown as the redox energy function (~e). Coupling factor F_1, the ATPase, is associated with the inner membrane spheres. Coupling between electron transport energy and phosphate bond energy involves intermediates (~X) presumed to be located in or associated with the spheres and are dependent on magnesium. These reactions also can accumulate ions as driven either by redox energy (~e) or phosphate bond energy (~P). In the case of mitochondrial inner membranes, translocator and selector functions (Ts) are important in determining access of ions (~i) to the coupling factors.

lipase C results in inactivation of glucose-6-phosphatase. This enzyme inactivation can be reversed by addition of phospholipids following which the enzyme activity returns to control levels. Phospholipids that can be used include microsomal phospholipid fractions, mixtures of phospholipids such as asolectin, or individual phospholipids such as phosphatidylethanolamine. To correlate with these changes we have made ultrastructural studies of the microsomes in the three states. Studies of untreated microsome fractions reveal a population of vesicles containing a rather sparse flocculent material and limited by a membrane which shows the typical trilaminar structure though suggestive evidence of cross-striations across the center of the unit membrane were observed. Microdensitometry traces across the membrane in areas cut normal to the surface revealed two distinct peaks, corresponding to the dense laminae, and were separated by a trough corresponding to the central clear zone. In the figure a frequency distri-

bution plot of peak-to-peak thickness is shown. The mean thickness was 50 Å, however there was a small secondary population with a thickness of 75 Å. After treatment with phospholipase C the microsomes showed general preservation of vesicular structure, but the ribosomes appeared to be reduced in number. Although the trilaminar structure of the membrane was well preserved and, in fact, appeared more distinct than in untreated vesicles, measurement of the spacing revealed a single population with a mean value of approximately 1.5 times that of the untreated fractions; this differs at the 1% level from the control population. In addition to the general increase in thickness, focal accumulations of homogeneous material were seen eccentrically located at the surface of vesicles. These homogeneous areas were continuous with the clear space between the outer and inner dense laminae of the vesicle giving a "signet ring" appearance. These droplets, we assume, represent the released diglyceride following the phospholipase treatment. We also noted that the increase in center-to-center spacing was not merely due to an increase in the dense layer thickness but we observed that the spacing between the dense layers actually increased.

Following reconstitution with microsomal phospholipid or asolectin, vesicular structures were again observed and the eccentric homogeneous densities disap-

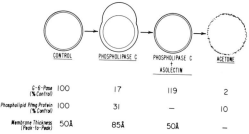

Figure 5.25. Diagram showing effects of phospholipase C on structure and function of hepatic microsomes from the rat. The diagrams at the top show ultrastructural changes in microsomal vesicles (see text).

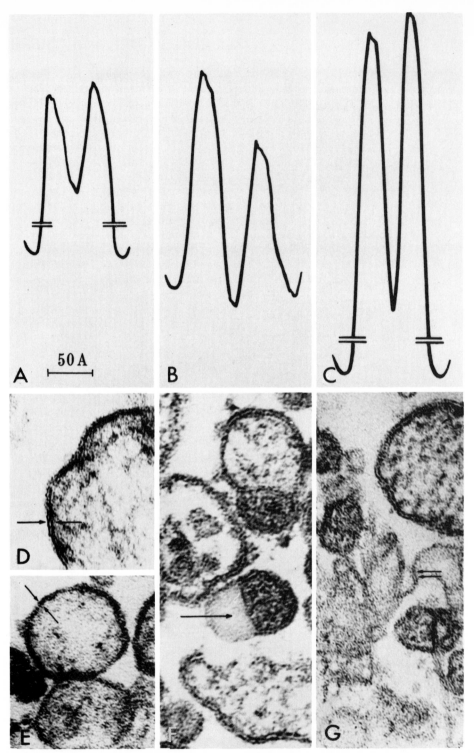

Figure 5.26. Electron micrograph and microdensitometer traces of hepatic microsomes treated with phospholipase C. A, D, and E show traces and electron micrographs of control microsomes. The arrows indicate the membrane. F and G show trace and micrograph of microsomes after treatment with phospholipase C. The arrow indicates areas of homogeneous densities continuous with the space between the inner and outer laminae of the membrane, thought to represent accumulated diglycerides. C and G show trace and micrograph of microsomes following addition of phospholipid. Note the disappearance of eccentric densities. ×195,000. (From Trump, B. F., Duttera, S. M., Byrne, W. L., and Arstila, A. U., *Proc. Nat. Acad. Sci. U.S.A. 66:* 433, 1970.)

peared. Measurements of the thickness of these membranes revealed a large population similar to untreated preparations, however, there were in addition populations representing thicker membranes suggesting a bi- or triphasic population and indicating that some membranes did not return to control thickness. Reconstitution in the presence of a sulfhydryl protective agent, dithiothreitol, appeared to give better reconstitution; however, statistically there was no improvement.

These studies indicate that microsomal membranes are capable of rather dramatic and reversible changes in conformation as well as function which are related to modification of most membrane phospholipid. These results emphasize the importance of phospholipid and lipid-protein interactions in maintaining structure as well as glucose-6-phosphatase activity. It is also interesting that accumulations can occur in the central pale laminae of the unit membrane. Since these probably represent released diglyceride, they emphasize the liquidity and self-sealing properties of the membrane, phenomena well-known to workers studying artificial membrane bilayers who often note "lenses" which move about within the bilayer. These "lenses" are probably analogous to the accumulations described here.

We have suggested that the membrane thickens because hydrophobic binding of membrane proteins with lipid is important for normal conformation and, when phospholipids are modified, the proteins change in a way which influences the enzymatic activity. This recalls the concept of cooperativity on conformational changes in membrane protomers. The results also emphasize that membrane phospholipids are readily accessible to the membrane surface. If microsomal membrane vesicles were treated with acetone, inactivation of glucose-6-phosphatase as well as breakdown of the membrane itself was observed. Reconstitution did not occur with added phospholipid. If lipids are completely removed the membrane structure breaks

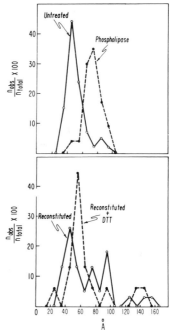

Figure 5.27. Frequency distribution plots of peak-to-peak membrane thickness in untreated, phospholipase-treated, and reconstituted microsomes with or without dithiothreitol. For explanation, see text. (From Trump, B. F., Duttera, S. M., Byrne, W. L., and Arstila, A. U., *Proc. Nat. Acad. Sci. U.S.A. 66:* 433, 1970.)

down. This is in contrast to studies on the inner membrane of mitochondria which are resistant to acetone-water extraction, again emphasizing differences in membranes as described above.

Peroxidized Microsomes (Figs. 5.28–5.31)

Somewhat similar effects were observed when microsomal peroxidation was initiated through the NADPH electron transport system by addition of ferrous iron, NADP, and ADP to isolated microsomes. It has been shown by Hochstein and Ernster (56) that under these conditions a burst of oxygen consumption occurs which is associated with the release of peroxidation end products such as malonyldialdehyde. It has been suggested that activation of this or a simi-

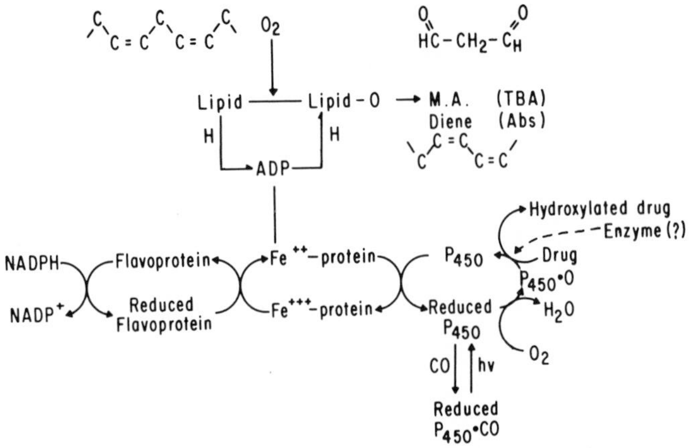

Figure 5.28. Relationship of NADPH-dependent electron transport system in microsomes in relation to drug metabolism and lipid peroxidation. Lipid peroxidation is believed to be catalyzed in an intermediate portion of the system, possibly involving the iron-protein complex. In the presence of nucleotides such as ADP, iron (Fe^{++}) catalyzes the formation of lipid-peroxidation products such as malonyl dialdehyde and conjugated dienes which can be measured by the thiobarbituric acid (TBA) reaction or ultraviolet absorption (Abs), respectively. (Modified from Goldstein, A., Aronow, L., and Kalman, S. M. (Editors). Drug metabolism. In *Principles of Drug Action*. pp. 206–279. New York, Harper and Row, Publishers, Inc., 1968.)

lar process may be of great importance in certain specific types of cell injury such as the hepatotoxicity following administration of carbon tetrachloride, effects of ionizing or ultraviolet irradiation on cells, the effects of vitamin E deficiency, and the primaquine sensitivity of glucose-6-phosphate dehydrogenase-deficient erythrocytes (57). Ultrastructural examination of peroxidized microsomes revealed very striking changes. The polysomes were rapidly lost from the membrane surface leaving smooth surfaced, membrane-bound vesicles. These vesicles rapidly clumped together; in osmium-fixed preparations dense material appeared between the vesicles. Measurement of the peak-to-peak thickness of the unit membrane of the microsomes revealed a 50% increase in thickness which was significant at the 1% level.

The third example is the alterations of ultrastructure of the mitochondrial inner membrane during the development of mitochondrial structural changes following cellular ischemia and is described in the following section.

Effects of Aging and Ischemia on the Mitochondrial Inner Membrane (Figs. 5.32–5.44)

As mentioned above, the mitochondria in ischemic cells show progressive and sequential changes in their ability to transduce the three equivalent energy forms, ~e, ~P, and ~i (Fig. 5.24). Cellular ATP levels drop rapidly (Fig. 5.32). Ultimately there is a loss of ability for oxidative phosphorylation and ion accumulation and finally in electron transport. Since these are of such overwhelming importance to the economy of the cell following lethal injury, we have begun a systematic exploration of the pathogenesis and sequence of these morphochemical alterations. Since the changes during aging of mitochondria in sucrose solution at 0–4°C are quite similar to those occurring in the mitochondria of ischemic cells, these are being studied in parallel and ultimately since the conditions are more capable of being controlled, examination of aging mitochondria may become more important.

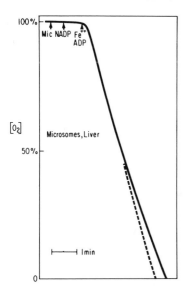

Figure 5.29. Oxygen electrode tracing showing oxygen uptake induced by peroxidation of hepatic microsomes. The microsomes (Mic) were added at the arrow, followed by the addition of NADH and a ferrous iron-ADP complex. Note the burst of oxygen consumption.

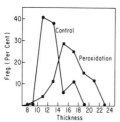

Figure 5.30. A frequency distribution plot showing thickness in arbitrary units of peak-to-peak measurements of microsome membranes in control and peroxidized microsome preparations. Experiment conducted as in Figure 5.25.

Functional analysis of the mitochondrial inner membrane reveals that, of the three functions, electron transport is maintained significantly longer in either ischemic (Fig. 5.35) or aging mitochondria. This is reflected by the unimpaired respiration with succinate or NADH-linked substrates in the intact mitochondria as well as by respiration in A (ammonia) particles. The A particles are prepared by

sonication of mitochondria in a dilute solution adjusted to pH 9 with ammonium hydroxide (58). These A particles consist of small vesicles with very few or no attached knobs or F_1 particles; they are limited by a unit membrane (Fig. 5.42A). Ultrastructural analysis of the inner membrane reveals no basic change in the mem-

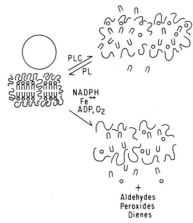

Figure 5.31. Diagram showing conceptualization of effects of phospholipase C and peroxidation on microsomal membranes. In both cases the ribosomes are rapidly detached. With phospholipase C (PLC) the membrane thickens and diglycerides accumulate within the membrane center. Change in the spacing of the inner and outer laminae is shown. It may be accompanied by change in protein conformation although this has not been proven. This change can be readily reversed by the addition of phospholipid (PL). Following peroxidation, as in Figures 5.25 and 5.26, a similar increase in thickness occurs. However, the reversibility has not been assessed.

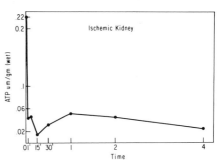

Figure 5.32. Graph showing concentration of ATP as a function of time in rat kidneys made ischemic at 37° C.

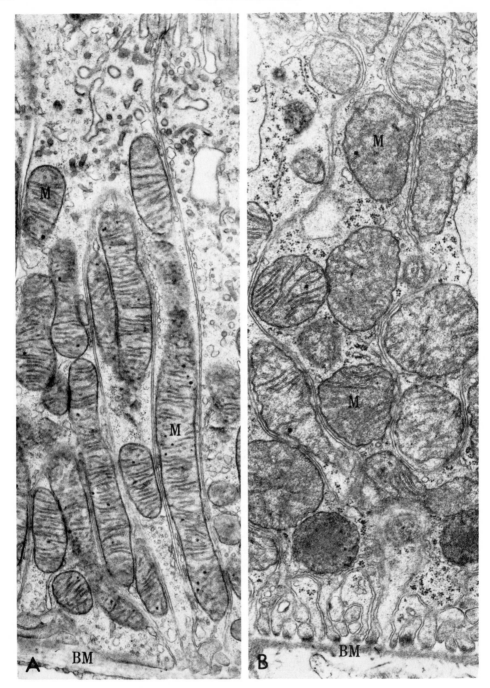

Figure 5.33A. Portion of proximal convoluted tubule from control rat showing elongate appearance of mitochondria (M). Basement membrane (BM). ×20,000.

Figure 5.33B. Proximal tubule, 5 minutes of ischemia at 37° C. Note rounding up of mitochondrial profiles and slight pallor of matrix. ×20,000.

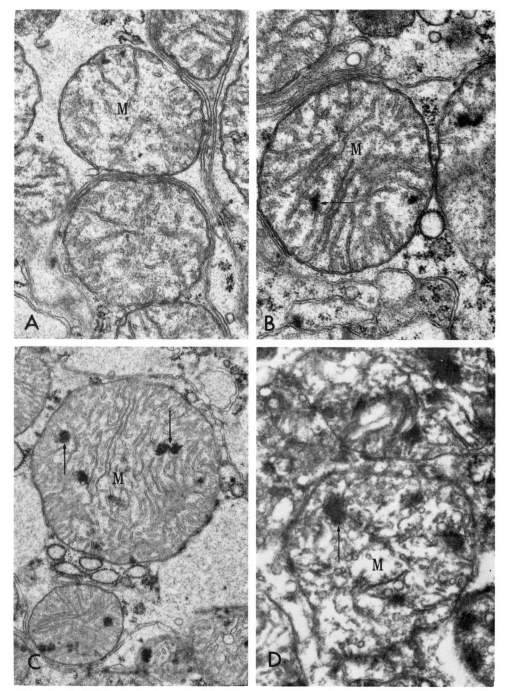

Figure 5.34A. Proximal tubule mitochondria (M) after 15 minutes of ischemia. Note swelling of inner compartment. ×35,000.

Figure 5.34B. Same system after 80 minutes of ischemia. Note beginning flocculent densities (*arrow*) in the matrix compartment. ×35,000.

Figure 5.34C. Same after 4 hours of ischemia showing greater development of matrix densities (*arrows*). ×35,000.

Figure 5.34D. Same after 24 hours showing dense flocculent accumulations (*arrow*) and fragmentation of cristae. Again note in this entire series of changes, the absence of mitochondrial calcifications. ×35,000.

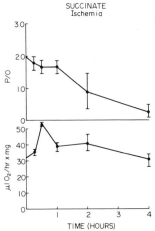

Figure 5.35. Graph showing P/O ratios and respiration with succinate of mitochondria isolated from ischemic kidneys at serial time intervals. Note the dissociation between loss of respiration ability and loss of phosphorylating ability. Note also that although the P/O ratios approach zero, they are slightly greater than 0 by 4 hours. This is believed to be also reflected by the fact that mitochondria even after this period of ischemia can still accumulate calcium though slowly.

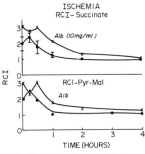

Figure 5.36. Plot showing respiratory control index with succinate and pyruvate-malate in mitochondria from ischemic kidneys. Note rapid loss of respiratory control and partial reversal with albumin.

brane architecture, though the configuration or external shape of the membrane varies considerably during this period (Figs. 5.33 and 5.34). That is, instead of plate-like cristae the inner membrane forms tubular and vesicular images. This is especially evident in negative staining where these worm-like profiles extend through the broken inner membrane. It

is on these tubular profiles that the membrane knobs or F_1 particles are most apparent (Fig. 5.41A). It appears from these studies that an excellent correlation between ultrastructure and function of the electron transport portion itself is maintained. Ultimately when the respiration does decrease to zero, the inner membrane is observed to undergo fragmentation, and smudgy images presumably representing residual membrane components are seen.

Ion gradient energy can be studied by measuring rates of accumulation of calcium in an *in vivo* loading system either driven by ATP or substrate using mitochondria isolated at various periods of ischemia or aging (Fig. 5.22). A progressive decrease in ion-accumulating ability measured in this way is evident by as

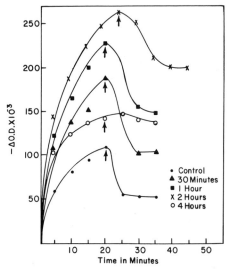

Figure 5.37. Plot showing kinetics of swelling as measured by change in optical density of mitochondria isolated from control kidneys and kidneys after various periods of ischemia. Note the gradual increase in initial rate of swelling and increase of total degree of swelling through 2 hours. By 4 hours the initial rate is similar though the maximum degree is less than at 2 hours, possibly because the mitochondria were swollen, when they were placed in the cuvette. ATP, magnesium, and serum albumin were added at the arrows. In all cases except the 4-hour mitochondria, this was followed by partial reversal of swelling.

early as 30 minutes. By 2 hours the rate of accumulation is markedly depressed; however, if mitochondria are incubated in the loading medium for longer periods, mitochondrial accumulations of calcium can be observed (Fig. 5.23D). These accumulations are microcrystalline and in close association with inner membrane resembling those occurring *in vivo* in injured cells. Using control mitochondria in a substrate-containing medium, long microcrystals of calcium phosphate are observed (Fig. 5.23C). The ability to accumulate calcium decreases roughly in proportion to the decrease in oxidative phosphorylation and the decrease in ATPase activity.

Intramitochondrial levels of magnesium and potassium are also an indication of ion transport energy capability (Fig. 5.38). These are lost in aging by 24 hours at 0–4°C and over 2 to 4 hours in ischemic mitochondria. A change in the translocator or selector function of the mitochondrial inner membrane is suggested by experiments in which mitochondria are placed in isosmotic potassium chloride medium *in vitro* and the rate of swelling measured by changes in absorbance (Fig. 5.37). These experiments were mentioned above and indicate a marked change in the permeability characteristics of the membrane to potassium chloride.

Phosphate bond energy conserving mechanisms decrease as a function of time following ischemia or aging. This is initially most apparent with the respiratory control index which initially undergoes a rapid decrease which then levels off slowly (Fig. 5.36). Initially this can be reversed to control levels by incubating the mitochondria with albumin (Fig. 5.36). Phosphorylation as measured by the P/O ratio decreases, reaching zero or near zero levels by 2 hours. It seems to be more sensitive with any NAD-linked substrates though presently we cannot explain whether this means that coupling site I is more sensitive or whether it is related to loss of co-factors from the mitochondria.

The ATPase activity measured with magnesium and/or DNP stimulation undergoes a gradual decrease reaching roughly 50% by 4 hours though at that time partial reversal can be obtained by adding albumin (Fig. 5.40). The ATPase in the presence of magnesium alone is not stimulated; thus the effects of ischemia may differ slightly from those seen after addition of uncoupler. This may indicate that the fundamental defect might reside in a change in the F_1 particle as well as in the coupling mechanism itself.

Electron microscopic examination of the inner membrane particles by negative staining reveals many typical F_1 particles in control mitochondria (Fig. 5.41A) and in mitochondria from cells ischemic for as long as 1 hour. By 2 hours, however, (Fig.

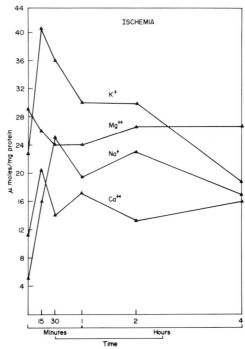

Figure 5.38. Ion content of mitochondria isolated at serial time intervals from ischemic kidneys. Note the early increase in sodium and potassium and the later fall of potassium. Note also that the calcium content is maintained at roughly zero time levels through the 4-hour period as seen also in the electron micrographs.

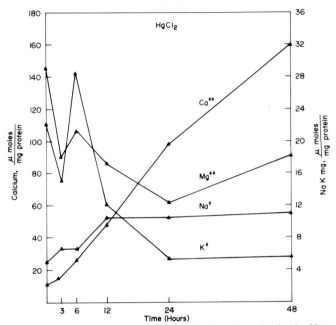

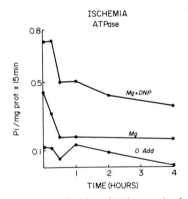

Figure 5.40. Graph showing mitochondrial ATPase activity as a function of time following ischemia. Note that the maximum activity seen with magnesium plus dinitrophenol falls rapidly to about 60% of zero time value after which it decreases very slowly. This seems to indicate that although the ATPase activity is reduced, it is still present in significant amounts and indicates that the defect in the P/O ratios can only be partly explained by loss of the so-called F_1 coupling factor.

5.41B) the number of knobs undergoes a significant decrease and many of the knobs appear abnormal in that they are irregular with rough contours. By 4 hours (Fig. 5.41C) no knobs can be visualized; in their place is a fuzzy granulofibrillar material along the outer surface of the inner membrane.

Racker's group (59–61) has shown that F_1 particles can be stripped from the inner membrane and purified by mechanical agitation followed by ammonium sulfate and protamine precipitation (Fig. 5.41D). We have prepared such particles from normal rat kidney mitochondria and are presently experimenting with reconstitution of damaged mitochondrial inner membrane using normal F_1 particles. Experiments to date have shown that if F_1 particles from control mitochondria are added together with magnesium to A particles prepared from mitochondria that

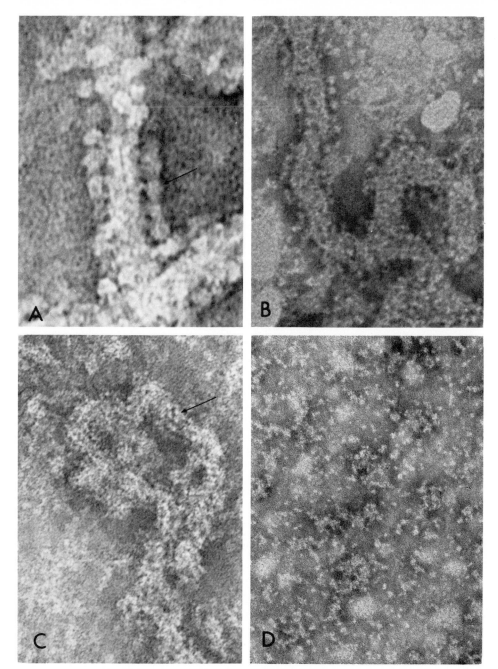

Figure 5.41A. Inner membrane of control rat kidney mitochondria prepared by suspending mitochondria in distilled water and staining with 2% ammonium molybdate. Note that the inner membrane spheres (*arrow*) are associated with a thin neck piece. It is to be noted that other experiments from our laboratory strongly suggest that this appearance may not reflect the *in vivo* situation and that the inner membrane spheres may be embedded upon or even within the inner membrane (67, 68). ×500,000.

Figure 5.41B. Same type of preparation after hours of ischemia showing focal loss of inner membrane spheres in patches along the inner membrane. ×250,000.

Figure 5.41C. Same type of preparation after 4 hours showing no discernible spheres on stalks but flocculent material attached to the inner membrane (*arrow*). ×200,000.

Figure 5.41D. Negative stained preparation of isolated ATPase particles (F₁ fraction). ×100,000.

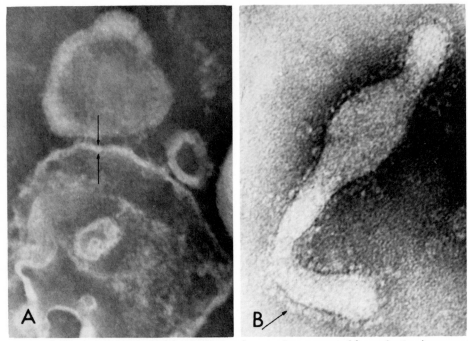

Figure 5.42A. Preparation of A particles (inner membrane spheres prepared by sonication in ammoniacal solution) showing appearance of membrane with no attached spheres (*arrow*). These preparations show respiration but no phosphorylation. ×100,000.

Figure 5.42B. Preparation of A particles from ischemic mitochondria to which control F_1 particles and magnesium were added. Spheres again appear along the surface of the membrane (*arrow*). ×250,000.

have been ischemic for 2 hours, restitution of phosphorylative ability with succinate is observed (Table 5.3). In fact the P/O ratios obtained are indistinguishable from those seen with control A particles and control F particles.

SUMMARY

We propose the following model of subcellular alterations following acute lethal injury such as ischemia (Fig. 5.44). Obviously, the initial interactions will vary depending on the type of injury. For example with chemical toxins such as carbon tetrachloride the initial interaction may involve metabolism to a free radical followed by an interaction with the cell membrane. For ischemic injury these considerations are diagrammed in Figure 5.44. In this case the initial interaction results

in depression of ATP synthesis by the mitochondrion with a resulting increase in the ADP/ATP ratio. This in turn stimulates anaerobic glycolysis which tends to further lower the pH and is associated with clumping of nuclear chromatin. The decreased energy supply to the pump leads to decreased sodium efflux and a net increase in water and sodium in the cell; the first compartment to expand is the endoplasmic reticulum which undergoes dilation. These changes comprise stage 2. In stage 3, the mitochondria become contracted because of the increased ADP/ATP ratio; further sodium and influx leads to swelling of cell sap and lysosomes. Additional swelling leads to blebbing of the cell surface with plasma membrane protrusions. At this stage, polysomes may become detached and scattered within the cell sap. In stage 4, the swell-

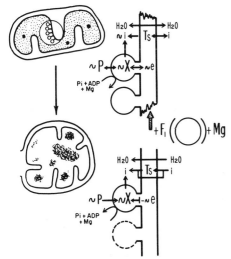

Figure 5.43. Diagram illustrating morphological and functional changes in ischemic mitochondria. After ischemia, the inner compartment shows high amplitude swelling and flocculent densities appear. The functional defect includes persistent redox function but partial block in phosphorylation indicated by the vertical bar. Some inner membrane spheres disappear as indicated by the dotted line. The translocator function of the inner membrane is modified; the membrane becomes permeable explaining in part the onset of high amplitude swelling. Ion-accumulating ability, though greatly impaired, is still present under appropriate conditions. The upper diagram shows the appearance of control mitochondria and the effects of adding F_1 particles (inner membrane spheres) plus magnesium.

ing results in further increase in permeability of the cell membrane or secondary leak which leads to influx of other ions such as calcium as well as to entry of vital dyes. Mitochondria undergo high amplitude swelling and hydrolases are probably released from lysosomes.

Recent experiments by Hawkins (62) in our laboratory strongly indicate that proteins are not released from lysosomes prior to the point-of-no-return in Chang cells lethally injured with cyanide and iodoacetate or with antibody plus complement. Thus, at least in these two models the suicide bag hypothesis does not seem to apply.

In stage 5, mitochondria show marked

uptake of calcium, forming calcium phosphate deposits, if conditions are appropriate. That is, if blood supply is restored or if the injury is applied with an intact blood supply so that substrate and oxygen are available. The mitochondria accumulate calcium phosphates near the inner membrane. The second type of mitochondrial density is comprised of fluffy or flocculent dense material which may represent denatured matrical proteins. The conformation of the plasma membrane is altered forming wrappings around organelles especially in regions where the plasma membrane shows multiple invaginations. Later these convert to complex myelin figures. Attack of components by lysosomal hydrolsases at this stage results in digestion of all cell structures as the systems approach equilibrium. This is represented by stage 6. In this sequence, stages 2 and 3 are regarded as reversible stages; stage 4 a transitional stage; and stages 5 and 6 irreversible stages of necrosis. It is to be emphasized in this model that alterations of nucleic acid and protein

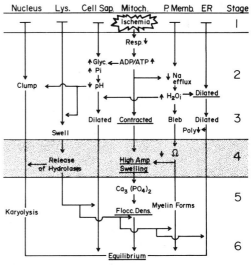

Figure 5.44. Diagram summarizing our working hypothesis of the progression of change in pathogenetic mechanisms following ischemic injury to cells. The stages at the right correspond to those depicted in Figure 5.3 and discussed in the text.

TABLE 5.3

Oxidative Phosphorylation in Reconstituted
Inner Membrane Preparations from
Ischemic Mitochondria

Succinate	No addition	F_1 control
A—control	0	1.3
A—2-hr ischemic	0	1.1

synthesis are not included since, though these commonly occur, they seem to represent parallel phenomenon not on the direct path leading to necrosis in acute injury. The entire sequence is to be applied to interphase cells, that is G_o or sterile cells; slightly different sequences may occur in cells which are in the mitotic cycle.

In the foregoing we have attempted to show the importance of ion and water movements and hence of structural and functional changes in cell membranes in the pathogenesis of change following acute lethal cell injury. The development of membranes with restricted permeability characteristics must have been of great strategic importance in the evolution of primitive cells. If, as is often suggested, life originated in brackish waters, the evolution of a sodium extrusion mechanism, perhaps driven by a high energy compound resembling ATP must have occurred very early to enable to protocells to resist the tendency toward Gibbs-Donnan equilibrium. The evolution of membranes may therefore be an even more primitive step than the evolution of the present DNA-RNA-protein synthesis scheme, since replication has been observed in systems not involving nucleic acid. It is therefore perhaps not surprising that loss or modification of the structure and function of cell membranes are of such key importance in the development of pathological changes following lethal or sublethal injury. These can be thought of as loss of the most primitive cell functions without which life cannot be sustained. It is also apparent that the evolution of intracellular enzyme systems has

proceeded in the type of environment provided by cell membrane activity that is relatively high concentrations of potassium and magnesium and low concentrations of sodium and calcium. It is therefore to be expected that reversal of the intracellular sodium/potassium and calcium/magnesium ratios can be extremely harmful and damaging to intracellular enzyme systems (40). For example, pyruvate kinase is inhibited by elevated concentrations of sodium and activated by potassium. Phosphofructokinase and fructokinase are markedly activated by potassium (39). Protein synthesis cannot proceed with depletion of intracellular potassium and changes in intracellular calcium have marked damaging effects on the mitochondria. Although presently the mechanisms involved in the calcium and magnesium relationships have not been established, the concept of secondary leaks following membrane conformational changes induced by swelling may account for some changes in the divalent ion ratios.

When these ideas are examined it becomes of interest to begin thinking of changes in these ion ratios as important pathogenetic factors in themselves rather than mere accompaniments of cell injury. This seems to be related to the concept of the "sick" cells as proposed by Welt (63). Welt has found evidence that in a population of patients with uremia, advanced cancer, burns, and other chronic illnesses there is a transport defect in the membranes of erythrocytes which seems to be associated with diminished activity of the ouabain-sensitive ATPase. It is conceivable that such membrane lesions are generalized, involving many other cell types and possibly other transport mechanisms. According to the arguments presented in the present paper, this should have serious consequences on cell function generally in the patient and bring about generalized disturbances that may be incompatible with life. Other evidence in this direction comes from the work of Bajusz (64, 64a) and Selye (65) who have considerable evidence that modifications of body electrolyte composition by combinations of electrolyte administration and stress result in non-vascular necroses in organs such as the myocardium.

Some of the experiments reported in the present chapter represent attempts to restore functional activity to damaged membrane systems such as A particles. This can be thought of as a restoration of the ~P function to a damaged "protocell." Extension of this approach should yield much more information regarding the precise morphochemical defects in membranes of "sick" cells and possibly to restoration of function to cells that would otherwise be irretrievable.

REFERENCES

1. SMUCKLER, E. A., AND ARCASOY, M. Structural and functional changes of the endoplasmic reticulum of hepatic parenchymal cells. *Int. Rev. Exp. Path. 7:* 305, 1969.

2. TRUMP, B. F., AND ERICSSON, J. L. E. Some ultrastructural and biochemical consequences of cell injury. In *The Inflammatory Process*, edited by Zweifach, B. W., Grant, L., and McCluskey, L., pp. 35–120. New York, Academic Press, 1965.

3. TRUMP, B. F., AND ARSTILA, A. U. Cellular and subcellular reactions of cells to injury. In *Principles of Pathobiology*, edited by LaVia, M., and Hill, R. New York, Oxford University Press, in press.

4. ARSTILA, A. U., SMITH, M. A., AND TRUMP, B. F. The characterization of peroxidation lesions in the endoplasmic reticulum of the rat kidney liver *in vivo* and *in vitro* (abstr.). *Lab. Invest. 22:* 490, 1970.

5. BULGER, R. E., AND TRUMP, B. F. Ca^{++} and K^+ ion effects on ultrastructure of isolated flounder kidney tubules. *J. Ultrastruct. Res. 28:* 301, 1969.

6. GINN, F. L., SHELBURNE, J. D., AND TRUMP, B. F. Disorders of cell volume regulation. I. Effects of inhibition of plasma membrane adenosine triphosphatase with ouabain. *Amer. J. Path. 53:* 1041, 1968.

7. GINN, F. L., HOCHSTEIN, P. E., AND TRUMP, B. F. Membrane alterations in hemolysis: Internalization of plasmalemma induced by primaquine. *Science 164:* 843, 1969.

8. LAIHO, K. U., AND SHELBURNE, J. D. Ultrastructural and volume changes in Ehrlich ascites tumor cells produced by metabolic inhibitors (abstr.). *Fed. Proc. 29:* 688, 1970.

9. SMUCKLER, E. A., AND TRUMP, B. F. Early changes in hepatic microsomal and polysomal structure and function during *in vitro* necrosis (abstr.). *J. Histochem. Cytochem. 13:* 721, 1965.

10. SALADINO, A. J., BENTLEY, P. J., AND TRUMP, B. F. Ion movements in cell injury. Effect of amphotericin B on the ultrastructure and function of the epithelial cells of the toad bladder. *Amer. J. Path. 54:* 421, 1969.

11. SAHAPHONG, S. Role of plasma membrane SH groups in pathogenesis of cell death (abstr.). *Fed. Proc. 29:* 752, 1970.

12. TRUMP, B. F., AND GINN, F. L. The pathogenesis of subcellular reaction to lethal injury. In *Methods and Achievements in Experimental Pathology*, edited by Bajusz, E., and Jasmin, G., Vol. IV, pp. 1–29. Chicago, Year Book Medical Publishers, 1969.

13. TRUMP, B. F. Ion movements in cell injury: Effects of inhibition of sodium transport on ultrastructure of the nephron and related systems. Symposium on Nephrology, Stockholm, Sweden, pp. 82–83. 1969.

14. TRUMP, B. F., AND BULGER, R. E. Studies of cellular injury in isolated flounder tubules. I. Correlation between morphology and function of control tubules; observations of autophagocytosis and mechanical cell damage. *Lab. Invest. 16:* 453, 1967.

15. TRUMP, B. F., AND BULGER, R. E. Studies of cellular injury in isolated flounder tubules. III. Light microscopic and functional changes due to cyanide. *Lab. Invest. 18:* 721, 1968.

16. TRUMP, B. F., AND BULGER, R. E. Studies of cellular injury in isolated flounder tubules. IV. Electron microscopic observations of changes during the phase of altered homeostasis in tubules treated with cyanide. *Lab. Invest. 18:* 731, 1968.

17. TRUMP, B. F., CALDER, J., AND SMITH, M. A. Correlation between structure and function in mitochondria from injured cells (abstr.). *Fed. Proc. 26:* 514, 1967.

18. TRUMP, B. F., DUTTERA, S. M., BYRNE, W. L., AND ARSTILA, A. U. Membrane structure: Lipid protein interactions in microsomal membranes. *Proc. Nat. Acad. Sci. U.S.A. 66:* 433, 1970.

19. TRUMP, B. F., AND GINN, F. L. Studies of cellular injury in isolated flounder tubules. II. Cellular swelling in high-potassium media. *Lab. Invest. 18:* 341, 1968.

20. TRUMP, B. F., GOLDBLATT, P. J., AND STOWELL, R. E. An electron microscopic study of early cytoplasmic alterations in hepatic parenchymal cells of mouse liver during necrosis *in vitro* (autolysis). *Lab. Invest. 11:* 986, 1962.

21. TRUMP, B. F., GOLDBLATT, P. J., AND STOWELL, R. E. Nuclear and cytoplasmic changes during necrosis *in vitro* (autolysis): An electron microscopy study (abstr.). *Amer. J. Path. 43:* 23a, 1963.

22. TRUMP, B. F., GOLDBLATT, P. J., AND STOWELL, R. E. Studies on necrosis of mouse liver *in vitro*. Ultrastructural alterations in the mitochondria of hepatic parenchymal cells. *Lab. Invest. 14:* 343, 1965.

23. TRUMP, B. F., GOLDBLATT, P. J., AND STOWELL, R. E. Studies of necrosis *in vitro* of mouse hepatic parenchymal cells. Ultrastructural alterations in endoplasmic reticulum, Golgi apparatus, plasma membrane, and lipid droplets. *Lab. Invest. 14:* 2000, 1965.

24. TRUMP, B. F., GOLDBLATT, P. J., AND STOWELL, R. E. Studies on necrosis of mouse liver *in vitro*. Ultrastructural alterations in cytosomes, cytosegresomes, multivesicular bodies, and microbodies and their relations to the lysosome concept. *Lab. Invest. 14:* 1946, 1965.

25. TRUMP, B. F., GOLDBLATT, P. J., AND STOWELL, R. E. Studies of mouse liver necrosis *in vitro*. Ultrastructural and cytochemical alterations in hepatic parenchymal cell nuclei. *Lab. Invest. 14:* 1969, 1965.

26. TRUMP, B. F., AND HAGADORN, J. F. Unpublished observations.

27. TRUMP, B. F., MERGNER, W. J., AND SMITH, M. A. Correlation between ultrastructure and function in mitochondria during renal ischemia (abstr.). *Amer. J. Path. 59:* 61a, 1970.

28. TRUMP, B. F., TISHER, C. C., AND SALADINO, A. J. The nephron in health and disease. In *The Biological Basis of Medicine*, edited by Bittar, E. E., and Bittar, N., Vol. 6, pp. 387–494. New York, Academic Press, 1969.

29. JENNINGS, R. B., HERDSON, P. B., AND SOMMERS, H. M. Structural and functional abnormalities in mitochondria isolated from ischemic dog myocardium. *Lab. Invest. 20:* 548, 1969.

30. GRITZKA, T. L., AND TRUMP, B. F. Renal tubular lesions caused by mercuric chloride. I. Electron microscopic observations. Degenera-

tion of the pars recta. *Amer. J. Path. 52:* 1225, 1968.

31. DANIELS, C. A. Unpublished observations.

32. PRIGOGINE, I. (EDITOR). *Thermodynamics of Irreversible Processes*, Ed. 2. New York, John Wiley and Sons, Inc., 1961.

33. CROKER, B. P., SALADINO, A. J., AND TRUMP, B. F. Ion movements in cell injury. Relationship between energy metabolism and the pathogenesis of lethal injury in the toad bladder. *Amer. J. Path. 59:* 247, 1970.

34. TOSTESON, D. C. Regulation of cell volume by sodium and potassium transport. In *The Cellular Functions of Membrane Transport*, edited by Hoffman, T. F., pp. 3–22. Englewood Cliffs, New Jersey, Prentice-Hall, Inc., 1969.

35. ARSTILA, A. U., AND TRUMP, B. F. Autophagocytosis: Origin of membrane and hydrolytic enzymes. *Virchow Arch. [Zellpath.] 2:* 85, 1969.

36. KORN, E. D. Cell membranes: Structure and synthesis. *Ann. Rev. Biochem. 38:* 263, 1964.

37. STOECKENIUS, D., AND ENGELMAN, M. Current models for the structure of biological membranes. *J. Cell Biol. 42:* 613, 1969.

38. JOBSIS, F. F. Basic processes in cellular respiration. In *Handbook of Physiology*, *Section Respiration*, edited by Finn, W. O., and Rahn, H., Vol. 1, pp. 63–124. Washington, D.C., American Physiological Society, 1964.

39. LUBIN, M. Intracellular potassium and macromolecular synthesis in mammalian cells. *Nature (London) 213:* 451, 1967.

40. USSING, H. H. Alkali metal ions in isolated systems and tissues. In *Handbuch der Experimentellen Pharmakologie*, edited by Eichler, O., and Farah, A., pp. 1–195. New York, Springer-Verlag New York Inc., 1960.

41. MUELLER, P., AND RUDIN, D. O. Translocators in bimolecular lipid membrane; their role in dissipative and conservative bioenergy transduction. In *Current Topics in Bioenergetics*, edited by Sanadi, D. R., Vol. 3, p. 157. New York, Academic Press, 1969.

42. MERGNER, W. J., AND TRUMP, B. F. Ultrastructural and functional changes in mitochondria aged *in vitro*. *Lab. Invest 22:* 505, 1970.

43. HACKENBROCK, C. R. Ultrastructural bases for metabolically linked activity in mitochondria. I. Reversible ultrastructural changes with change in metabolic steady state in isolated liver mitochondria. *J. Cell Biol. 30:* 269, 1967.

44. HACKENBROCK, C. R. Ultrastructural bases for metabolically linked mechanical activity in

mitochondria. II. Electron transport linked ultrastructural transformation in mitochondria. *J. Cell Biol. 37:* 345, 1968.

45. HARRIS, R. A., ASBELL, M. A., ASAI, J., JOLLY, W. W., AND GREEN, D. E. The conformational basis of energy transduction in membrane systems. V. Measurement by light scattering. *Arch. Biochem. 132:* 545, 1969.

46. CHANCE, B., AND WILLIAMS, G. R. Respiratory enzymes in oxidative phosphorylation. III. The steady state. *J. Biol. Chem. 217:* 409, 1955.

47. BLONDIN, G. A., VAIL, W. J., AND GREEN, D. E. The mechansim of mitochondrial swelling. *Arch. Biochem. 129:* 158, 1969.

48. REYNAFARJE, B., AND LEHNINGER, A. L. High affinity binding of Ca^{++} by rat liver mitochondria. *J. Biol. Chem. 244:* 584, 1969.

49. REYNOLDS, E. S. Liver parenchymal cell injury. III. The nature of calcium-associated electron-opaque masses in rat liver mitochondria following poisoning with carbon tetrachloride. *J. Cell Biol. [Suppl.]:* 53, 1965.

50. CHAPMAN, D. (EDITOR). *Biological Membranes, Physican and Function,* pp. 125–203. New York, Academic Press, 1968.

51. WALLACH, D. F. H., AND GORDON, A. S. Lipid protein interaction in cellular membranes. In *Symposium on Regulatory Functions of Biological Membranes, BBA Library,* Edited by Jarnefelt, J., Vol. 11, pp. 87–98. New York, Elsevier Publishing Co., 1968.

52. WALLACH, D. F. H. Membrane lipids and the conformation of membrane proteins. *J. Gen. Physiol. 54:* 3s, 1969.

53. CHANGEAUX, J., THIERY, J., TUNNY, Y., AND KITTEL, C. On the cooperativity of biological membranes. *Proc. Nat. Acad. Sci. U.S.A. 57:* 335, 1967.

54. DICKERSON, R. E., AND GEIS, I. (EDITORS). *The Structure and Action of Proteins,* pp. 1–120. New York, Harper and Row Publishers, Inc., 1969.

55. PERUTZ, M. F., KENDREN, J. C., AND WATSON, H. C. Structure and function of haemoglobin. II. Some relations between polypeptide chain configuration and amino acid sequence. *J. Molec. Biol. 13:* 669, 1965.

56. HOCHSTEIN, P., AND ERNSTER, L. Microsomal peroxidation of lipids and it possible role in cellular injury. In *Ciba Foundation Symposium, Cellular Injury,* edited by deReuck, A. V. S., and Knight, J., pp. 123–135. Boston, Little, Brown and Co., 1963.

57. BARBER, A. A., AND BERNHEIM, F. Lipid peroxidation. Its measurement, occurrence and significance in animal tissues. *Advances Geront. Res. 2:* 355, 1967.

58. FESSENDEN, J. M., AND RACKER, E. Partial resolution of the enzymes catalyzing oxidative phosphorylation. XI. Stimulation of oxidative phosphorylation by coupling factors and oligomycin; inhibition by an antibody against coupling factor F_1. *J. Biol. Chem. 241:* 2483, 1966.

59. LAM, K. W., WARSHAW, J. B., AND SANADI, D. R. The mechanism of oxidative phosphorylation. *Arch. Biochem. 119:* 477, 1967.

60. PULLMAN, M. E., PENEFSKY, H. S., DALLA, A., AND RACKER, E. Partial resolution of the enzymes catalyzing oxidative phosphorylation. I. Purification and properties of a soluble dinitrophenol stimulated adenosine triphosphatase. *J. Biol. Chem. 235:* 3322, 1961.

61. VALLEJOS, R. H., VANDER BERGH, S. G., AND SLATER, E. C. On coupling function of oxidative phosphorylation. *Biochim. Biophys. Acta 153:* 509, 1968.

62. HAWKINS, H. K. Lysosome stability in lethal cell injury (abstr.). *Fed. Proc. 29:* 784, 1970.

63. WELT, L. Membrane transport defect: The sick cell. *Trans. Ass. Amer. Physicians 80:* 217, 1967.

64. BAJUSZ, E. (EDITOR). *Electrolytes and Cardiovascular Diseases, Physiology-Pathology-Therapy,* Vol. I, *Fundamental Aspects.* Baltimore, The Williams and Wilkins Co., 1965.

64a. BAJUSZ, E. (EDITOR). *Electrolytes and Caridovascular Diseases, Physiology-Pathology-Therapy,* Vol. II, *Clinical Aspects.* Baltimore, The Williams and Wilkins Co., 1966.

65. SELYE, H. (EDITOR). *The Chemical Prevention of Cardiac Necroses,* pp. 3–194. New York, The Ronald Press Co., 1958.

66. GOLDSTEIN, A., ARONOW, L., AND KALMAN, S. M. (EDITORS). "Drug metabolism," In *Principles of Drug Action,* pp. 206–279. New York, Harper and Row, Publishers, Inc., 1968.

67. MERGNER, W. J., AND TRUMP, B. F. Functional and morphological evaluation of ammonium molybdate and phosphotungstic acid negative staining on rat kidney mitochondria. (abstr.). *Fed. Proc. 29:* 814, 1970.

68. MERGNER, W. J., PENDERGRASS, R. E., AND TRUMP, B. F. The influence of ammonium molybdate, silicotungstic acid and phosphotungstic acid on function and structure of mitochondria. In *Proceedings of the Electron Microscopic Society of America,* Vol. 28, p. 70, 1970.

69. GREEN, D. E., ASAI, J., HARRIS, R. A., AND

PENNISTON, J. T. Conformation basis of energy transformation in membrane systems. III. Conformational changes in the mitochondrial inner membrane induced by changes in functional states. *Arch. Biochem.* *125:* 684, 1968.

70. SHELBURNE, J. D., AND TRUMP, B. F. Inhibition of protein synthesis in flounder kidney tubules (abstr.), *Fed. Proc. 27:* 410, 1968.

71. REYNOLDS, E. S. Liver parenchymal cell injury. I. Initial alteration of the cell following poisoning with carbon tetrachloride. *J. Cell Biol. 19:* 139, 1963.

72. HACKENBROCK, C. R., AND REHN, T. Transformation in ultrastructural and energy state of mitochondria in the intact ascites tumor cell. (abstr.). *Fed. Proc. 29:* 734, 1970.

6

ENDOCYTOSIS AND THE VACUOLAR SYSTEM

Zanvil A. Cohn

Within the past decade a large number of studies have delineated the pathways within cells by which endogenous and exogenous substrates are segregated within membrane systems and degraded by hydrolytic enzymes. This process of intracellular digestion has its origins in the last century and is largely derived from the now classic studies of Ilya Metchnikoff and colleagues. Extrapolating from observations on protozoa and simple metazoans he clearly visualized the role of endocytosis and the subsequent importance of "cytases" in the economy of the mammal. Although largely directed toward the problems of host defense against microbial invasion, these concepts have now been expanded and encompass many important aspects of cell physiology.

The renaissance in this area is clearly related to the initial biochemical studies of de Duve and his colleagues on the localization and properties of acid hydrolases in rat liver. Combined with the morphological and cytochemical observations of Alex Novikoff and related observations of Werner Straus on renal cells, this work soon expanded into a working hypothesis which formulated a unique, digestive organelle called the lysosome. The lysosome concept was rapidly expanded in a burgeoning literature and this

cytoplasmic structure can now be described as being delimited by a semipermeable membrane containing a wide variety of hydrolytic enzymes all of which have acid pH optima. The concerted efforts of these enzymes have been studied in some detail and are capable of degrading most biologically important macromolecules to the building block level. As far as can be ascertained at this time the lysosome remains the only clearly established locus in which intracellular digestion takes place.

For the purposes of our discussion, the lysosome or digestive body will constitute the central organelle of the vacuolar apparatus. Plasma membrane flowing from the cell periphery through endocytosis represents one important pathway whereas Golgi and smooth endoplasmic reticulum membrane represent the other. The interaction between these membrane compartments, the resulting membrane fusions which occur, and the factors governing both the flow of membrane and the fate of substrate will be the focus of this chapter. Most of our studies have been conducted with monocytes and macrophages, cells in which the vacuolar system plays a prominent role and in which detailed information is at hand concerning the regulation of its various compartments. Table 6.1 presents a simplified version of the components to be covered.

ENDOCYTOSIS

Endocytosis is a general term to describe the interiorization of the plasma

The Rockefeller University, New York, New York 10021.

This study was supported in part by Grant AI 07012-05, U.S. Public Health Service, National Institute of Allergy and Infectious Diseases, National Institutes of Health, Bethesda, Maryland.

TABLE 6.1

The Vacuolar System

1. Endocytic vesicles and vacuoles: plasma membrane-derived
    a. Pinocytic vesicles: soluble exogenous molecules
    b. Phagocytic vacuoles: particulate exogenous molecules
2. Secondary lysosomes or digestive bodies
    a. Heterophagic: exogenous substrates
    b. Autophagic: endogenous substrates
    c. Mixed
3. Primary lysosomes
    a. Storage type: PMN azurophil granule
    b. Golgi vesicle: an organelle containing newly synthesized hydrolases which have not as yet interacted with their ultimate substrates.

membrane in the form of vesicles and larger vacuoles. It entails the fusion of the plasma membrane following either the invagination or evagination of this organelle. The process varies markedly in terms of the size of the structures formed and in terms of their intracytoplasmic fate but in general it is separated into two major categories based upon the state of the exogenous material which is interiorized. On this basis, pinocytosis represents the uptake of soluble molecules either free in solution or bound to the plasma membrane and usually takes the form of small vesicles. In contrast, phagocytosis is defined as the uptake of solid or insoluble particulates which may range from tiny polystyrene beads to intact erythrocytes, and in general represents the formation of a larger vacuole. Endocytic mechanisms therefore represent the only clear-cut examples of the quantal uptake of exogenous molecules by intact cells. This is not to deny the existence of the transmembranous transport of macromolecules but merely to point out that our knowledge of this phenomenon is too rudimentary to deserve further discussion at this time.

Pinocytosis

The discovery of pinocytosis or the uptake of fluid-filled droplets was reported by Warren Lewis in 1931 (1), employing cultured macrophages. In the next four decades it has been studied in more or less detail in many cell types but most rigorously by Holter and Chapman-Andresen (2, 3) at the Carlsberg Laboratories. These workers using the free living amoebae *Chaos chaos* and *Amoeba proteus* systematically examined the requirements for induction of and consequences of pinocytosis in these protozoa. Their studies are now the classic descriptions of the process and by far the most comprehensive. However, more recently many examples of pinocytosis have accumulated in mammalian systems. Although we will not describe these in detail they illustrate the markedly different fate of pinocytic vesicles as compared to the macrophage. For example, Palade (4) and Bruns and Palade (5) and others have examined the formation of micropinocytic vesicles which are very prominent in capillary endothelium and mesothelium. These vesicles form as tiny pits or caveolae and pinch off from the plasma membrane. They then shuttle across the narrow cytoplasm of the endothelial cell and readily fuse with the plasma membrane on the other cell face. In this and other similar instances little or no interaction takes place with other cytoplasmic components, presumably digestion of exogenous molecules does not occur, and the resulting effect is the transport of intravascular components to the extravascular space. Such a transport phenomenon may also occur in the neonatal small intestine with the uptake of maternal antibody. In these examples we have little information concerning the regulation of "micropinocytosis" under *in vivo* conditions.

Studies in our laboratory have been primarily concerned with the metabolic requirements of pinocytosis and those agents which induce vesicle formation

(6–8). Two techniques have been employed to measure the interiorization of plasma membrane and these have in general given comparable results. The first is morphological and measures the formation of new pinosomes visible under oil immersion phase contrast microscopy. These vesicles are formed most often in cell pseudopods, the locus of ruffled membrane, and then flow centripetally into the perinuclear region. The other method employs the uptake of isotopically labeled macromolecules (9). As in the amoeba, pinocytosis in macrophages is critically dependent upon ambient temperature and a source of energy. A 10° reduction in temperature ($\pm 27°$ C) results in a 75% inhibition of vesicle formation. The "Q_{10}" is in the range of 3.3. Through the use of inhibitors vesicle formation is most sensitive to those agents which inhibit the respiratory chain and oxidative phosphorylation. This suggests the importance of mitochondrially derived energy and the role of adenosine triphosphate as the ultimate energy source. Studies with the inhibitors appear to be correlated with morphological observations in which the presence of mitochondria within pseudopods is closely correlated with the formation of pinosomes in this portion of the cell. The withdrawal of mitochondria from pseudopods, a process which can be initiated by a number of agents, i.e., Colcemid, results in the prompt cessation of this form of endocytosis. Under the conditions employed in this laboratory, the phagocytosis of either opsonized bacteria or erythrocytes is unaffected by agents which alter respiration or oxidative phosphorylation. Pinocytosis may also be depressed to low levels by agents which inhibit glycolysis and protein synthesis. Cycloheximide, p-fluorophenylalanine, and puromycin at concentrations which inhibit the incorporation of amino acids into proteins by 75% are effective blocking agents. Recent studies suggest that a portion of this requirement may be for new proteins neces-

sary for the formation of plasma membrane. Under active conditions of pinocytic activity we have calculated that approximately 50% of the macrophage plasma membrane may be interiorized within 2.5 hours and since the cell volume remains essentially unchanged, considerable synthesis of new membrane must occur. This assumes that internalized membrane does not serve as a subsequent source of plasma membrane.

The actual mechanisms by which energy is utilized for the interiorization of plasma membrane are unknown. It is becoming clearer, however, that the energy derived from respiration-oxidative phosphorylation pathways are necessary for the motion of the membrane in pseudopods. Membrane movement or undulations, therefore, seem to play an important role for pinocytic mechanisms and are less critical for the uptake of particles by phagocytosis. Whether or not membrane movement is also required for "micropinocytosis" in the macrophage and other cell types is unclear.

The factors responsible for the induction of pinocytosis have been examined in only a few systems and no sweeping generalizations can be made at this time. In the macrophage culture system, inducing molecules may be separated into at least three categories. The first group are relatively non-specific and depend upon their size and anionic nature for activity. These include acidic polysaccharides, nucleic acids, amino acid homopolymers, proteins, amino acids, and small carbohydrates. Their activity is unrelated to whether or not they are susceptible to cellular hydrolases. Neutral molecules and cationic species had low activity. This finding is quite different from studies in the amoeba in which cationic inducers are quite effective and in which some form of direct interaction with a surface acidic polysaccharide presumably takes place. It is also the opposite of Ryser's observations (10) on Sarcoma 180 cells in which polycations stimulate the "uptake" of iodinated albumin. In the macrophage, however, the polycations are quite lytic and at subtoxic levels do not appear to stimulate vesicle formation at any concentration. They do complex readily with anionic molecules in the medium and cell surface to form large aggregates which may then be ingested by a phagocytic mechanism.

A second group of agents encompasses adenosine and its 5'-phosphates (11). These are potent inducers whose mechanism of action is still not clear. Since the macrophage plasma membrane contains an active divalent cation dependent ATPase it seemed possible that the energy derived from the reaction might be converted into membrane activity. However, the situation is more complex since adenosine itself is an excellent inducer of vesicle formation. In addition, adenosine has other effects on the structural organization of the cytoplasm which may be indirectly involved in vesicle formation. One of these is to produce a highly oriented population of mitochondria in the peripheral pseudopods which under phase contrast are imbedded in a central core of denser hyaloplasm. These mitochondria extend to the tips of the pseudopods and under the electron microscope are in close association with typical, oriented microtubules. One may speculate that the presence of mitochondria in close apposition to the plasma membrane may facilitate the transfer of ATP or other high energy compounds.

A third class of agents are immunological in nature and do not depend upon charge but upon their ability to bind firmly to the plasma membrane. One example is the macroglobulin present in bovine serum which behaves as an interspecies antibody directed against the mouse macrophage membrane (12). In the absence of hemolytic complement (C') it stimulates pinocytosis in a dose-dependent fashion and ultimately the accumulation of lysosomes and lysosomal enzymes. When C' is present in the system, there is an almost immediate lysis of the plasma membrane and cell death. The antigen on the plasma membrane with which this γ-globulin interacts has not as yet been characterized but from absorption experiments is also shared by the mouse erythrocyte. In fact, immunization of rabbits with mouse RBC leads to an antibody with similar properties to that in normal bovine serum. The bovine macroglobulin is absent in fetal calf serum and increases in titer during early neonatal life.

Phagocytosis

We will not dwell on the process of phagocytosis in any great detail since it is the subject of recent review articles (13, 14). There are a number of points which should be stressed in comparison to the uptake of soluble molecules by pinocytosis. First, there appear to be differences in the metabolic requirements for pinocytosis and phagocytosis in at least the mouse macrophage. Whereas phagocytosis is unaffected by inhibitors of respiration and oxidative phosphorylation which block pinocytosis, it is markedly inhibited by inhibitors of glycolysis such as fluoride and iodoacetate. In addition, phagocytosis is a much more effective mechanism in quantitative terms for interiorizing large amounts of exogenous agents in short periods of time. For example, the uptake of heat-aggregated albumin or γ-globulin is roughly 10-fold greater than the interiorization of soluble molecules on a similar time scale.

There are other important differences which relate to the surface of the particle to be ingested. Immunoglobulins play an important role in preparing a particle for interiorization. IgG is quite effective in the absence of C' and a particle coated with it appears to bind to receptors present on the macrophage plasma membrane. In contrast, particles coated with IgM require the presence of complement to be interiorized. It is not clear whether immunoglobulins react with surface receptors *per se* or whether an initial interaction with antigen is required to produce configurational changes which are then recognized by the cell surface.

THE INTRACYTOPLASMIC FATE OF ENDOCYTIC VACUOLES

Phagocytic Vacuoles

Some years ago, from studies with polymorphonuclear leukocytes, it became clear that phagocytic vacuoles fused with cytoplasmic granules and were thereby converted to digestive bodies or secondary lysosomes. This occurred by the fusion of granule and phagosome membrane and the subsequent mixing of contents. The digestive body-limiting membrane then contained components of both the plasma membrane (phagosome) and Golgi membrane (granule) in varying proportions depending upon the degree of degranulation. Little is known of the mechanism by which this form of membrane fusion takes place or whether it represents an active or passive process.

Similar events take place within the macrophage cytoplasm (15, 16). In this case, however, the cytoplasmic "granules" are not primary lysosomes as in the case of the polymorphonuclear neutrophilic leukocyte (PMN) but are already digestive bodies. The transfer of hydrolases can be ascertained by a variety of cytochemical and biochemical methods. Perhaps the most direct comes from electron microscopic cytochemistry in which the process of fusion can be visualized and the discharge of acid phosphatase demonstrated. A second procedure depends upon cell fractionation and traces the distribution of acid hydrolases in control and phagocytizing cells. *In vitro* conditions can be employed in which 50 to 70% of the lysosomal enzymes are released from pre-existing organelles. Employing the method of Korn it is now possible to isolate intact macrophage phagosomes after the ingestion of polystyrene and flotation in discontinuous sucrose gradients.

Pinocytic Vesicles

The pathway taken by pinocytic vesicles appears to be more complex than with the larger phagosome. Small pinosomes which enter the cytoplasm exhibit a directed migration into the perinuclear area and usually come to rest adjacent to the Golgi complex. These vesicles often will fuse with each other as they move through the cell, most often in the pseudopods and form larger phase and electron lucent vacuoles. Both the vesicles and larger vacuoles may fuse with pre-existing digestive bodies and secondary lysosomes in a manner analogous to the fusion of phagosomes. In this case, however, the secondary lysosome is usually larger than the pinosome although in both instances new substrate from the environment is transferred to a hydrolase-containing organelle.

A second pathway results in the conversion of the pinosome into a secondary lysosome by means of fusions with Golgi vesicles (17, 18). In this case, newly synthesized hydrolases which are thought to be packaged within Golgi vesicles enter the pinosome and initiate intravacuolar digestion. Although the fusion of Golgi vesicles with pinocytic vacuoles is relatively common in thin sections of macrophages, their fusion with larger phagosomes or secondary lysosomes has not as yet been demonstrated.

THE FATE OF ENDOCYTIZED MOLECULES

Once a soluble or particulate macromolecule enters the confines of a lysosome, intracellular digestion may ensue. It is now clear that the lysosomes of many cells contain a wide spectrum of acid hydrolases which through their concerted efforts have the ability to degrade most if not all biologically important substrates. The importance of intracellular digestion is of obvious importance in the economy of the cell and is emphasized under conditions in which specific deficiencies in lysosomal enzymes are found. Many new examples of storage diseases have been described in which the absence of a single lysosomal enzyme is associated with the accumulation of its natural substrate.

A few examples of the degree of intra-lysosomal digestion will suffice to illustrate the efficiency of the macrophage. Some years ago we examined the degradation of a variety of bacteria which had been uniformly labeled with both ^{32}P and ^{14}C (19). Figure 6.1 illustrates the time course of the degradation of *Escherichia coli* macromolecules after phagocytosis by rabbit macrophages. Within 3 hours large amounts of protein, lipid, and RNA had been reduced to acid soluble fragments whereas the digestion of DNA took considerably longer. More recently we have examined the digestion of proteins pinocytized by cultured mouse macrophages (9, 20, 21). Iodinated albumin and γ-globulin were rapidly degraded to acid soluble fragments which by gel chromatography turned out to be monoiodotyrosine. ^{3}H-leucine labeled hemoglobin was also digested to the level of amino acids and either excreted into the medium or utilized for new protein synthesis by the cell. From other studies it appears that intralysosomal digestion proceeds to the level of either amino acids or very small peptides (22, 23). Larger fragments are retained within the confines of the lysosome and do not enter the cytosol.

FUTURE STUDIES

Although many problems related to endocytosis and the vacuolar system remain to be resolved there are a few which deserve special comment. One of the more interesting relates to the mechanism by which energy produced by metabolism is converted into membrane movement and other forms of activity. A second is the mechanism of membrane fusion and the manner in which specific cytomembranes are recognized as "compatible" for fusion. A third represents a large field of plasma membrane biogenesis and physiology in which methods are just becoming available to investigate membrane flow and the turnover of individual constituents. The solution of these problems should have many important implications in the biology and pathology of eukaryotic cells.

SUMMARY

The various members of the vacuolar system are described and their interrelationships examined. Factors which control endocytosis regulate the flow of plasma membrane and exogenous substrates into the cytoplasm. Hydrolytic enzymes present within primary and secondary lysosomes enter the newly formed pinocytic and phagocytic vacuoles by membrane fusion and begin the process of intracellular digestion. The degradation of selected molecules are reviewed and their escape through the lysosomal membrane and subsequent fate delineated.

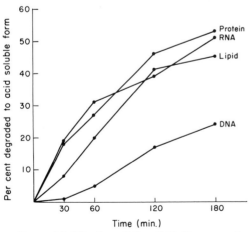

Figure 6.1. The fate of *E. coli* K-12 macromolecules following ingestion by rabbit macrophages.

REFERENCES

1. LEWIS, W. H. Pinocytosis. *Johns Hopkins Med. J. 49:* 17, 1931.
2. HOLTER, H. Pinocytosis. *Int. Rev. Cytol. 8:* 481, 1959.
3. CHAPMAN-ANDRESEN, C. Pinocytosis in amoebae. *C.R. Lab. Carlsberg 33:* 73, 1962–1963.
4. PALADE, G. E. Transport in quanta across the

endothelium of blood capillaries. *Anat. Rec. 136:* 254, 1960.

5. BRUNS, R. R., AND PALADE, G. E. Studies on blood capillaries. II. Transport of ferritin molecules across the wall of muscle capillaries. *J. Cell Biol. 37:* 277, 1968.

6. COHN, Z. A. The regulation of pinocytosis in mouse macrophages. I. Metabolic requirements as defined by the use of inhibitors. *J. Exp. Med. 124:* 557, 1966.

7. COHN, Z. A., AND PARKS, E. The regulation of pinocytosis in mouse macrophages. II. Factors inducing vesicle formation. *J. Exp. Med. 125:* 213, 1967.

8. COHN, Z. A. The requirements and consequences of pinocytosis in mouse macrophages. In *Cellular Recognition*, edited by Smith, R. T., and Good, R. A., p. 39. New York, Appleton-Century-Crofts, 1969.

9. EHRENREICH, B. A., AND COHN, Z. A. The uptake and digestion of iodonated human serum albumin by macrophages *in vitro. J. Exp. Med. 126:* 941, 1967.

10. RYSER, H. Uptake of protein by mammalian cells: An underdeveloped area. *Science 159:* 390, 1968.

11. COHN, Z. A., AND PARKS, E. The regulation of pinocytosis in mouse macrophages. III. The induction of vesicle formation by nucleosides and nucleotides. *J. Exp. Med. 125:* 457, 1967.

12. COHN, Z. A., AND PARKS, E. The regulation of pinocytosis in mouse macrophages. IV. The immunological induction of pinocytic vesicles, secondary lysosomes and hydrolytic enzymes. *J. Exp. Med. 125:* 1091, 1967.

13. RABINOVITCH, M. Phagocytosis: The engulfment stage. *Seminars Hemat. 5:* 134, 1968.

14. COHN, Z. A. The structure and function of mono-cytes and macrophages. *Advances Immun. 9:* 163, 1968.

15. COHN, Z. A., HIRSCH, J. G., AND WIENER, E. The cytoplasmic granules of phagocytic cells and the degradation of bacteria. In *Ciba Symposium on Lysosomes*, edited by de Reuck, A. V. S., and Cameron, M. P., p. 126. London, J. and A. Churchill, Ltd., 1962.

16. COHN, Z. A., AND WIENER, E. The particulate hydrolases of macrophages. II. Biochemical and morphological response to particle ingestion. *J. Exp. Med. 118:* 1009, 1963.

17. COHN, Z. A., FEDORKO, M. E., AND HIRSCH, J. G. The *in vitro* differentiation of mononuclear phagocytes. V. The formation of macrophage lysosomes. *J. Exp. Med. 123:* 757, 1966.

18. COHN, Z. A., AND FEDORKO, M. E. The formation and fats of lysosomes. In *"Lysosomes in Biology and Pathology,"* edited by Dingle, J. T., and Fell, H. B. Vol. 1, p. 43. London, North Holland, 1968.

19. COHN, Z. A. The fate of bacteria within phagocytic cells. I. The degradation of isotopically labeled bacteria by polymorphonuclear leucocytes and macrophages. *J. Exp. Med. 117:* 27, 1963.

20. EHRENREICH, B. A., AND COHN, Z. A. Fate of hemoglobin pinocytosed by macrophages *in vitro. J. Cell Biol. 38:* 244, 1968.

21. EHRENREICH, B. A., AND COHN, Z. A. Pinocytosis by macrophages. *J. Reticuloendothel. Soc. 5:* 230, 1968.

22. COHN, Z. A., AND EHRENREICH, B. A. The uptake, storage and intracellular hydrolysis of carbohydrates by macrophages. *J. Exp. Med. 129:* 201, 1969.

23. EHRENREICH, B. A., AND COHN, Z. A. The fate of peptides pinocytosed by macrophages *in vitro. J. Exp. Med. 129:* 227, 1969.

7

INVOLVEMENT OF MEMBRANES IN THE INFECTIOUS CYCLE OF VACCINIA

Samuel Dales

The cycle of vaccinia virus biogenesis, reconstructed from a large body of experimental work (1–5), can be separated into five, temporally interconnected phases and commences with uptake and penetration of the inoculum in preparation for intracytoplasmic uncoating. In the second stage of the cycle, virus cores, containing the DNA, are released into the cytoplasmic matrix. A transcriptase enzyme contained inside the core can transcribe from the coated DNA template "early" messenger RNA species (6) that are required for the uncoating (i.e., release from the core) and subsequent reduplication of the DNA genome. During the third phase, progeny strands of replicated DNA become incorporated inside lipoprotein envelopes that are assembled de novo and surround spherical particles of immature virus. The fourth stage is associated with macromolecular synthesis of "late" factors required for transformation of immature forms into mature infectious particles (7). In the fifth and final stage of the cycle the maturing or mature progeny move out of the foci of virus assembly termed viroplasmic matrices or factories into other regions of the cytoplasm. The earliest mature progeny

to be formed during the infectious cycle are wrapped in cell-derived smooth cisternae and thereupon migrate to the cell surface, where release through the plasma membrane can occur.

In the first section of this chapter a brief recapitulation is made of some previously published information concerning the formation of virus-specific envelopes. The second section deals with hitherto unpublished observations regarding the envelopment of vaccinia progeny in host-derived membranes and release of particles through the cell surface.

BIOGENESIS OF THE VACCINIA MEMBRANE

The envelopes of vaccinia meet several of the criteria for cellular membranes. Chemically they are constituted from protein and lipid, of which lecithin is the predominant phospholipid (8). Morphologically these envelopes exhibit a trilaminar or "unit" membrane structure of approximately the same dimensions as that of host cell membranes. The unit membrane is coated externally by a layer of closely packed and uniformly distributed dense rodlets, termed spicules. From the reconstructed sequence of virus morphopoeisis as examined by means of thin sections these membranes appear to be unique to this agent and discontinuous from any of the cellular membranes present during virus development. In this re-

Department of Cytobiology, The Public Health Research Institute of the City of New York, Inc., 455 First Avenue, New York, New York 10016.

Supported by U.S. Public Health Service Grant AI-07477.

spect formation of the vaccinia membranes contrasts with that of envelopes surrounding other animal agents such as Sindbis, influenza, parainfluenza, and vesicular stomatitis viruses, which utilize segments of either the endoplasmic reticulum or plasma membrane during envelopment of progeny particles (9–12).

Membranes of vaccinia and the other poxviruses are assembled within viroplasmic matrices or factories which develop in the cytoplasm. First evidence of membrane formation is the appearance of short, arched segments consisting of a unit membrane and spicule coat. During "growth" of the membrane, the surface area increases in all directions presumably by accretion of material around the initial site of condensation while maintaining the original curvature, so as to enclose completely the immature vaccinia in a spherical envelope. The predetermined and constant curvature of the membrane results in the assembly of spheres of a very uniform diameter. It appears likely that the arching is imposed or determined at the very beginning of membrane assembly by the attached spicules because in the absence of a monolayer of spicules the envelopes possess irregular shapes. For example, treatment of cells at the appropriate times following inoculation with actinomycin D or Rifampicin, two inhibitors of the transcription process, results in the formation of unit membranes that acquire only an intermittent coat of spicules. The regions of unit membrane lacking spicules are flexible, highly convoluted, and frequently sealed into micelles (8).

Regarding the regulation of synthesis of protein components for the vaccinia membranes, experiments in which inhibitors of transcription and translation are added to cell cultures at defined time intervals reveal that proteins destined for assembly into membranes commence to be synthesized about 3 hours following infection, while the bulk of virus DNA is reduplicated earlier, at 1.5 to 3 hours after infection. During normal cycles of infection the assembly of enveloped immature particles commences 3 to 5 hours after infection, then continues at an exponential rate for 8 hours or longer, utilizing an expanding intracytoplasmic pool of viral protein. However, if the prevailing synthesis of RNA is blocked 60 minutes in advance and protein synthesis 20 to 30 minutes in advance of the time that membranes start to appear in factories, formation of virus envelopes can be completely arrested (8).

By definition (13), *early* virus functions can be transcribed from the infecting, parental genome while *late* functions are expressed following replication of the genome. In the case of vaccinia, inhibitors of DNA replication such as fluorodeoxyuridine and hydroxyurea can disrupt the infectious cycle without preventing synthesis and assembly of spherical, immature particles. Such particles lack the DNA nucleoids formed during normal infection, but have envelopes of morphologically normal appearance (14–17). These observations are consistent with data from experiments using inhibitors of transcription and translation, which demonstrate that components of the immature forms of vaccinia, including the membranes, belong in the category of *early* virus functions (8, 18–20).

The information that has been accumulated concerning the assembly of vaccinia-specific membranes has certain implications about the biogenesis of non-viral membranes, especially those of the plastids. In this regard the inner membrane discs or grana within chloroplasts of the alga *Chlamydomonas* are apparently assembled *de novo* from their lipid and protein constituents, including several enzymes, in a single step process (21). Comparative information on the formation of other membranes may demonstrate in the future whether biogenesis of the vaccinia-specific envelopes can be considered a satisfactory model for assembly of biological membranes in general.

ENVELOPMENT OF PROGENY VIRUS IN CELLULAR MEMBRANES AND EMERGENCE AT THE SURFACE

Developing vaccinia particles migrate out of the viroplasmic matrix during a period of transition from an immature spherical form into the mature progeny (Fig. 7.1). The first group of mature particles that are formed during the infectious cycle are observed to concentrate frequently in the centrosphere region (Fig. 7.1). At this site the particles are often associated with smooth membranous cisternae, tentatively identified as vesicles of the Golgi complex (Figs. 7.1-7.3). Judging by the association that is developed there appears to exist some specific as yet not understood recognition between the vaccinia particles and these cisternae. Examination of samples taken 5 hours after infection reveals that individual virus particles are surrounded by several small vesicles, contiguous with Golgi cisternae, some possessing a dense covering layer (coated vesicles) as illustrated in Figures 7.1-7.4A. In samples preserved at later times, 6 to 12 hours after inoculation, some virus particles appear to be completely surrounded by single flattened cisternae (Fig. 7.4D). These observations can be considered as suggestive evidence indicating that several small vesicles that become attached to the surface of vaccinia coalesce to form a continuous, double membrane sac investing the progeny virus. Whether fusion between vesicles is controlled by the virus is not known at present. It is, however, worthwhile to draw the readers attention to the possibility that this phenomenon may be related to cell fusion observed in cultures infected with the same IHD strain of vaccinia (7).

The complex of virus and associated cisternae is moved toward the cell surface in preparation for emergence (Fig. 4E). Occasionally, cisternal membranes facing the cytoplasmic matrix possess a dense layer like that found on coated vesicles (Fig. 7.4G and H). This morphological observation suggests that coated and smooth vesicles may fuse with one another into a single wrapping cisterna. Fusion of virus-associated vesicles prior to migration of the complex toward the cell surface sometimes may not occur as evident in Figures 7.4B and C. However, in the usual case, when the outer cisternal membrane comes to lie adjacent to the plasma membrane, there appears to occur fusion between the contiguous layers whereby a channel is opened to the exterior. Following this event only the inner cisternal membrane surrounds the virus on the surface facing the extracellular space (Fig. 7.4F and H-J). Finally, the mature infectious virus may be released into the extracellular fluid either wrapped in a single, inner cisternal membrane or as a naked particle, should the inner membrane become ruptured (Fig. 7.4K). Wrapping of progeny in cell-derived membranes does not always occur. Occasionally unenveloped or naked particles become lodged in the cytoplasm immediately subjacent to the plasma membrane. In other instances, naked particles may be transported into microvilli (Fig. 7.4L). It should be mentioned that immature vaccinia which occasionally emigrate from the factories may also become wrapped in smooth cisternae and released at the cell surface in the same way as the mature progeny.

The reconstructed morphological sequence, thought to represent a process of wrapping and release of vaccinia (Figs. 7.1-7.4), is in evidence during the early phases of virus production and may be controlled by either the virus or the host cell or by both. Examination of samples, taken 14 to 24 hours following infection, reveals that most intracellular virus progeny which accumulate in large numbers throughout the cytoplasm are either naked or only partially enveloped. Cessation of virus wrapping and release at the surface may result from a limitation in the avail-

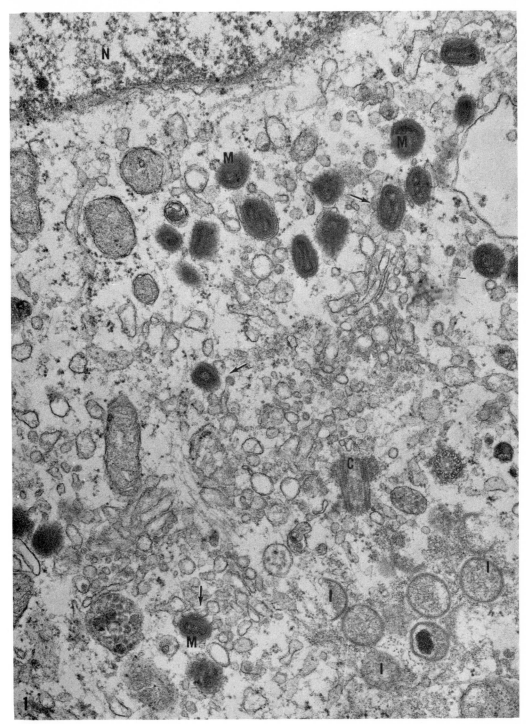

Figure 7.1. Portion of an L cell from a culture sampled 7 hours after inoculation with vaccinia virus as described in reference 7. In the centrosphere region are present centrioles (C) and a large number of Golgi vesicles. Several mature vaccinia (M) are enveloped by groups of vesicles continuous with those of the Golgi complex (*arrows*). I, immature vaccinia progeny; N, nucleus. ×40,000.

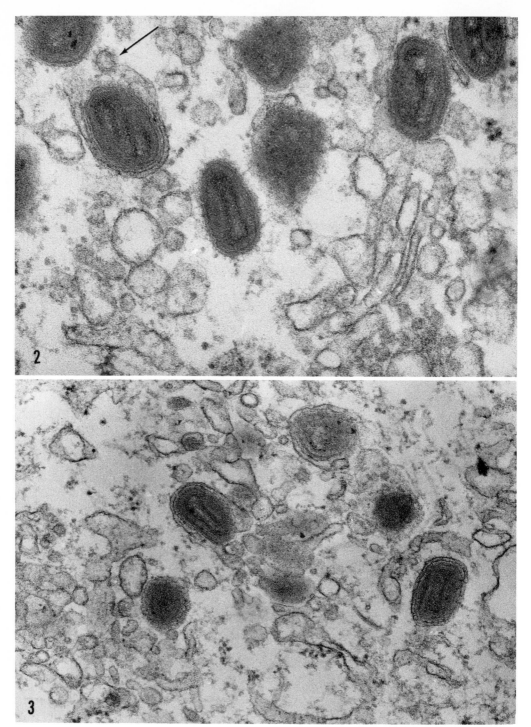

Figure 7.2. Selected region from Figure 7.1 shown at a higher magnification to illustrate the wrapping of mature vaccinia by host cell cisternae. Note the presence of a coated vesicle near one virus particle (*arrow*). ×92,000.

Figure 7.3. Another example, as in Figure 7.1, selected to illustrate the association between Golgi (?) cisternae and progeny particles. ×57,000.

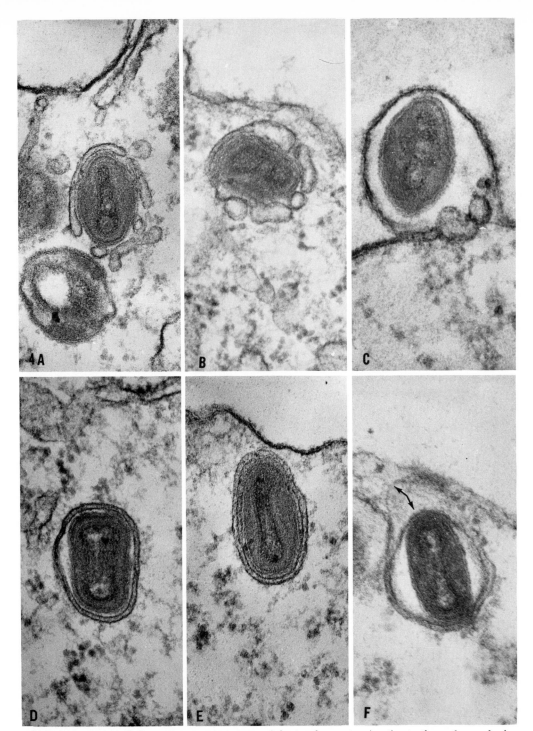

Figure 7.4. A through L, reconstructed sequence of the envelopment, migration to the surface and release through the plasma membrane of progeny vaccinia. The examples were selected from cells preserved 6 to 8 hours after infection. ×100,000.

A and B, envelopment by vesicles that have not fused into a continuous cisterna. B is near the cell surface; C, two small vesicles interposed between the plasma membrane and a single membrane surrounding the discharged virus particle; D, virus particle lying in the centrosphere region surrounded by a flattened cisterna; E, a vaccinia particle and enveloping by a cisterna is presumed to have migrated to the vicinity of the cell surface; F, separation of the inner and outer membranes of the enveloping cisterna in the vicinity of the plasma membrane (*arrows*).

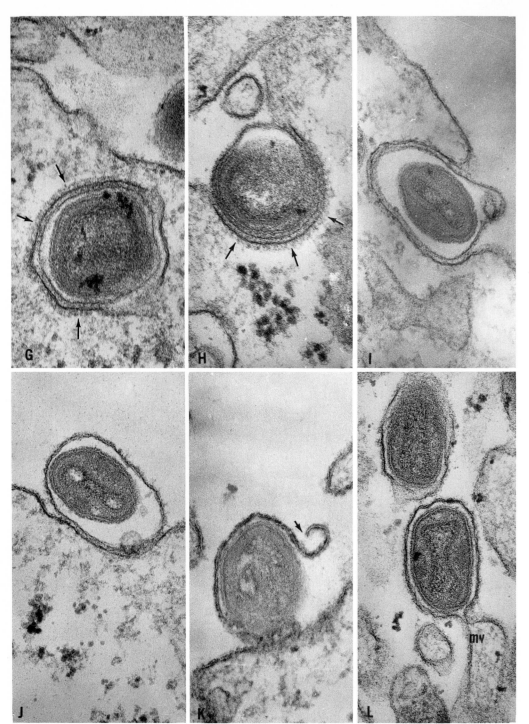

Figure 7.4. G, portion of the cisternal membrane facing the cytoplasmic matrix possesses a dense coat (*arrows*); H, vaccinia in the process of release at the cell surface. A single membrane, originating from the inner membrane of the enveloping cisterna, now surrounds the particle facing toward the cell exterior. The outer membrane of the cisterna in the interior of the cell possesses a dense coat (*arrows*); I and J, stages in the process of release at the cell surface, as in H; K, single membrane surrounding an extracellular vaccinia particle has become ruptured. Note the free end of the unit membrane clearly evident near the arrow.

ability of the smooth vesicles. However, other equally plausible ·explanations cannot be eliminated at this time.

SUMMARY

The envelopes of vaccinia and other poxviruses meet several of the criteria for cellular membranes. Chemically they are constituted from protein and lipid of which lecithin is the predominant phospholipid. Morphologically the envelopes possess a "unit" membrane structure, coated externally by a layer of uniform, dense spicules. The virus membranes are unique structures, assembled *de novo* within virus factories and discontinuous from any of the cellular membranes. Experiments using inhibitors of transcription and translation demonstrate that materials synthesized for the virus envelopes belong in the category of early functions.

Regarding the egress of the progeny, initially maturing or mature vaccinia of the strain employed in these studies migrate out of virus factories and become concentrated in the centrosphere region of the host cell. Individual particles become surrounded by vesicles apparently originating from the Golgi complex and these vesicles fuse with one another, investing each virus particle in double membrane sacs or cisternae. The complex of virus plus cisternae moves toward the cell membrane where the outer cisternal membrane appears to fuse with the cell membrane, creating a channel for the release of progeny vaccinia to the exterior.

Acknowledgment. I am grateful to Mr. Mark Mellinger for assistance.

REFERENCES

1. DALES, S. The uptake and development of vaccinia virus in strain L cells followed with labeled viral deoxyribonucleic acid. *J. Cell Biol. 18:* 51, 1963.
2. DALES, S. Replication of animal viruses as studied by electron microscopy. *Amer. J. Med. 38:* 699, 1965.
3. AVAKYAN, A. A., AND BYCKOVSKY, A. F. Ontogenesis of human smallpox virus. *J. Cell Biol. 24:* 337, 1965.
4. JOKLIK, W. K. The poxviruses. *Bact. Rev. 30:* 33, 1966.
5. WOODSON, B. Recent progress in poxvirus research. *Bact. Rev. 32:* 127, 1968.
6. KATES, J. R., AND MCAUSLAN, B. R. Poxvirus DNA-dependent RNA polymerase. *Proc. Nat. Acad. Sci. U.S.A. 58:* 134, 1967.
7. DALES, S., AND SIMINOVITCH, L. The development of vaccinia virus in strain L cells as examined by electron microscopy. *J. Biophys. Biochem. Cytol. 10:* 475, 1961.
8. DALES, S., AND MOSBACH, E. Vaccinia as a model for membrane biogenesis. *Virology 35:* 564, 1968.
9. PFEFFERKORN, E. R., AND HUNTER, H. S. The source of the ribonucleic acid and phospholipid of Sindbis virus. *Virology 20:* 446, 1963.
10. KATES, M., ALLISON, A. C., TYRELL, D. A. J., AND JAMES, A. T. Origin of lipids in influenza virus. *Sympos. Quant. Biol. 27:* 293, 1962.
11. COMPANS, R. W., HOLMES, K. V., DALES, S., AND CHOPPIN, P. W. An electron microscopic study of moderate and virulent virus-cell interactions of the parainfluenza virus SV5. *Virology 30:* 411, 1966.
12. CARTWRIGHT, B., AND PEARCE, C. A. Evidence for a host cell component in vesicular stomatitis virus. *J. Gen. Virol. 2:* 207, 1968.
13. LURIA, S. W. Genetics of bacteriophage. *Amer. Rev. Micribiol. 16:* 205, 1962.
14. ROSENKRANTZ, H. S., ROSE, H. M., MORGAN, C., AND HSU, K. C. The effect of hydroxyurea on virus development. *Virology 28:* 510, 1966.
15. EASTERBROOK, K. B. Conservation of vaccinial DNA during an abortive cycle of multiplication. *Virology 21:* 508, 1963.
16. KAJIOKA, R., SIMINOVITCH, L., AND DALES, S. The cycle of multiplication of vaccinia virus in Earle's strain L cells. *Virology 24:* 295, 1964.
17. POGO, B. G. T., AND DALES, S. Regulation of the synthesis of nucleotide phosphohydrolase and neutral DNAse: Two activities present within purified vaccinia virus. *Proc. Nat. Acad. Sci. U.S.A. 63:* 1297, 1969.
18. EASTERBROOK, K. B. Interference with the maturation of vaccinia virus by isatin-β-thiosemicarbazone. *Virology 17:* 245, 1962.
19. MOSS, B., ROSENBLUM, E. N., KATZ, E., AND GRIMLEY, P. M. Rifampicin: A specific inhibitor of vaccinia virus assembly. *Nature (London) 224:* 1280, 1969.
20. NAGAYAMA, A., POGO, B. G. T., AND DALES, S.

Biogenesis of vaccinia: Separation of early stages from maturation by means of rifampicin. *Virology 40:* 1039, 1970.

21. OHAD, I., SIEKEVITZ, P., AND PALADE, G. E. Bio- genesis of chloroplast membranes. II. Plastid differentiation during greening of a dark-grown algal mutant (*Chlamydomonas rein- hardi*). *J. Cell Biol. 35:* 553, 1967.

8

SOME PROPERTIES OF MEMBRANE GLYCOPROTEINS

V. T. Marchesi

Histochemical staining experiments provided the first clear indication that carbohydrate-containing macromolecules formed part of the surface membranes of animal cells (1). These studies were carried out by light microscopy, but more recent studies combining electron microscopy with specific staining methods have largely confirmed these results. Under appropriate conditions the outer surfaces of a variety of cell types can be stained by periodic acid-silver methenamine and this reaction is inhibited by specific glycosidases (2). Some cells have a visible surface coat which binds the stain, but in most cases (the red blood cell is one example), a distinct structure is not visible.

Other evidence that glycoproteins are present on cell surfaces has been obtained by studying the biological effects of treating cells with specific hydrolytic enzymes. For example, it has been shown that removal of sialic acid residues from the glycoproteins of tumor cell surfaces by neuraminidase alters the capacity of the cells to metastasize (3). In a similar kind of experiment Sanford (4) found that neuraminidase treatment of transplantable tumor cells altered their immunological reactivity.

The studies by Gesner and co-workers (5, 6) have provided further support for the idea that membrane glycoproteins are involved in cell recognition phenomena.

Laboratory of Experimental Pathology, National Institute of Arthritis and Metabolic Diseases, National Institutes of Health, Bethesda, Maryland 20014.

They have shown that the capacity of lymphocytes to "home" to lymphoid organs is modified if the glycoproteins of the surface of the lymphocytes are partially hydrolyzed either by proteases or specific glycosidases.

The role that carbohydrates play in determining the chemical specificity of cell surfaces is best documented in the case of the ABO and Lewis blood group antigens of human red cells (7). Other antigens on cell surfaces have carbohydrate determinants and recent studies also suggest that some of the histocompatibility antigens which are involved in homograft reactions may be glycoproteins (8).

On the basis of these and other studies it has been suggested that glycoproteins (and glycolipids) mediate the "social behavior" of mammalian cells. This hypothesis implies that contacts between cells are regulated in some way by macromolecules on their exposed surfaces, and the specificity of the reaction is determined by unique carbohydrate configurations.

CHEMISTRY OF MEMBRANE GLYCOPROTEINS

Glycoproteins are made up of sugars linked covalently to polypeptide chains. The sugars commonly found in glycoproteins of cell membranes are shown in Figure 8.1. Although there are only six individual residues, these can be linked in a variety of combinations. As a result an enormous number of unique chemical configurations are possible. The sugars are linked to each other by glycosidic bonds, and they can form oligosaccharide chains of varying length. The oligosaccharide chains are attached to the peptide portions of the glycoproteins *via* an amino sugar linkage to either threonine or serine or to asparagine (9). Sialic acids and fucose are usually attached to the outermost portions of the oligosaccharide chains.

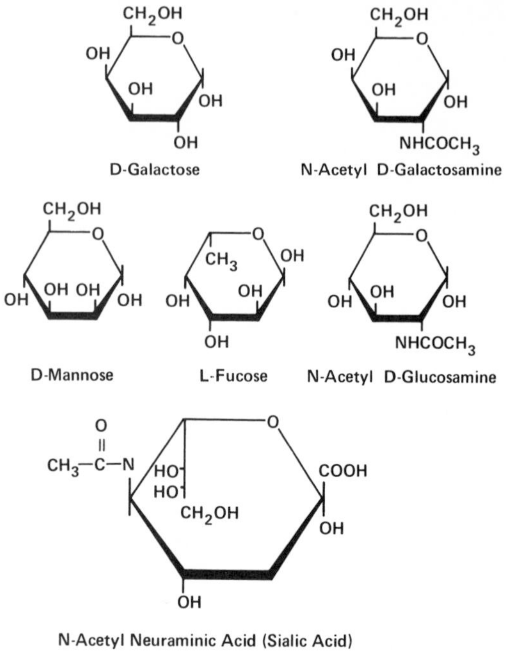

Up until recently little was known about the physical properties of the intact glycoproteins of membranes. This was due primarily to the lack of suitable methods for their isolation. A number of different approaches have been used to isolate glycoproteins from red cell membranes (10, 11), but the results have been contradictory and difficult to evaluate.

Recently we have developed a new method for extracting glycoproteins from membranes (12), and the results of this approach are summarized below.

RBC MEMBRANE GLYCOPROTEIN ISOLATED WITH LITHIUM DIIODOSALICYLATE (LIS)

Approximately 4 to 5% of the dry mass of human red blood cell membranes (equivalent to ~10% of the total membrane protein) is composed of a single type of glycoprotein which contains MN blood group activity and the receptor sites for influenza virus attachment and for phytohemagglutinin. This protein is tightly bound to the lipid components of the membrane and cannot be extracted from the membrane by the neutral salts and buffers commonly used for protein isolation. However, it was found that LIS in low concentrations (0.1–0.3 M) was remarkably effective in freeing the glycoprotein from the membrane (12). As a result of this treatment the glycoprotein could be purified and characterized by standard techniques.

This glycoprotein appears to have a monomeric molecular weight of ~125,000 as determined by its migration in acrylamide gels in the presence of sodium dodecyl sulfate (Fig. 8.2A). The purified pro-

Figure 8.1. Sugars found in membrane glycoproteins.

tein is soluble in water and in neutral salts, and has a $s_{20, w}$ of 7 (Fig. 8.2B). Approximately 60% of the mass of the glycoprotein is carbohydrate, and one-third of the carbohydrate is sialic acid residues.

Experiments on the effect of tryptic digestion of the isolated glycoprotein suggest that the molecule may be constructed as drawn in Figure 8.3. This is a loose interpretation of the data, but it is consistent with results obtained by proteolytic digestion of intact red cells (13). These latter studies indicate that most of the carbohydrate of the glycoprotein is located on the part of the molecule which extends outside of the cell.

The diagram in Figure 8.3 also shows a 15,000 molecular weight segment of the glycoprotein at one end of the molecule which has relatively few oligosaccharide chains. The coiled loops are supposed to indicate that this segment has a high content of non-polar, hydrophobic amino acids. A peptide with these properties

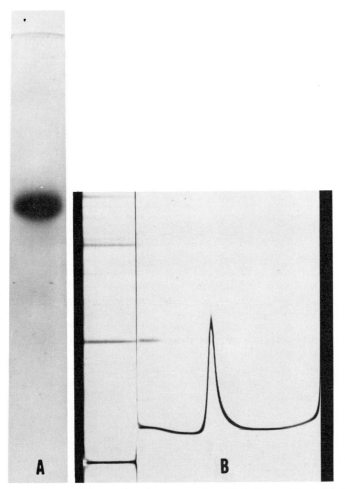

Figure 8.2A. Polyacrylamide gel electrophoresis pattern of purified glycoprotein isolated from human red blood cells. Sample run in 0.1% sodium dodecyl sulfate and 0.1 M PO_4, pH 7.0. Stained with periodic acid-Schiff.

Figure 8.2B. Ultracentrifugal pattern of purified membrane glycoprotein dissolved in 0.1 M NaCl and 0.05 M citrate buffer, pH 5.0.

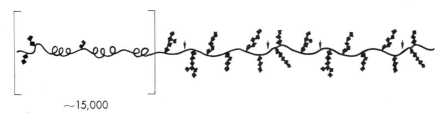

~15,000

Figure 8.3. A schematic representation of the isolated membrane glycoprotein.

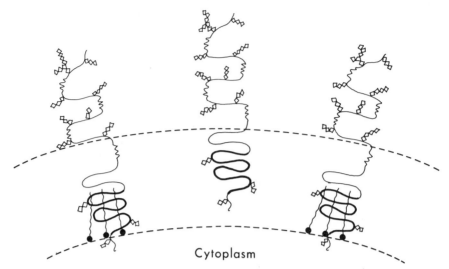

Cytoplasm

Figure 8.4. Glycoproteins may be arranged in the membrane as depicted in this drawing. This arrangement is consistent with the available experimental evidence but other interpretations are also possible.

which also has some tightly bound lipid has been isolated from the glycoprotein by trypsin treatment (14). It seems reasonable to suggest that this end of the molecule extends into the lipid portion of the membrane. A drawing of this possibility is shown in Figure 8.4. This model is similar to those proposed by previous workers (15, 11).

This diagram postulates that part of the glycoprotein extends into the interior of the membrane and interacts with the hydrocarbon chains of phospholipids. Electron micrographs of red cell membranes obtained by the usual thin sectioning techniques do not show any structures within the membrane which might correspond to these glycoprotein-lipid complexes. However, recent studies using the freeze-cleaving technique indicate that there are globular particles within the interior of the membrane (Fig. 8.5). The particles which measure ~75 to 85 Å were originally thought to be located on the surfaces of membranes (16), but more recent studies show that they are actually intramembranous structures (17, 18).

The chemical composition and functional properties of these particles are still unknown. Experiments now in prog-

ress (19) suggest the possibility that the globular particles might be formed by the glycoprotein-lipid complex described above. However, the evidence in support of this idea is circumstantial, and other interpretations must also be considered.

This discussion has focused almost entirely on the properties of the glycoproteins associated with the red cell membrane. This reflects the fact that this red cell glycoprotein is the only species of membrane glycoprotein which has been studied in any detail. Hopefully the methods used to study this glycoprotein and the concepts derived from its study will soon be applied to other cell types.

SUMMARY

Glycoproteins associated with the surface membranes of cells appear to play a major role in governing cell-cell interactions. The chemical and physical properties of these molecules are as yet largely unknown. The principal glycoprotein of the human red blood cell membrane has has recently been isolated and partially characterized, and the results are presented here.

We anticipate that the data and experience obtained from studies of red cell

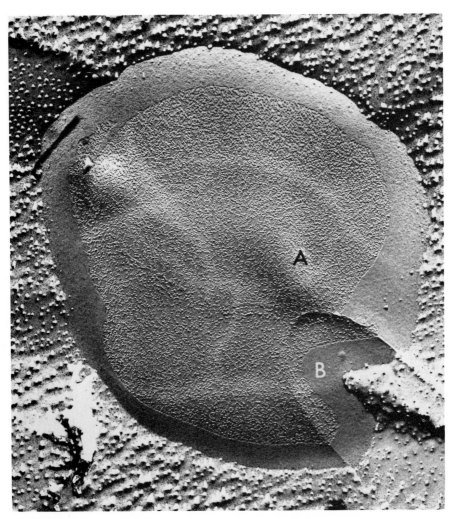

Figure 8.5. Electron micrograph of part of a red cell ghost membrane prepared by freeze-etching. Globular particles are present on the surface (A) exposed by cleavage but are not seen on the outside surface of the membrane which was exposed by etching (B). ×40,000.

membrane glycoproteins will be applicable to studies of cell membranes in general.

REFERENCES

1. GASIC, G., AND GASIC, T. Removal of PAS positive surface sugars in tumor cells by glycosidases. *Proc. Soc. Exp. Biol. Med. 114:* 660, 1963.

2. RAMBOURG, A., AND LEBLOND, C. P. Electron microscope observations on the carbohydrate-rich cell coat present at the surface of cells in the rat. *J. Cell Biol. 32:* 27, 1967.

3. GASIC, G., AND GASIC, T. Removal of sialic acid from the cell coat in tumor cells and vascular endothelium, and its effects on metastasis. *Proc. Nat. Acad. Sci. U.S.A. 48:* 1172, 1962.

4. SANFORD, B. H. An alteration in tumor histocompatibility induced by neuraminidase. *Transplantation 5:* 1273, 1967.

5. GESNER, B. M., AND GINSBURG, V. The effect of glycosidases on the fate of transfused lymphocytes. *Proc. Nat. Acad. Sci. U.S.A. 52:* 750, 1964.

6. WOODRUFF, J. J., AND GESNER, B. M. The effect of neuraminidase on the fate of transfused lymphocytes. *J. Exp. Med. 129:* 551, 1969.

7. MARCUS, D. M. The ABO and Lewis blood group system. Immunochemistry, genetics, and relation to human disease. *New Eng. J. Med. 280:* 994, 1969.

8. MURAMATSU, T., AND NATHENSON, S. G. Isolation of a chromatographically unique glycopeptide from murine histocompatibility-2 (H-2) membrane alloantigens labeled with H³-fucose or H³-glucosamine. *Biochem. Biophys. Res. Commun. 38:* 1, 1970.

9. GINSBURG, V., AND NEUFELD, E. F. Complex heterosaccharides of animals. *Ann. Rev. Biochem. 38:* 371, 1969.

10. MADDY, A. H. The solubilization of the protein of the ox erythrocyte ghost. *Biochim. Biophys. Acta 88:* 448, 1964.

11. WINZLER, R. J. A glycoprotein in human erythrocyte membranes. In *Red Cell Membrane,* edited by Jamieson, G. A., and Greenwalt, T. J., p. 157. Philadelphia, J. B. Lippincott Co., 1969.

12. MARCHESI, V. T., AND ANDREWS, E. M. The use of lithium diiodosalicylate (LIS) to extract glycoproteins from cell membranes, in preparation.

13. WINZLER, R. J., HARRIS, E. D., PEKAS, D. J., JOHNSON, C. A., AND WEBER, P. Studies on glycopeptides released by trypsin from intact human erythrocytes. *Biochemistry (Wash.) 6:* 2195, 1967.

14. MARCHESI, V. T. Isolation and characterization of a sialic acid containing glycoprotein from red cell membranes (abstr.). *Fed. Proc. 29:* 600, 1970.

15. MORAWIECKI, A. Dissociation of M and N-group glycoproteins into subunits in detergent solutions. *Biochim. Biophys. Acta 83:* 339, 1964.

16. WEINSTEIN, R. S. Electron microscopy of surfaces of red cell membranes. In *Red Cell Membrane,* edited by Jamieson, G. A., and Greenwalt, T. J., p. 36. Philadelphia, J. B. Lippincott Co., 1969.

17. PINTO DA SILVA, P., AND BRANTON, D. Membrane splitting in freeze-etching. Covalently bound ferritin as a membrane marker. *J. Cell Biol. 45:* 598, 1970.

18. TILLACK, T. W., AND MARCHESI, V. T. Demonstration of the outer surface of freeze-etched red blood cell membranes. *J. Cell Biol. 45:* 649, 1970.

19. TILLACK, T. W., SCOTT, R. E., AND MARCHESI, V. T. Cell-membrane ultrastructure studied by freeze-etching (abstr.). *Fed. Proc. 20:* 489, 1970.

EXPERIMENTAL MODIFICATION OF MITOCHONDRIAL BIOGENESIS IN RAT LIVER CELLS

D. G. Scarpelli, M. Chiga, and E. Haynes

Since the initial demonstration of mitochondria by Altmann in 1890 (1), questions concerning their origin, biogenesis, and function have continued to occupy the attention of biologists (2–8). Recently rapid advances have been made along these lines, and it is now clearly established that mitochondria arise from pre-existing ones (9–11), that they contain systems capable of protein synthesis which differ from those in the cytoplasm (12–17), that they contain genetic information which is distinct from that contained in the nucleus (18–22), and finally, that they contain DNA polymerase (23) capable of replicating information in the DNA. These developments have greatly increased interest in the role of these organelles in cell function and their possible role in cytoplasmic inheritance (4, 5). Much of our knowledge relating to mitochondrial membrane synthesis and assembly has come from intensive studies involving metabolic manipulation of yeast (24–26). Yeast cells are excellent models for the investigation of mitochondriogenesis because as facultative anaerobes they respond to anoxia by repression of mitochondrial biogenesis and depletion of their mitochondrial population which are reversed when aerobic conditions are re-established. Although, mitochondrial growth and population in mammalian cells are not as readily subject to experimental manipulation, depletion of such mitochondria as a consequence of prolonged inanition and their restitution by refeeding has been known for many years (27–30). The present chapter deals with such experiments on liver cells, and of various alterations of mitochondrial structure and function induced *in vivo*.

THE EXPERIMENTAL MODEL AND METABOLIC INHIBITORS

Sprague-Dawley male rats weighing 220 to 250 g were deprived of all food and allowed water *ad libitum* for 7 days and subsequently refed by pair feeding for 3 days. This leads first to a quantitative depletion of hepatic mitochondria followed by their return to normal levels. Since the nuclear DNA content of hepatocytes remains constant throughout the period of starving and refeeding, it serves as an excellent reference against which to measure alterations of mitochondrial population in these cells. The mitochondriogenesis which occurs during refeeding provides an excellent system for the *in vivo* study of the various synthetic systems involved. The effects of selective metabolic inhibitors for DNA biosynthesis, and cytoplasmic and mito-

Department of Pathology and Oncology, University of Kansas Medical Center, Kansas City, Kansas 66103.

Supported in part by a grant from Human Growth Incorporated.

chondrial protein synthesis were studied by refeeding Purina chow pellets supplemented with the appropriate drug, or by daily intraperitoneal injection of the drug during the period of refeeding. The following drugs were administered, 1.5 to 2.0% chloramphenicol added to the diet; erythromycin injected at a dosage of 200 mg/kg body weight; cycloheximide injected at a dosage of 1 to 1.5 mg/kg body weight; hydroxyurea injected every 6 hours at a dosage of 500 mg/kg body weight for a total of 24 hours; and acriflavin injected either intraperitoneally or into the tail vein at a dose level of 5 μg/kg body weight.

ISOLATION OF MITOCHONDRIA

Rat liver was homogenized in cold 0.44 M mannitol by 60 strokes with a Potter-Elvehjem homogenizer in which the pestle was rotated at a speed of 650 rpm. The homogenate was centrifuged at $750 \times g$ for 10 minutes. The nuclear fraction was resuspended, washed twice and the supernatant combined with the mitochondrial fraction. It was found that this maneuver increased the mitochondrial yield by 10 to 15%. The mitochondrial suspension was then centrifuged at $8400 \times g$ for 15 minutes, resuspended and washed twice. Although electron micrographs of the mitochondrial pellets showed a high degree of purity, the presence of occasional vesicles of endoplasmic reticulum were quite disturbing since this could lead to considerable errors in counting (Fig. 9.1). This is due to the inability of the electronic counter to discriminate between particles representing mitochondria and those due to vesicles of endoplasmic reticulum, which have undergone osmotic swelling and thus approach the size of mitochondria. In an effort to determine the degree of contamination by endoplasmic reticulum, the activity of glucose-6-phosphatase, a marker enzyme for endoplasmic reticulum was determined for the fractions at each of the steps during centrifugation. It was found

that contamination by endoplasmic reticulum was about 10% for fed animals and 6% for starved ones and that this degree of contamination was quite reproducible from one experiment to another. A typical experiment on microsomal contamination is shown in Figure 9.2. The magnitude of counting errors caused by microsomal contamination of the mitochondrial fraction was determined by counting a 10% microsomal suspension in a Celloscope III (Particle Data Inc., Elmhurst, Ill.) particle counter under conditions identical for mitochondrial counting. The mean value obtained from 10 such experiments was applied as a correction factor by subtracting it from the uncorrected mitochondrial counts.

QUANTITATIVE AND SEMIQUANTITATIVE ANALYSIS OF MITOCHONDRIAL POPULATION CHANGES DURING INANITION AND REFEEDING

Methods employed for the measurement of mitochondrial populations included not only counting of isolated organelles by means of an electronic particle counter but also by quantitative electron microscopy of mitochondria in thin sections, and by assay of the activity of succinoxidase, a marker multienzyme system localized on the inner membrane of mitochondria.

Electronic Particle Counting

Since quantitation of mitochondria by electronic particle counters is limited by the inability of these instruments to accurately count particles smaller than 0.15 μ^3 (31), results obtained by this method must be regarded as semiquantitative estimations rather than true quantitative ones. An additional potential error posed by the present experimental model was that of a possible diminution in size of mitochondria as a consequence of inanition so that many of them would be smaller than 0.15 μ^3, not counted by the instrument and thus lead to the erroneous

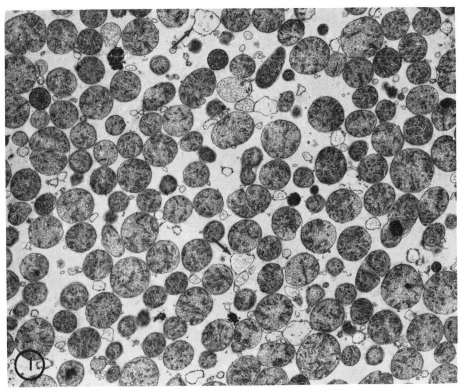

Figure 9.1. Mitochondria isolated in 0.44 M mannitol. Note the contamination by vesicles of endoplasmic reticulum some of which have swollen to a size comparable to mitochondria. ×7,600.

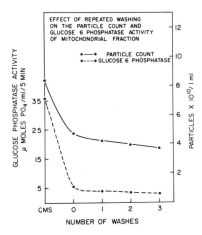

Figure 9.2. The relation between the electronic particle count of the mitochondrial fraction and the activity of glucose-6-phosphatase as a function of the number of washes.

conclusion that the mitochondrial population had decreased in number. Careful size measurements of 500 mitochondria isolated from livers of normal rats and those starved for 7 days showed that mitochondria became significantly larger during prolonged starvation, as is shown in Figure 9.3, thus indicating that the decreased mitochondrial population data obtained from the livers of starved rats by particle counting was not in error due to a change of mitochondrial size.

Although the mechanism of mitochondrial enlargement in starvation has not been critically studied, it is probably largely the result of swelling. This conclusion is supported by electron micrographic evidence of mitochondrial swelling and more rarely what may be interpreted

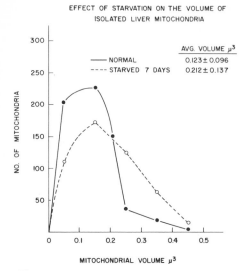

EFFECT OF STARVATION ON THE VOLUME OF
ISOLATED LIVER MITOCHONDRIA

	AVG. VOLUME μ^3
—— NORMAL	0.123 ± 0.096
---- STARVED 7 DAYS	0.212 ± 0.137

Figure 9.3. The volume of hepatic mitochondria isolated from normal rats and those starved for 7 days as determined by measurement of 500 mitochondrial profiles from electron micrographs from each group of animals.

as fusion of several organelles in hepatocytes following starvation. Counts accomplished by electronic particle counters of mitochondria isolated from the whole liver of normal, starved, and refed animals are shown in Table 9.1.

Quantitative Electron Microscopy

Quantitative estimation of mitochondria by means of lineal analysis of electron micrographs was undertaken to ascertain the degree of error imposed by the sensing limitations of the electronic particle counter. This consisted of the technique described by Loud and his co-workers (32) which is based on the principle that the fractional volume V_{vc} of a given cytoplasmic component c in a cell can be estimated by measuring the fractional area A_{ac} of a random section containing transections of c according to the following relation:

$$V_{vc} = A_{ac}.$$

Results obtained by this technique were recently shown by Weibel *et al.* (33) to correspond well with data obtained by a

more elaborate morphometric method. Results of the present study are summarized in Table 9.2. A comparison of these results with those obtained with the electronic counter shows a surprising degree of agreement, and indicates that although absolute counts are not possible, a comparison of relative counts obtained by elec-

TABLE 9.1

Semiquantitative Analysis by Electronic Particle Counter of Mitochondrial Population Following Inanition and Refeeding

Counting accomplished with Celloscope III using a 12-μ aperture. Instrument calibrated with 1.099-μ diameter polystyrene latex spheres (The Dow Chemical Company) to give a value of 0.01 μ^3/ threshold division. The counting solution consisted of 0.25 M mannitol containing 0.45% KCl.

Group	Ratio of Mit (>0.15 μ^3 $\times$ 10^{10}) to mg N-DNA (±S.E.)*	P Value	N-DNA
			mg
Normal†	6.35 ± 0.56		18.8
7 day starved	3.20 ± 0.35	< .001	19.2
3 day refed	3.62 ± 0.23	< .005	19.1
5 day refed	5.10 ± 0.29	> .05	20.1
9 day refed	5.81 ± 0.32	> .05	19.8

* Mit, mitochondrial population; N-DNA, nuclear DNA.

† Represents 12 animals, all other groups 8 animals each.

TABLE 9.2

Lineal Morphometric Analysis of Liver Mitochondria During Starvation and Refeeding

Magnification of electron micrographs was $\times 15,000$. Central cross-section profiles of 50 individual hepatocytes measured in each group.

Group	Ratio of Mit to μ^3 of Cytoplasm (±S.E.)*	Average Cytoplasmic Volume	Average Mit/Cell
	μ^3		
Normal	0.292 ± 0.119	4790	1398
Starved 7 days	0.268 ± 0.151	2877	771
Refed 9 days	0.288 ± 0.138	4821	1388

* Mit, mitochondrial number.

tronic counting can be used for the semi-quantitative estimation of mitochondrial populations.

Succinoxidase Activity

Succinoxidase activity of rat liver decreased following starvation and returned to normal levels upon refeeding. The results are shown in Table 9.3. Although there is an acceptable agreement between the mitochondrial population values obtained by the various techniques of measurement (Table 9.4), a precise quantitative relationship between succinoxidase activity and the number of mitochondria remains to be established by concomitant morphometric and biochemical studies on the same tissue as done recently for NADPH cytochrome c reductase and endoplasmic reticulum by Stäubli et al. (34).

MITOCHONDRIAL DNA (M-DNA) AND PROTEIN SYNTHESIS DURING STARVATION AND REFEEDING

In view of the marked decrease of hepatic mitochondrial population following starvation and its return to normal levels upon refeeding, studies on the synthesis of mitochondrial DNA and protein were undertaken to determine the rapidity and extent to which these metabolic events were modified by these various experimental conditions. Data on the incorporation of tritiated thymidine into M-DNA (Table 9.5) clearly showed that 1 day of refeed-

TABLE 9.4

Comparison of Semiquantitative Estimation of Mitochondrial Population Changes during Inanition

Method	Decrease
	$\%$
Particle counter	49.7
Lineal morphometry	44.9
Succinoxidase assay	44.2

TABLE 9.5

Incorporation of ^{3}H Thymidine into Mitochondrial DNA in Starved and Refed Rat Liver Mitochondria

^{3}H-thymidine (100 μC) injected intraperitoneally. Animals were sacrificed 12 hours later and M-DNA isolated from DNAase-treated mitochondria solubilized in 1% sodium dodecyl sulfate, incubated in pronase, and extracted with phenol. Purity of M-DNA checked by its buoyant density in cesium chloride.

Experiment	Specific Activity
	$dpm/\mu g$ M-DNA
Starved 7 days	294
Refed 1 day	1603
Refed 2 days	1051
Refed 3 days	1008

ing led to approximately a 5-fold increase in the rate of thymidine incorporation which decreased substantially by the 3rd day of refeeding. The pattern of leucine incorporation (Table 9.6) was comparable to

TABLE 9.3

Succinoxidase Activity of Liver Homogenates following Starvation and Refeeding

Oxygen consumption was recorded by an Oxygraph, model K (Gilson Medical Electronics). The reaction mixture consisted of 1.5 ml of 10 mM Tris–phosphate buffer, pH 7.4. After reaching equilibrium 0.5 ml of liver homogenate (filtered through a double layer of gauze) was added, followed by 0.1 ml of 0.1 M sodium succinate.

Group	O_2 Consumption ($\pm$S.E.)	P	O_2 Consumption ($\pm$S.E.)	P
	$\mu l/min/g$		$\mu l/min/liver$	
Normal	3.09 ± 0.54		40.77 ± 9.7	
Starved 7 days	5.11 ± 0.81	$< .001$	26.83 ± 7.1	$< .001$
Refed 6 days	4.12 ± 0.61	$< .001$	41.22 ± 7.7	$> .09$

CELL MEMBRANES

TABLE 9.6

Incorporation of ³H-Leucine into Mitochondrial
Proteins of Rat Liver following
Starvation and Refeeding

³H-leucine (100 µC) injected intraperitoneally.
Animals were sacrificed 12 hours later.

Experiment	Specific Activity
	*dpm/mg Mit protein**
Starved 7 days	282
Refed 1 day	1480
Refed 2 days	1263
Refed 3 days	1190

* Mit, mitochondria.

that of thymidine suggesting a parallel
stimulation of mitochondrial DNA and protein synthesis by refeeding. This is not un-
expected since chemical, autoradiographic,
and morphological data indicate that new
mitochondria are formed from pre-existing
ones and separate from them as completely
assembled organelles.

THE EFFECT OF METABOLIC INHIBITORS

Although manipulation of mitochondrial biosynthesis has been accomplished
in a variety of cell systems by the use of

various metabolic inhibitors, there are no
studies correlating the effect of inhibitors
with quantitative alterations of the mitochondrial population in cells.

Alterations of Mitochondrial Population and Structure

Chloramphenicol, erythromycin, cycloheximide, hydroxyurea, and acriflavin inhibited the restitution of mitochondria
when they were administered during refeeding; results are shown in Table 9.7.
Chloramphenicol and acriflavin were most
effective by refeeding. Since numerous
studies have established that the biogenesis of mitochondria depends on synthetic
events occurring in the endoplasmic reticulum as well as in the mitochondrion (15,
16, 26), it seemed important to determine
what effect starvation, refeeding, and refeeding in the presence of certain inhibitors
had on the structural integrity of hepatic
polyribosomes. Seven days of starvation led
to a decrease of the larger polyribosome
aggregates (Fig. 9.4B). These were reconstituted after 3 days of refeeding (Fig.
9.5A). It is of interest to note that the reconstitution of normal polyribosome patterns was not inhibited by either acriflavin
(Fig. 9.5B) or chloramphenicol (Fig. 9.6)

TABLE 9.7

Effect of Various Inhibitors on Mitochondrial Restitution following 3 days of Refeeding*

Inhibitor	Ratio of Mit ($>0.15~\mu^3 \times 10^{10}$) to mg N-DNA ($\pm$S.E.)†	P Value	Ratio of Mit Protein to mg N-DNA	P Value
Chloramphenicol (2% in diet)	2.35 ± 0.24	$>.005$	3.00	$<.001$
Erythromycin (200 mg/kg $\times$ 3)	2.66 ± 0.38	$>.025$	3.72	$<.005$
Cycloheximide (1.5 mg/kg $\times$ 3)	2.64 ± 0.21	$>.025$	3.85	$<.005$
Hydroxyurea (500 mg/kg $\times$ 4)	2.81 ± 0.33	$>.025$	4.11	$<.025$
Acriflavin (5 µg/kg i.v. $\times$ 3)	2.49 ± 0.38	$>.025$	3.36	$<.005$
3 day refed controls	3.62 ± 0.23		6.30	

* Each experimental group consisted of 5 animals; control group 12 animals.
† Mit, mitochondrial population; N-DNA, nuclear DNA.

administered during refeeding. This indicates that the inhibitory effect of these substances on mitochondriogenesis is not due to a structural disorganization of cytoplasmic protein synthetic systems.

Ultrastructural studies of livers from animals refed for 3 days on a diet containing 1.5% chloramphenicol showed that such treatment led to the formation of morphologically abnormal mitochondria. These were characterized by single (Fig. 9.7A) or multiple saccular extensions of the outer membrane (Fig. 9.7B), which were not accompanied by any structural abnormalities of the inner membrane. Although these were present in small numbers in any given hepatocyte, they were encountered in all hepatocytes of chloramphenicol refed animals, regardless of whether the tissue was fixed in osmium alone, or in glutaraldehyde followed by osmium. This coupled with the fact that such organelles were not encountered in hepatocytes of non-treated

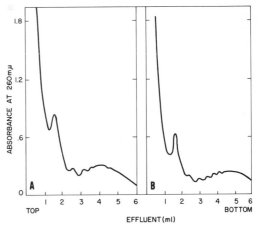

Figure 9.5A. The ribosomal-polysomal profile is reconstituted as soon as 24 hours after refeeding. The profile shown here is from an animal after 3 days of refeeding.

Figure 9.5B. The ribosomal-polysomal profile from an animal injected daily intravenously with acriflavin 7.5 μg/g body weight during refeeding. The profile has been reconstituted to the normal pattern.

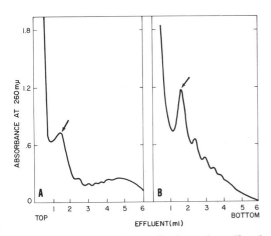

Figure 9.4A. The ribosomal-polysomal profile of the postmitochondrial fraction from the liver of a normal fed rat. The initial peak (*arrow*) is due to single ribosomes, subsequent peaks are due to the other various ribosomal aggregates (polysomes).

Figure 9.4B. The ribosomal-polysomal profile isolated from the liver of a rat starved for 7 days. Note the sharp increase in the peak due to single ribosomes (*arrow*) and the gross alteration of the curve characteristic of polysomal aggregates. This is due to the dissociation of these aggregates.

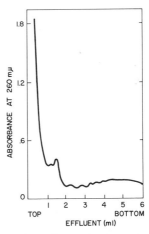

Figure 9.6. The ribosomal-polysomal profile from an animal *refed* on a diet containing 1.5% chloramphenicol. It has been reconstituted to the normal pattern by refeeding despite the presence of chloramphenicol in the diet.

refed animals and were not seen following cycloheximide administration led us to conclude that they were in some way related to chloramphenicol treatment. The saccular extensions were interpreted as redun-

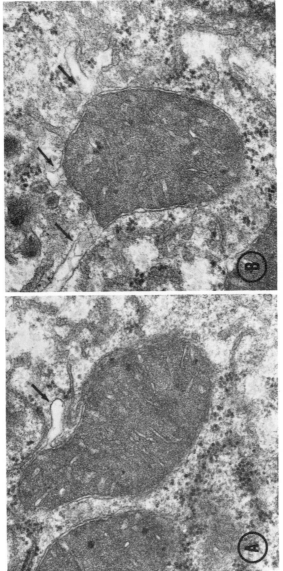

Figure 9.7A. A hepatic mitochondrion from a rat refed on a diet containing 1.5% chloramphenicol. The arrow points to a saccular extension of the outer membrane which is interpreted as redundant membrane. ×34,000. (From Coggi, G., and Scarpelli, D.G., *Proc. Soc. Exp. Biol. Med. 134:* 328, 1970 (35).)
Figure 9.7B. A hepatic mitochondrion from an animal treated in an identical fashion. The arrows point to multiple extensions of the outer membrane. ×31,000.

dant outer membrane, due possibly to lesser growth of the inner membrane as compared to the outer one as a consequence of antibiotic treatment. In an effort to determine whether this was the mechanism responsible for the morphologically abnormal mitochondria, the incorporation of labeled leucine into the various membranes, and matrical fraction of mitochondria in normal, chloramphenicol-, and cycloheximide-treated refed animals was studied. The results are shown in Table 9.8.

ALTERATIONS OF MITOCHONDRIAL BIOGENESIS INDUCED BY THYROIDECTOMY AND RIBOFLAVIN DEFICIENCY

Thyroidectomy

In a series of systematic studies, Tata and his co-workers (36) have firmly established that thyroid hormones increased the formation of mitochondrial respiratory enzymes. Furthermore, since thyroid hormone also stimulated incorporation of amino acid by mitochondria it was tempting to suggest that mitochondrial biogenesis was enhanced. However, there was no evidence that these biochemical events were accompanied by an increase in the number of mitochondria. In an effort to extend our

study we investigated the effect of thyroidectomy and subsequent administration of triiodothyronine on the population of hepatic mitochondria. The results of such a study are shown in Table 9.9. Thyroidectomy led to a significant decrease in the number of hepatic mitochondria as compared to normal. The population was lowered further by starvation and returned to the level normal for thyroidectomized animals by refeeding. After 3 days of refeeding the cytoplasm of hepatocytes from thyroidectomized rats contained few mitochondria and an occasional array of rough surfaced endoplasmic reticulum (Fig. 9.8). A single dose of triiodothyronine caused a marked acceleration of mitochondrial restitution after only 3 days of refeeding to a level almost approaching normal. Hepatocytes from similar animals that had received a single dose of triiodothyronine on the 1st day of refeeding contained numerous mitochondria and arrays of endoplasmic reticulum (Fig. 9.9). On the other hand, three doses of hormone administered daily during refeeding totally inhibited the increase of mitochondria characteristic of refeeding. The inhibition of mitochondrial protein synthesis by excess levels of triiodothyronine shown in Table 9.10 indicates that the failure of mitochondrial restitution in hyperthyroidism is probably due to an interruption of their biogenesis.

TABLE 9.8

Incorporation of ^{3}H-Leucine into Various Mitochondrial Fractions in Refed Rats[*]

Fractionation of mitochondria was accomplished by the method of Sottocasa *et al.* (*J. Cell Biol. 32:* 415, 1967). Purity of the outer and inner membrane fractions was ascertained by spectrophotometric assays of monoamine oxidase, and β-hydroxybutyric, and succinic dehydrogenases. Matrical protein was isolated by sonication of the inner membrane fraction (Branson sonifier 110 seconds, at 100 W followed by centrifugation at $120,000 \times g$ for 45 minutes).

Experiment	Radioactivity of Mitochondrial Fractions CPM/mg Protein $\pm$ S.E.		
	Outer membrane	Inner membrane	Matrical proteins
Refed 3 days	1983 $\pm$ 40	1970 $\pm$ 182	1452 $\pm$ 153
Same + cycloheximide	1323 $\pm$ 111	1964 $\pm$ 52	1075 $\pm$ 166
Same + chloramphenicol	1286 $\pm$ 207	989 $\pm$ 59	922 $\pm$ 46

* (From Coggi, G., and Scarpelli, D. G., *Proc. Soc. Exp. Biol. Med. 134:* 328, 1970 (35).)

TABLE 9.9

Effect of 3,5,3'-Triiodothyronine (T_3) on the Mitochondrial Population of Liver
in Thyroidectomized Rats following Inanition and Refeeding

Triiodothyronine (T_3), 25 μg/100 g body weight, was injected intraperitoneally from the 1st day of refeeding, animals sacrificed 48 hours after the last injection.

Experiment*	Ratio of Mit ($>0.15 \mu^3 \times 10^{10}$) to mg N-DNA ($\pm$S.E.)†	P Value
Normal control	6.22 ± 0.61	
Thyroidectomized (6 weeks)	4.16 ± 0.38	< .005
Thyroidectomized, starved 7 days (7/0)	2.66 ± 0.35	< .001
Thyroidectomized, refed 3 days (7/3)‡	3.80 ± 0.33	< .005
Thyroidectomized, refed 9 days (7/9)	4.19 ± 0.43	< .005
Thyroidectomized (7/3) + 25 μg T_3 × 1§	5.13 ± 0.55	> .05
Thyroidectomized (7/3) + 300 μg T_3 × 3¶	2.71 ± 0.49	< .001

* Each experimental group consists of five animals.
† Mit, mitochondrial population; N-DNA, nuclear DNA.
‡ Basal metabolic rate = 0.88 ml of O_2/hr/g.
§ Basal metabolic rate = 1.30 ml of O_2/hr/g.
¶ Basal metabolic rate = 2.48 ml of O_2/hr/g.

Riboflavin Deficiency

Riboflavin is an important component of the flavoprotein enzymes, members of which are responsible for the bulk of electron transport in mitochondria and the endoplasmic reticulum (37,38). Riboflavin deficiency is known to lead to a variety of morphological and functional alterations of mitochondria notable among which are gigantism (39), depressed oxygen consumption and oxidative phosphorylation, and a marked reduction of succinic dehydrogenase and NADPH levels (40). Recovery from riboflavin deficiency (41) is characterized by a return of mitochondria to normal size and the appearance of mitochondria with transverse membranous partitions which often constricted the organelle in a fashion reminiscent of the budding seen in yeast and other microorganisms during their division. These findings suggest that recovery from riboflavin deficiency is accompanied by the synthesis of new organelles.

The results of electronic particle counting of mitochondria isolated from the whole livers of riboflavin-deficient and riboflavin-treated rats are shown in Table 9.11. Riboflavin deficiency caused a marked decrease in the mitochondrial population which was reversed rapidly by the administration of riboflavin. Hepatocytes of riboflavin-deficient rats contained moderately enlarged polymorphous mitochondria, large aggregates of smooth surfaced endoplasmic reticulum, and an occasional array of the rough surfaced variety (Fig. 9.10). Twenty-four hours following a single dose of riboflavin the cytoplasm contained more normal appearing mitochondria and rough surfaced endoplasmic reticulum (Fig. 9.11). Forty-eight hours following the daily intraperitoneal administration of riboflavin the cytoplasm contained numerous normal appearing mitochondria and arrays of rough surfaced endoplasmic reticulum (Fig. 9.12). Some of the mitochondria contained transverse membranous partitions with localized constriction of the mitochondrial body (Figs. 9.13 and 9.14).

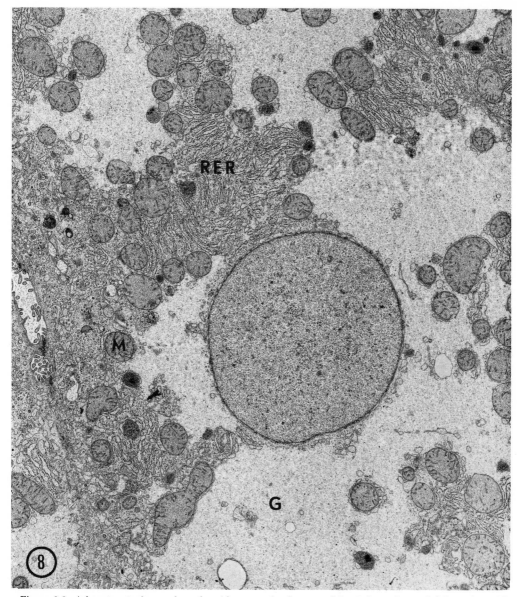

Figure 9.8. A hepatocyte from a hypothyroid rat previously starved for 7 days, then refed for 3 days. The cytoplasm contains several patches of rough surfaced endoplasmic reticulum (RER), mitochondria (M), and large amounts of glycogen (G). ×7,000.

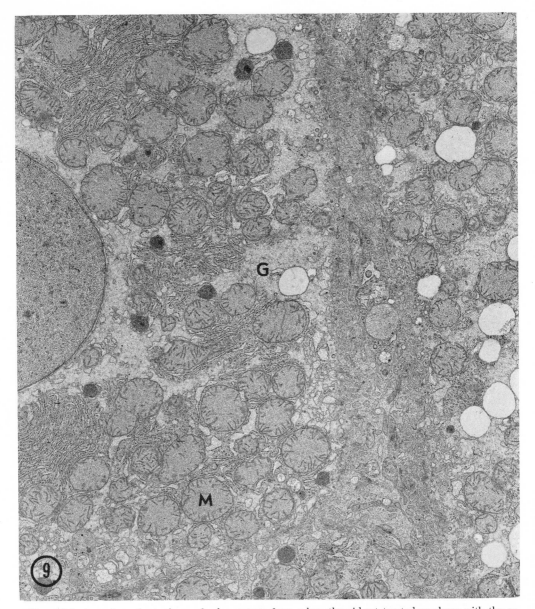

Figure 9.9. A portion of cytoplasm of a hepatocyte from a hypothyroid rat treated as above with the exception that 3,5,3'-triiodothyronine, 25 µg/100 g body weight was injected intraperitoneally at the time of refeeding and sacrificed 3 days later. The cytoplasm is filled with numerous mitochondria (M) which appear somewhat swollen. Small amounts of glycogen (G) are visible in the ground cytoplasm. ×7,400.

TABLE 9.10

Effect of 3,5,3′-Triiodothyronine on ^{3}H-Leucine Incorporation into Protein of Outer and Inner Mitochondrial Membranes

Fractionation of mitochondrial membranes was accomplished by the method of Sottocasa et al. (J. Cell Biol. 32: 415, 1967).

Experiment	Radioactivity of Mitochondrial Fractions ($\pm$S.E.)	
	Outer membrane	Inner membrane
	cpm/mg protein	
Normal control	1899 $\pm$ 72	1912 $\pm$ 103
Hypothyroidism (8 weeks)	1023 $\pm$ 111	979′ $\pm$ 88
Hyperthyroidism (T_3, 300 μg/100 g body weight daily $\times$ 4)*	799 $\pm$ 68	863 $\pm$ 52

* Basal metabolic rate = 2.59 ml of O_2/hr/g.

NON-ENZYMATIC "STRUCTURAL PROTEINS" OF INNER MEMBRANE OF RAT LIVER MITOCHONDRIA DURING VARIOUS EXPERIMENTAL STATES

Preliminary experiments were undertaken to determine whether mitochondrial inner membrane was altered by the various experimental manipulations described in the previous sections of this chapter. This was approached by a study of the heterogeneous proteins of the mitochondrion

which are insoluble at physiological pH, are devoid of enzymatic activity, and are termed "structural proteins" (42). These proteins were isolated from inner membrane of rat liver mitochondria by the method of Richardson et al. (43). The proteins were resolved by discontinuous electrophoresis in acrylamide gel according to the method of Lesjek and Lusena (44).

Inner membrane "structural protein" was resolved into five separate bands (Fig. 9.15). These bands remained unchanged in mitochondria isolated from hypothyroid rats and in animals subsequently treated with triiodothyronine. On the other hand, riboflavin deficiency of 4-weeks' duration resulted in a decrease of the resolvable bands to three with deletion of bands 2 and 4. Forty-eight hours after the intraperitoneal injection of riboflavin band 2 was again present with a suggestion of the return of band 4.

DISCUSSION

It is of historical interest to note that in his classical treatise on mitochondria, Altmann (1) considered the problem of their nature and formation. Although these considerations were purely speculative, they have proven to be surprisingly close to the current view based on an ever growing number of investigations in this area.

The early literature on these organelles contains many reports of experiments on their qualitative and quantitative altera-

TABLE 9.11

Mitochondrial Population of Rat Liver during Riboflavin Deficiency and Subsequent Recovery

Riboflavin, 1 mg/100 g body weight, was injected intraperitoneally daily.

Experiment*	Ratio of Mit (>0.15 μ^3 $\times$ 10^{10}) to mg N-DNA ($\pm$S.E.)†	P Value
Normal control	6.08 $\pm$ 0.61	
Riboflavin deficiency (3 weeks)	2.88 $\pm$ 0.32	$< .001$
Riboflavin deficiency (6 weeks) + riboflavin 48 hours	4.02 $\pm$ 0.39	$> .005$
Riboflavin deficiency (6 weeks) + riboflavin 72 hours	5.37 $\pm$ 0.58	$> .05$

* Each experimental group consists of five animals.

† Mit, mitochondrial population; N-DNA, nuclear DNA.

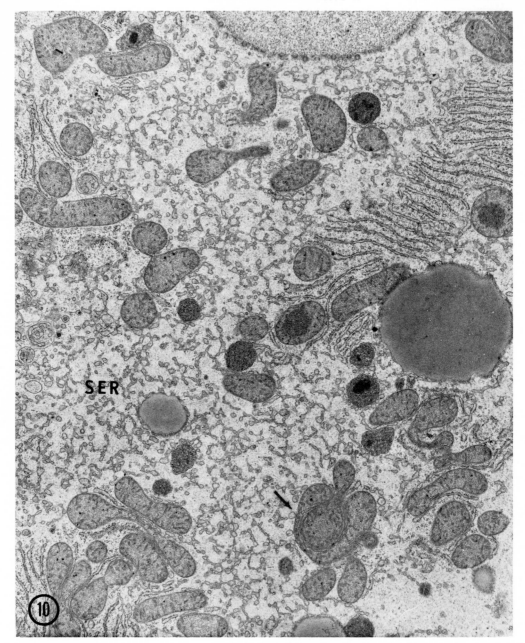

Figure 9.10. A hepatocyte from a rat on riboflavin-deficient diet for 4 weeks. The cytoplasm contains numerous small vesicles which are probably smooth endoplasmic reticulum (SER) and a number of polymorphous and elongate mitochondria. The arrow points to a mitochondrion closely applied to the surface of a second one. ×9,000.

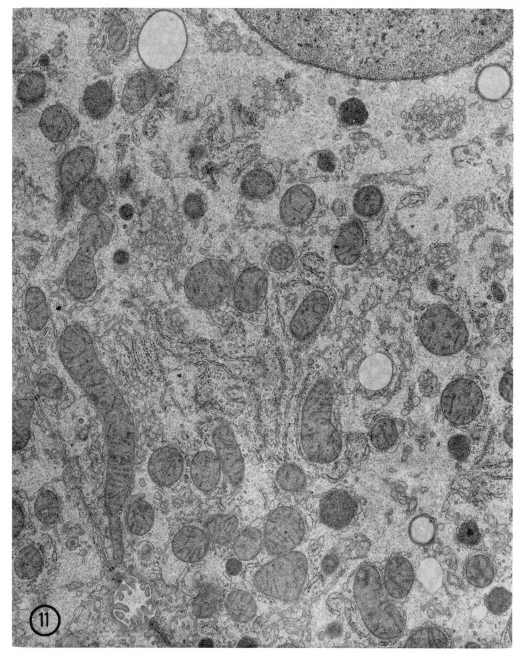

Figure 9.11. A hepatocyte from a rat on riboflavin-deficient diet for 4 weeks, then injected intraperitoneally with 1 mg of riboflavin/100 g body weight and sacrificed 24 hours later. The cytoplasm is devoid of the
small vesicles and the mitochondria more closely resemble normal ones in size and shape. ×9,400.

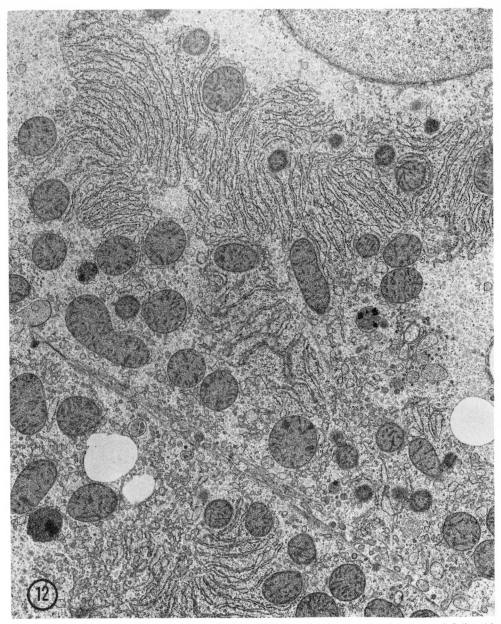

Figure 9.12. A hepatocyte from a rat on a riboflavin-deficient diet for 4 weeks, then injected daily with 1 mg of riboflavin/100 g body weight and sacrificed 48 hours after the initial injection. The cytoplasm contains numerous arrays of rough surfaced endoplasmic reticulum and numerous normal appearing mitochondria. A comparison of Figures 9.10, 9.11, and 9.12 indicates that restitution of both the endoplasmic reticulum and mitochondria occurs following the administration of riboflavin. ×9,400.

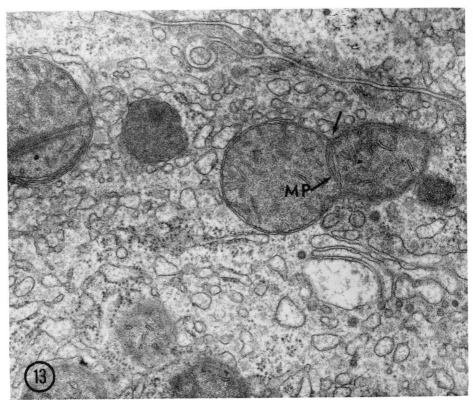

Figure 9.13. A hepatic mitochondrion 48 hours following the daily administration of riboflavin to an animal that had been on a riboflavin-deficient diet for 4 weeks. Note the constriction (*arrow*) at the point of the transverse membranous partition (MP). ×39,000.

tions in a variety of physiological and pathological states (3, 27–30). The majority of the quantitative data is of questionable value since it is based on the estimation of mitochondrial population obtained by the study of tissue sections, with little or no attention to changes in cell volume, uniformity of section thickness, and tinctorial staining. The first attempts at accurate quantitation were those of Thurlow (45) on the mitochondrial complement of neurons. In this study the number of mitochondria per unit volume of neuronal cytoplasm was found to be fairly constant irrespective of whether sensory or motor neurons were studied. Such investigations require very rigid control of tissue section thickness and staining, and are quite tedious.

The development of methods for the isolation of mitochondrial fractions of high purity and good yield, coupled with those of electronic particle-counting instruments has offered a feasible approach to such studies. These have been refined to the point that quantitative estimation of the mitochondrial population can be readily obtained from tissues consisting of a relatively homogeneous cell population such as liver. For a variety of reasons, the results of electronic particle counting of isolated mitochondria must be considered as semiquantitative at best. This is predicated on the limitations of particle-counting instruments to accurately discriminate particles smaller than 0.15 μ^3, and the inability to recover all the mitochondria in liver tissue by differential centrifugation (46).

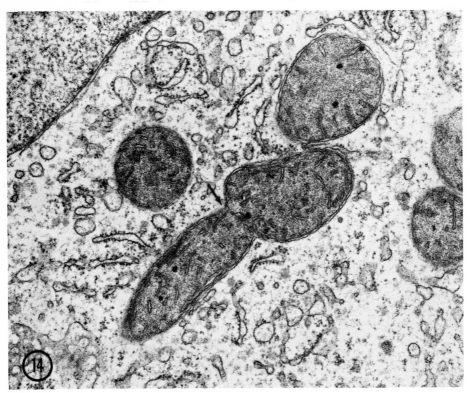

Figure 9.14. A mitochondrion in a hepatocyte of an animal treated identically as in Figure 9.13. A more elongate organelle appears to be budding. Note the point of constriction (*arrow*). ×34,000.

Furthermore, any consideration of the complement of mitochondria in hepatocytes must be tempered by the fact that approximately 30% of the cell population (47) in liver consists of Kupffer cells which cannot be readily or quantitatively separated from hepatocytes by current techniques. Despite these problems, the data obtained by electronic particle counting compare favorably with those of morphometric and biochemical studies.

The present experiments establish that inanition leads to a decrease of the mitochondrial population in liver which returns to normal levels upon refeeding. A diminution of the mitochondrial population as a consequence of extended starvation and its restitution by refeeding is consonant with the concept that mitochondrial growth in liver is, in part, dependent on adequate nutrition. Such modifications

of the mitochondrial population also offers an *in vivo* model for the study of mitochondrial biogenesis which is reproducible and subject to experimental manipulation. The time required for the return of the mitochondrial population from approximately 50% of normal to normal levels as determined by electronic particle counting is approximately 10 days. This compares favorably with the half-life of from 8.5 to 12.4 days obtained by Fletcher and Sanadi (48) from turnover studies employing labeled precursor substances incorporated into mitochondrial membranes, and with 9.4 days obtained more recently by Bergeron and Droz (11) by means of quantitative ultrastructural autoradiography. The increased incorporation of labeled precursors into the DNA and membrane proteins of hepatic mitochondria during refeeding as compared to that observed in

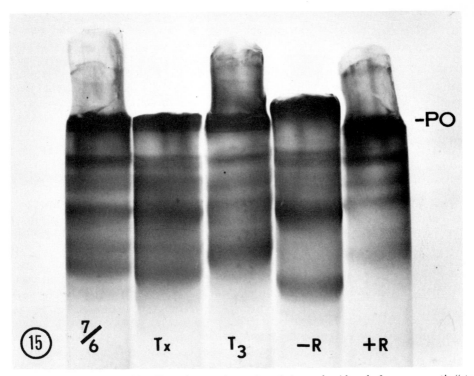

Figure 9.15. Patterns obtained by discontinuous electrophoresis in acrylamide gel of non-enzymatic "structural" proteins derived from inner membrane of hepatic mitochondria. 7/6 is protein isolated from a rat starved for 7 days and refed for 6 days. The stacking gel is at the top, PO = point of origin, 1–5 represent the various bands isolated. T_x is from a rat that was thyroidectomized for 6 weeks and T_3 from a rat that had received 20 μg of 3,5,3'-triiodothyronine/100 g body weight 48 hours before sacrifice. There is no appreciable difference from the normal pattern of bands seen in 7/6—R is from a rat on a riboflavin-deficient diet for 8 weeks, the number of bands has decreased to three with a deletion of bands 2 and 4. +R is from a rat that had received 1 mg of riboflavin/100 g body weight daily intraperitoneally for 1 week, the pattern of bands is identical to that seen in animal 7/6. "Structural protein" was isolated from inner membrane by the method of Richardson *et al.* (43). The protein was solubilized in 8 M urea and 0.22% formic acid. Discontinuous electrophoresis was performed according to the method of Lesjek and Lusena (44).

starved animals is consistent with increased synthesis of mitochondrial components. The concomitant increase in the number of mitochondria isolated from the liver during this period supports the view that new mitochondria are being formed in response to refeeding. The high degree of reproducibility of these alterations corroborates, and lends quantitative support, to the results of earlier reports of this phenomenon based on the microscopic study of hepatocytes and the epithelial cells of a variety of other tissues (27–30). In a carefully done quantitative study on the neu-

rons of the woodchuck, Rasmussen (49) found no alteration of the mitochondrial population per unit volume of cytoplasm as a consequence of hibernation or inanition. This implies that cells may vary with respect to the ease with which their mitochondrial complement can be modified. It may be that cells vital for survival of the organism are more resistant to the effects of prolonged starvation than are other somatic cells. Such a suggestion must remain entirely speculative until a systematic, comparative quantitative study is undertaken of the responses of a variety of cell types to a single environmental change known to alter the mitochondrial population.

The *in vivo* effects of a variety of metabolic inhibitors on the restitution of hepatic mitochondria following refeeding indicate that interference with mitochondrial DNA, or protein synthesis, or cytoplasmic protein synthesis will effectively interrupt the formation of new organelles. Unfortunately, the toxicity of some of the inhibitors precluded the extension of their use beyond 3 days of refeeding. The profound inhibitory effect of cycloheximide on the incorporation of labeled leucine into proteins of the outer mitochondrial membrane as compared to an almost negligible effect on synthesis of inner membrane proteins is direct evidence that the biogenesis of mitochondrial membranes is mediated by two different protein synthetic systems. Since this antibiotic is known to specifically inhibit the protein synthetic system localized in the endoplasmic reticulum, it may be presumed that the outer membrane of the mitochondrion is synthesized by this organelle. Although such a conclusion had been suggested by previous studies, it was based on such indirect proof as the failure of isolated mitochondria *in vitro* to incorporate amino acid into the outer membrane in contrast to heavy labeling of the inner one. The strikingly parallel inhibition by cycloheximide of leucine incorporation into proteins of the outer membrane and matrix of mitochondria suggests that both components are synthesized in the cytoplasm. In an early study on the effects of starvation and refeeding on liver, Fawcett (50) pointed out the close proximity of endoplasmic reticulum to mitochondria during refeeding and suggested that the latter organelle might play a role in the growth of mitochondria. *In vivo* localization by means of specific inhibitors of protein synthesis responsible for inner membrane formation was less clear. Chloramphenicol, an antibiotic which *in vitro* inhibits incorporation of amino acid into inner membrane, *in vivo* inhibited incorpo-

ration into both inner and outer membranes, although it was more marked in outer membranes. Such an apparently anomalous effect can best be explained by the findings of Freeman and Haldar (51, 52) and others (53, 54) that chloramphenicol inhibits mitochondrial NADH oxidation which in turn leads to decreased ATP generation, and impaired synthesis of RNA, and cytoplasmic proteins. Since both intra- and extramitochondrial protein synthesis are driven by energy derived from ATP, such metabolic disturbances would be expected to interfere with the formation of new mitochondria.

The presence of saccular extensions of the outer mitochondrial membrane following chloramphenicol treatment during refeeding coupled with less inhibition by this antibiotic of amino acid incorporation *in vivo* into outer membrane protein as compared to that in inner membrane suggests that they may be due to greater growth of outer membrane. Although similar extensions of the outer mitochondrial membrane have been encountered in hepatocytes infected with yellow fever virus (55), and in Hurler's disease (56), their significance remains obscure since parallel biochemical studies are not available.

Quantitative alteration of the mitochondrial population by thyroidectomy, and subsequent administration of thyroid hormone supports the view that these organelles are subject to hormonal control. Furthermore, it establishes that the increased levels of respiratory enzymes encountered by Tata *et al.* (36) following the administration of a single dose of thyroid hormone to previously thyroidectomized animals is due to the biogenesis of additional mitochondria. The finding by Roodyn and his associates (57) that triiodothyronine induced parellel increased incorporation of ^{14}C-valine by both mitochondria and endoplasmic reticulum in thyroidectomized rats is consistent with the notion that the genesis of new mitochondria is dependent upon the integration of synthetic events in both these organelles. The deleterious effect of excess thyroid hormone on mitochondrial growth may be of central importance in our understanding of hyperthyroidism. Although it is readily appreciated that thyroid hormone has multiple biological effects which are clearly dose-dependent, the action of excess levels of hormone on mitochondria may be explained in part, at least, on two well documented effects. (a) The uncoupling of oxidative phosphorylation, since it has been shown that protein synthesis by mitochondria is dependent on their capacity to generate ATP (15,58) and it is well known that massive amounts of thyroid hormone uncouples phosphorylation by these organelles (59); and (b) the catabolic effects of excessive levels of hormone (60) which leads to an increased rate of tissue breakdown, thus disturbing the delicate balance between synthesis and removal of cell constituents which constitutes the "normal" steady state of cells.

The response of hepatic mitochondria to riboflavin deficiency and to subsequent riboflavin administration is of considerable interest since it suggests that a very vital cell function, such as the formation of new mitochondria, can be controlled by the absence or presence of riboflavin, a metabolite which is almost totally supplied by diet. This is no doubt due to the fact that mitochondrial membrane formation is dependent on the availability of the flavoprotein components which constitute the respiratory enzyme assemblies in these membranes. This dependence on riboflavin derived from the diet for mitochondrial membrane formation may be an obligatory one, since the interruption of riboflavin synthesis by intestinal bacteria by antibiotics does not lead to a detectable decrease in the level of riboflavin in liver and muscle (61).

An additional point of interest is the modification of the non-enzymatic protein components of the inner membrane as a consequence of riboflavin deficiency. Germane to our consideration of this effect are the preliminary observations of Skipski *et al.*, as reported by Tandler *et al.* (39), on the alterations of mitochondrial phospholipids by riboflavin deficiency. It appears that the absence of this metabolite leads to gross chemical modification of mitochondrial membranes which presumably are reflected in their altered structure and function.

SUMMARY

In vivo experiments on the biogenesis of mitochondria in the liver of rats have established that 7 days of inanition leads to approximately a 50% decrease in the number of mitochondria as determined by electronic particle counting, lineal morphometry, and succinoxidase activity. The mitochondrial population returned to normal levels after 9 to 10 days of refeeding. Restitution of mitochondria was reflected by marked paralleled increases in ^{3}H-thymidine incorporation into mitochondrial DNA, and ^{3}H-leucine into mitochondrial membrane protein. Mitochondrial growth was inhibited by the administration of the antibiotics chloramphenicol, erythromycin, and cycloheximide; the acridine dye, acriflavin, was also quite effective. A comparison of the inhibitory effect on amino acid incorporation exerted by cycloheximide with that of chloramphenicol indicates that the outer membrane and matrical proteins are synthesized by a protein-synthesizing system localized in the endoplasmic reticulum whereas those of the inner membrane are synthesized by systems localized both in the mitochondrion and the endoplasmic reticulum.

Mitochondrial biogenesis appears to depend on adequate levels of thyroid hormone and riboflavin as evidenced by the marked decrease in the mitochondrial population of liver and its subsequent increase when these substances are administered to deficient animals. Riboflavin deficiency is reflected by an alteration in the pattern of non-enzymic "structural" proteins isolated from the mitochondrial inner membrane which is returned to that obtained from normal inner membrane by riboflavin administration. Experimental manipulation of mitochondrial biogenesis either by the use of selective metabolic inhibitors or by deficiency of substances vital for mitochondrial membrane biosynthesis offers a promising approach to the study of membrane structure and function.

REFERENCES

1. ALTMANN, R. "*Die Elementarorganismen und ihre Beziehungren zu den Zellen,*" p. 145. Leipzig, Veit, 1890.
2. COWDRY, E. V. The general functional significance of mitochondria. *Amer. J. Anat. 19:* 423, 1916.
3. COWDRY, E. V. The reactions of mitochondria to cellular injury. *Arch Path. (Chicago) 1:* 237, 1926.
4. NOVIKOFF, A. B. Mitochondria (chondriosomes). In *The Cell*, edited by Brachet, J., and Mirsky, A. E., Vol. 11, p. 299. New York, Academic Press, 1961.
5. GIBOR, A. Inheritance of cytoplasmic organelles. In *Formation and Fate of Cell Organelles. Symposia of The International Society for Cell Biology*, edited by Warren, K. B. New York, Academic Press, 1967.
6. SAGER, R. Cytoplasmic genes and organelle formation. In *Formation and Fate of Cell Organelles. Symposia of The International Society for Cell Biology*, edited by Warren, K. B. New York, Academic Press, 1967.
7. ROODYN, D. B., AND WILKIE, D. *The Biogenesis of Mitochondria*. London, Methuen and Co. Ltd., 1968.
8. LEHNINGER, A. L. *The Mitochondrion*. New York, W. A. Benjamin, Inc., 1964.
9. LUCK, D. J. L. The influence of precursor pool size on mitochondrial composition in *Neurospora crassa. J. Cell Biol. 24:* 445, 1965.
10. LUCK, D. J. L. Formation of mitochondria in *Neurospora crassa. J. Cell Biol. 16:* 483, 1963.
11. BERGERON, M., AND DROZ, B. Protein renewal in mitochondria as revealed by electron microscopy. *J. Ultrastruct. Res. 26:* 17, 1969.
12. ROODYN, D. B., REIS, P. J., AND WORK, T. S. Protein synthesis in mitochondria. Requirements for the incorporation of radioactive amino acids into mitochondrial protein. *Biochem. J. 80:* 9, 1961.
13. KROON, A. M. Protein synthesis in mitochondria. III. On the effects of inhibitors on the incor-

poration of amino acids into protein by intact mitochondria and digitonin fractions. *Biochim. Biophys. Acta 108:* 275, 1965.
14. HALDAR, D., FREEMAN, K., AND WORK, T. S. Biogenesis of mitochondria. *Nature (London) 211:* 9, 1966.
15. BORST, P., KROON, A. M., AND RUTTENBERG, G. J. C. M. Mitochondrial DNA and other forms of cytoplasmic DNA. In *Genetic Elements: Properties and Function*, edited by Shuger, D., p. 81. New York, Academic Press, 1967.
16. KADENBACH, B. Synthesis of mitochondrial proteins: Demonstration of a transfer of proteins from microsomes into mitochondria. *Biochim. Biophys. Acta 134:* 430, 1967.
17. MAGER, J. Chloramphenicol and chlortetracycline inhibition of amino acid incorporation into proteins in a cell-free system from tetrahymena pyriformis. *Biochim. Biophys. Acta 38:* 150, 1960.
18. NASS, S., AND NASS, M. M. K. An electron histochemical study of mitochondrial fibrous inclusions. *J. Roy. Micr. Soc. 81:* 209, 1963.
19. NASS, M. M. K., NASS, S., AND AFZELIUS, B. A. The general occurrence of mitochondrial DNA. *Exp. Cell Res. 37:* 516, 1965.
20. KROON, A. M., BORST, P., VAN BRUGGEN, E. F. J., AND RUTTENBERG, G. J. C. M. Mitochondrial DNA from sheep heart. *Proc. Nat. Acad. Sci. U.S.A. 56:* 1836, 1966.
21. NASS, M. M. K. The circularity of mitochondrial DNA. *Proc. Nat. Acad. Sci. U.S.A. 56:* 1215, 1966.
22. SINCLAIR, J. H., AND STEVENS, B. J. Circular DNA filaments from mouse mitochondria. *Proc. Nat. Acad. Sci. U.S.A. 56:* 508, 1966.
23. WINTERSBERGER, E. Occurrence of a DNA-polymerase in isolated yeast mitochondria. *Biochem. Biophys Res. Commun. 25:* 1, 1966.
24. EPHRUSSI, B., SLONIMSKI, P. P., YOTSUYANAGI, Y., AND TAVLITZKI, J. Variations physiologiques et scytologiques de la levure au cours du cycle de la croissance aerobie. *C.R. Lab. Carlsberg, Ser. Physiol. 26:* 87, 1956.
25. SCHATZ, G. The isolation of possible mitochondrial precursor structures from aerobically grown Baker's yeast. *Biochem. Biophys. Res. Commun. 12:* 448, 1963
26. CLARK-WALKER, G. D., AND LINNANE, A. W. The biogenesis of mitochondria in saccharomyces cerevisiae. *J. Cell Biol. 34:* 1, 1967.
27. RUSSO, A. Aumento dei granuli protoplasmatici nelloocite delle Coniglie iniettate con lecitinia, loro diminuzione nelle Coniglie digiun-

anti e loro natura lipoide e mitochondriale. *Arch. f. Zellforsch. Bd. 8:* 203, 1912.

28. NICHOLSON, F. M. Changes in the mitochondria produced experimentally in the thyroid gland. *J. Exp. Med. 39:* 63, 1923.

29. MILLER, S. P. Effects of various types of inanition upon the mitochondria in the gastrointestinal epithelium and in the pancreas of the albino rat. *Anat. Rec. 23:* 205, 1922.

30. MA, W. C. The changes in the pancreatic cell of the guinea pig during inanition and refeeding. *Anat. Rec. 27:* 47, 1924.

31. GLAS, U., AND BAHR, G. F. Quantitative study of mitochondria in rat liver. Dry mass, wet mass, volume, and concentration of solids. *J. Cell Biol. 29:* 507, 1966.

32. LOUD, A. V., BARANY, W. C., AND PACK, B. A. Quantitative evaluation of cytoplasmic structures in electron micrographs. *Lab. Invest. 14:* 996, 1965.

33. WEIBEL, E. R., STÄUBLI, W., GNÄGI, H. R., AND HESS, F. A. Correlated morphometric and biochemical studies on the liver cell. I. Morphometric model, stereologic methods and normal morphometric data for rat liver. *J. Cell Biol. 42:* 68, 1969.

34. STÄUBLI, W., HESS, R., AND WEIBEL, E. R. Correlated morphometric and biochemical studies on the liver cell. II. Effects of phenobarbital on rat hepatocytes. *J. Cell Biol. 42:* 92, 1969.

35. COGGI, G., AND SCARPELLI, D. G. Biogenesis of mitochondrial membranes: Biochemical and morphological evidence of two protein-synthesizing systems. *Proc. Soc. Exp. Biol. Med. 134:* 328, 1970.

36. TATA, J. R., ERNSTER, L., LINDBERG, O., ARRHENIUS, E., PEDERSEN, S., AND HEDMAN, R. The action of thyroid hormones at the cell level. *Biochem. J. 86:* 408, 1963.

37. WISS, O., AND WEBER, F. The liver and vitamins. In *The Liver, Morphology, Biochemistry, Physiology,* edited by Rouiller, C., Vol. II, p. 133. New York, Academic Press, 1964.

38. ROBINSON, F. A. *The Vitamin Co-Factors of Enzymic Systems,* p. 206. New York, Pergamon Press, 1966.

39. TANDLER, B., ERLANDSON, R. A., AND WYNDER, E. L. Riboflavin and mouse hepatic cell structure and function. I. Ultrastructural alterations in simple deficiency. *Amer. J. Path. 52:* 69, 1968.

40. BURCH, H. B., HUNTER, F. E., COMBS, A. M., AND SCHUTZ, B. A. Oxidative enzymes and phosphorylation in hepatic mitochondria from riboflavin-deficient rats. *J. Biol. Chem. 235:* 1540, 1960.

41. TANDLER, B., ERLANDSON, R. A., SMITH, A. L., AND WYNDER, E. L. Riboflavin and mouse hepatic cell structure and function. II. Division of mitochondria during recovery from simple deficiency. *J. Cell Biol. 41:* 477, 1969.

42. GREEN, D. E., TISDALE, H. D., CRIDDLE, R. S., CHEN, P. Y., AND BOCK, R. M. Isolation and properties of the structural protein of mitochondria. *Biochem. Biophys. Res. Commun. 5:* 109, 1961.

43. RICHARDSON, J. H., HULTIN, H. O., AND FLEISCHER, S. Interactions of mitochondrial structural protein with phospholipids. *Arch. Biochem. 105:* 254, 1964.

44. LESJEK, K., AND LUSENA, C. V. Resolution of mitochondrial structural proteins by discontinuous electrophoresis in acrylamide gels. *Canad. J. Biochem. 47:* 753, 1969.

45. THURLOW, M. DEG. Quantitative studies on mitochondria in nerve cells. *Contrib. Embryol. (Carnegie Inst.) Wash. 6:* 35, 1917.

46. HOGEBOOM, G. H., SCHNEIDER, W. C., AND PALLADE, G. E. Cytochemical studies of mammalian tissues. I. Isolation of intact mitochondria from rat liver; Some biochemical properties of mitochondria and submicroscopic particulate material. *J. Biol. Chem. 172:* 619, 1948.

47. DAOUST, R., AND CANTERO, A. The numerical proportions of cell types in rat liver during carcinogenesis by 4-dimethylaminoazobenzene (DAB). *Cancer Res. 19:* 757, 1959.

48. FLETCHER, M. J., AND SANADI, D. R. Turnover of rat liver mitochondria. *Biochim. Biophys. Acta 51:* 356, 1961.

49. RASMUSSEN, A. T. The mitochondria in nerve cells during hibernation and inanition in the woodchuck (*Marmota monax*). *J. Comp. Neurol. 31:* 37, 1919.

50. FAWCETT, D. W. Observations on the cytology and electron microscopy of hepatic cells. *J. Nat. Cancer Inst. 15 (Suppl.):* 1475, 1955.

51. FREEMAN, K. B., AND HALDAR, D. The inhibition of mammalian mitochondrial NADH oxidation by chloramphenicol and its isomers and analogues. *Canad. J. Biochem. 46:* 1003, 1968.

52. HALDAR, D., AND FREEMAN, K. B. The inhibition of protein synthesis and respiration in mouse ascites tumor cells by chloramphenicol and its isomers and analogues. *Canad. J. Biochem. 46:* 1009, 1968.

53. FIRKIN, F. C., AND LINNANE, A. W. Biogenesis of mitochondria. 8. The effect of chloramphenicol

on regenerating rat liver. *Exp. Cell Res. 55:* 68, 1969.

54. KROON, A. M., AND DE VRIES, H. The effect of chloramphenicol on the biogenesis of mitochondria of rat liver *in vivo. Fed. Europ. Biochem. Soc. Letters 3:* 208, 1969.

55. BEARCROFT, W. G. C. Electron microscope studies on the livers of yellow-fever-infected African monkeys. *J. Path. Bact. 83:* 59, 1962.

56. HAUST, M. D. Mitochondrial budding and morphogenesis of cytoplasmic vacuoles in hepatocytes of children with the Hurler syndrome and Sanfilippo disease. *J. Exp. Molec. Path. 9:* 242, 1968.

57. ROODYN, D. B., FREEMAN, K. B., AND TATA, J. R. The stimulation by treatment *in vivo* with triiodothyronine of amino acid incorporation into protein by isolated rat-liver mitochondria. *Biochem. J. 94:* 628, 1965.

58. ROODYN, D. B., REIS, P. J., AND WORK, T. S. Pro-tein synthesis in isolated mitochondria: Its relationship to oxidative phosphorylation and its bearing upon theories of mitochondrial replication. In *Protein Synthesis*, edited by Harris, R. J. C., p. 37. New York, Academic Press, 1961.

59. TATA, J. R. Biological action of thyroid hormones at the cellular and molecular levels. In *Actions of Hormones on Molecular Processes*, edited by Litwack, G., and Kritchevsky, D., p. 58. New York, John Wiley and Sons, Inc., 1964.

60. FLETCHER, K., AND MYANT, N. B. Effects of thyroxine on the synthesis of cholesterol and fatty acids by cell-free fractions of rat liver. *J. Physiol. (London) 154:* 145, 1960.

61. SCHWEIGERT, B. S., TEPLY, L. J., GREENHUT, I. T., AND ELVEHJEM, C. A. The riboflavin and vitamin B_c potency of tissues from rats fed succinyl sulfathiazole with and without liver supplements. *Amer. J. Physiol. 144:* 74, 1945.

INDEX

176